New General Mathematics 2

J B Channon MA
formerly Assistant Master at Rugby School

A McLeish Smith BA
formerly Second Master at Lawrence Sheriff School, Rugby

H C Head MA
Assistant Master at Rugby School

Longman

LONGMAN GROUP LIMITED
London
Associated companies, branches and representatives throughout the world

First published 1957
New edition first published 1970
Sixth impression 1974

ISBN (with answers) 0 582 31843 2
ISBN (without answers) 0 582 31842 4

Printed in Great Britain by Butler & Tanner Ltd, Frome and London

Preface

This set of four books is based on the authors' **General Mathematics** series, which has been completely rewritten in order to meet modern demands. Decimal currency has been used throughout, and the metric system of measures has supplanted the Imperial system almost completely, though a few questions and examples still remain in which Imperial units are used.

With the introduction of decimal currency it is assumed that pupils at primary level will have acquired some knowledge of decimal notation—place value, multiplication and division by a whole number and so on.

The more ponderous and less useful features of traditional textbooks will not be found here, and their omission has left room for chapters on those new topics which appear to the authors to be of permanent value, and which are in no danger of being eliminated from the syllabus once the experimental period of trial and error is over. Such topics as binary numbers, statistics, set theory, matrices, vectors, probability and linear programming must find a place in any series of books which is attempting to fit pupils for the modern world of technological development, and all of these subjects are dealt with in this series.

At the time of writing the future of geometry is still in a state of considerable uncertainty and, for this reason, more of the subject is retained than some teachers may consider necessary. These chapters can of course be disregarded by those who wish to do so, but they are there for those who believe that the study of geometry still has something to offer to the intelligent pupil.

J.B.C.
A.McL.S.
H.C.H.

Rugby 1970

Contents

Theorems

Constructions

Tables

Metric Units

LENGTH

10 millimetres (mm) = 1 centimetre (cm)
10 cm = 1 decimetre (dm)
10 dm = 1 metre (m) = 1 000 mm
10 m = 1 decametre (dam)
10 dam = 1 hectometre (hm)
10 hm = 1 kilometre (km) = 1 000 m

The decimetre, decametre and hectometre are very rarely used

AREA

100 sq mm (mm^2) = 1 sq cm (cm^2)
100 sq cm = 1 sq dm (dm^2)
and so on
1 sq dam (dam^2) = 1 are
100 ares = 1 sq hm (hm^2) = 1 hectare

The hectare is the only unit in which the prefix hecto is in common use

VOLUME

1 000 cu mm (mm^3) = 1 cu cm (cm^3)
1 000 cu cm = 1 cu dm (dm^3)
and so on

CAPACITY

10 millilitres (ml) = 1 centilitre (cl)
10 cl = 1 decilitre (dl)
10 dl = 1 litre (l)
1 litre = 1 dm^3 = 1 000 cm^3

MASS

10 milligrammes (mg)	=	1 centigramme (cg)
10 cg	=	1 decigramme (dg)
10 dg	=	1 gramme (g) = 1 000 mg
10 g	=	1 decagramme (dag)
10 dag	=	1 hectogramme (hg)
10 hg	=	1 kilogramme (kg) = 1 000 g
1 000 kg	=	1 tonne (t)

The centigramme, decigramme, decagramme and hectogramme are very rarely used

1 gramme is the mass of 1 cm^3 of water at 4° C (celsius)
1 kilogramme is the mass of 1 litre of water at 4° C (celsius)

Imperial Units

LENGTH

12 inches (in)	=	1 foot (ft)	220 yards	=	1 furlong
3 feet	=	1 yard (yd)	1 760 yards	=	1 mile
22 yards	=	1 chain (ch)	5 280 feet	=	1 mile
10 chains	=	1 furlong (fur)	6 080 feet	=	1 sea mile
8 furlongs	=	1 mile (ml)			

AREA

144 sq in (in^2)	=	1 sq ft (ft^2)
9 sq ft	=	1 sq yd (yd^2)
484 sq yd	=	1 sq ch (ch^2)
4 840 sq yd	=	1 acre (ac)
640 acres	=	1 sq mile ($mile^2$)

VOLUME

1 728 cu in (in^3)	=	1 cu ft (ft^3)
27 cu ft	=	1 cu yd (yd^3)

MASS

16 ounces (oz)	=	1 pound (lb)	14 lb	=	1 stone (st)
28 lb	=	1 quarter (qr)	112 lb	=	1 cwt
4 qr	=	1 hundredweight (cwt)	2 240 lb	=	1 ton
20 cwt	=	1 ton			

CAPACITY

4 gills = 1 pint (pt)
2 pt = 1 quart (qt)
4 qt = 1 gallon (gall)

The gill is used only for liquids

PAPER

24 sheets = 1 quire
20 quires = 1 ream

FOREIGN MONEY

French:	100 centimes (c)	= 1 franc (F)
German:	100 pfennig (pf)	= 1 Deutschmark (DM)
American:	100 cents (c)	= 1 dollar ($)

APPROXIMATE EQUIVALENTS

1 inch	= 2·54 cm	1 are	= 120 yd² (roughly)
1 yard	= 0·914 m	1 hectare	= $2\frac{1}{2}$ acres (roughly)
1 metre	= 39·37 in	1 pound	= 0·454 kg
1 mile	= 1·609 km	1 kilogramme	= 2·205 lb
1 kilometre	= 0·621 miles	1 ton	= 1·016 tonnes
8 kilometres	= 5 miles (roughly)	1 tonne	= 0·984 tons
		1 litre	= 1·76 pints

A knot is a speed of 1 sea mile per hour, which is slightly more than 1 land mile per hour (1 knot = approx. $1\frac{1}{7}$ mile/h).

1 gallon of water weighs 10 pounds.

1 ft³ of water weighs about 1 000 oz ($62\frac{1}{2}$ lb).

1 ft³ of water is about $6\frac{1}{4}$ gallons.

THE CALENDAR

Thirty days hath September, April, June and November.
All the rest have thirty-one, excepting February alone,
And this has twenty-eight days clear,
And twenty-nine in each Leap Year.

For a Leap Year the date must be divisible by 4, except when it is divisible by 100. In this case it is a Leap Year only when the date is divisible by 400, e.g.

1896 was a Leap Year. 2000 will be a Leap Year.
1900 was not a Leap Year.

Chapter 1

Multiplication and division of monomials

Example 1 *Multiply a^2 by a^5.*

$$\begin{aligned} a^2 \times a^5 &= (a \times a) \times (a \times a \times a \times a \times a) \\ &= a \times a \times a \times a \times a \times a \times a \\ &= a^7. \end{aligned}$$

Notice that the index in the result is the **sum** of the indices given,

e.g. $x^4 \times x^7 = x^{4+7} = x^{11}$

$h^6 \times h = h^{6+1} = h^7$ (since $h = h^1$)

and in general $x^m \times x^n = x^{m+n}$.

Example 2 *Multiply $2c^3de^2$ by $-5c^2d^5e$.*

$$\begin{aligned} (2c^3de^2) \times (-5c^2d^5e) &= (2cccdee) \times (-5ccddddde) \\ &= -2 \times 5cccccddddddeee \\ &= -10c^5d^6e^3 \end{aligned}$$

or more briefly, by adding indices,

$$\begin{aligned} (2c^3de^2) \times (-5c^2d^5e) &= -2 \times 5c^{3+2}d^{1+5}e^{2+1} \\ &= -10c^5d^6e^3. \end{aligned}$$

Exercise 1a

By writing out each term in its fully expanded form, simplify

1 $a^3 \times a^2$ **2** $m^3 \times m^5$ **3** $3x^2 \times x^4$ **4** $n^5 \times n$

5 $b \times 5b^3$ **6** $3c^2 \times 2c^5$ **7** $a^3m^2 \times a^2m^3$

8 $b^2c \times bc^3$ **9** $5am^2u \times 2au^2$ **10** $4bc^2d^3 \times 3b^2cd$

Multiply

11 a^6 by a^4 **12** b^5 by b^9

13 c^8 ,, $-c^7$ **14** $-d^7$,, d^6

15 $-e^5$,, $-e^{11}$ **16** x^7 ,, x

17 $-y$ by y^{12}
18 $-5m^5$ by $-3m^3$
19 $2n^6$ „ $-6n^2$
20 a^3m^2 „ a^2m^4
21 $-dn^3$ „ $-d^2n^2$
22 pq „ pq
23 $3ex^2$ „ $-2ex^4$
24 $-4d^3n^4$ „ $5d^2n^5$
25 x^2yz^2 „ xy^2z^3
26 $2abc$ „ $4abc$
27 $-3a^2b^2c$ „ $-ac^2$
28 $-2m^2n^3$ „ $3mnx^2$
29 $6d^2e^5$ „ $5d^3e$
30 $4ad^3m^2$ „ $-5ad^2m$
31 $-p^3q^5$ „ $7p^4q^3$
32 h^4k „ $5hk^6$
33 $-3abc$ „ $3bcd$
34 $5p^3y$ „ $-2q^2y^2$
35 $-2d^3mn$ „ $-4a^2n^2$

Find the product of

36 a, ab and b^2
37 $3mn$, m^2 and $-2n$
38 $-2u^3v^2$, $-4u$ and u^2v^3
39 dxy, $-3d^2y$ and $4xy^2$
40 $-2muv$, $-4nu^2v$ and $-3mn^2v^2$

Example 3 *Divide a^5 by a^2.*

$$\frac{a^5}{a^2} = \frac{\not{a}\not{a}aaa}{\not{a}\not{a}}$$
$$= a^3.$$

Notice that the index in the result may be obtained by **subtracting** 2 from 5,

e.g. $m^8 \div m^3 = m^{8-3} = m^5$

$x^5 \div x = x^{5-1} = x^4$ (since $x = x^1$)

and in general $x^m \div x^n = x^{m-n}$.

Example 4 *Divide $-12c^4d^3e^2$ by $-4c^3d$.*

$$\frac{-12c^4d^3e^2}{-4c^3d} = +\frac{12\not{c}\not{c}\not{c}c\not{d}ddee}{4\not{c}\not{c}\not{c}\not{d}}$$
$$= 3cd^2e^2$$

or more briefly, by subtracting indices,

$$(-12c^4d^3e^2) \div (-4c^3d) = +3c^{4-3}d^{3-1}e^2$$
$$= 3cd^2e^2.$$

Exercise 1b

By writing out each term in its fully expanded form, simplify

1 $\frac{a^7}{a^3}$ **2** $\frac{c^4}{c}$ **3** $\frac{d^6}{d^5}$ **4** $\frac{10e^5}{2e^3}$ **5** $\frac{12m^7}{4m^4}$

6 $\frac{5n^7}{n^6}$ **7** $\frac{u^5}{u^5}$ **8** $\frac{7v^3}{v^3}$ **9** $\frac{5x^6}{5x}$ **10** $\frac{10x^9}{5x^6}$

Divide

11 a^6	by a^2	**12** b^8	by $-b^5$
13 $-c^9$	,, c^3	**14** $-d^{11}$	,, $-d^9$
15 e^8	,, e	**16** x^5	,, x^4
17 y^3	,, y^3	**18** $-6m^5$	,, $3m^2$
19 $-8n^8$	,, $-2n^2$	**20** $10u^5$	,, $-5u^3$
21 x^4y^5	,, $-x^2y^2$	**22** $12a^3m^4$	,, $3m^4$
23 $-15d^4n^6$	,, $-5n^3$	**24** $-8a^2b^3c^4$	,, $2abc$
25 $6m^3u^2v^4$	,, $-2mv^2$	**26** $8a^2b^3x$	,, a^2b^3
27 $10d^4bc$	,, $-d^2c$	**28** $-16p^{11}q^{10}$	,, $-8p^{10}q^9$
29 $-12h^5k^3m^2$	,, $4h^5m$	**30** $15p^6q^4r^3$	,, $-3p^3q^2r$

Simplify

31 $(-15m^5n^4u^6) \div (-3m^2n^2u^3)$ **32** $(2a^4b^2) \times (-4ab^2c^3)$

33 $\frac{-11a^5c^6d^7}{a^2c^3d^2}$ **34** $\frac{-15d^4e^2x^5}{-5de^2x^4}$

35 $-7ghk \times 3hk^2$ **36** $24a^3ce^4n \div 6aen$

37 $(-4muv) \times (-5nv^2x)$ **38** $-20a^7b^6c^2d \div 10a^2b^4d$

39 $\frac{4c^2d \times (-6de^3)}{-12ce}$ **40** $\frac{(-3a^3m^4) \times (-8a^4m^5)}{-6a^5m^6}$

Example 5 $(a^2)^3 = a^2 \times a^2 \times a^2$

$= a^{2+2+2}$

$= a^6.$

Notice that 6, the index in the result, is the **product** of 2 and 3.

Similarly $(b^4)^2 = b^{4\times 2} = b^8$

$(c^3)^5 = c^{3\times 5} = c^{15}$

and in general $(x^m)^n = x^{mn}.$

Example 6 $(-3d^3e)^2 = (-3d^3e) \times (-3d^3e)$
$= +9d^6e^2.$

Example 7 $-3(d^3e)^2 = -3 \times (d^3e) \times (d^3e)$
$= -3d^6e^2.$

Example 8 $(-4f^2g^5)^3 = (-4f^2g^5) \times (-4f^2g^5) \times (-4f^2g^5)$
$= -64f^{2+2+2}g^{5+5+5}$
$= -64f^6g^{15}$

or more briefly, $(-4f^2g^5)^3 = -4^3f^{2\times3}g^{5\times3}$
$= -64f^6g^{15}.$

(N.B. In multiplication or division, an odd number of minus signs gives a negative result, as in Book 1, Chap. 22.)

Example 9 $(-l^2m^3n)^7 = -l^{2\times7}m^{3\times7}n^{1\times7}$
$= -l^{14}m^{21}n^7.$

Exercise 1c

Simplify

1 $(a^3)^2$ **2** $(-c^3)^2$ **3** $(d^4)^3$

4 $(-e^4)^3$ **5** $(3m^4)^2$ **6** $(2n^5)^3$

7 $(-u^2)^5$ **8** $4(v^3)^2$ **9** $(4x^3)^2$

10 $-2(a^2)^3$ **11** $(-2b^2)^3$ **12** $-(c^5)^4$

13 $(-d^5)^4$ **14** $(-2e^2)^5$ **15** $(mn^2)^4$

16 $(-u^3v^2)^4$ **17** $-(x^2y)^4$ **18** $-3(a^2b^3)^2$

19 $-(3a^2b^3)^2$ **20** $(-3a^2b^3)^2$ **21** $(5mn^3)^3$

22 $(-4u^2v)^3$ **23** $2(a^2mv)^4$ **24** $-3(cde^3)^4$

25 $(-7m^3n^2u^4)^2$ **26** $\dfrac{(-x^3)^2}{-x^4}$ **27** $\dfrac{a^6}{(-a)^4}$

28 $\dfrac{(-c)^2 \times c^4}{(-c)^5}$ **29** $\dfrac{-(d^2)^3}{d^4 \times (-d)}$ **30** $\dfrac{(-e)^7 \times e^2}{(-e^3)^3}$

Example 10 $\sqrt{a^6} = \sqrt{a \times a \times a \times a \times a \times a}$
$= \sqrt{(a \times a \times a) \times (a \times a \times a)}$
$= a \times a \times a$
$= a^3$

or, since $a^6 = a^3 \times a^3$
$\sqrt{a^6} = a^3$.

Notice that the index in the result can be obtained by **dividing** 6 by 2,

e.g. $\sqrt{a^{10}} = a^{10 \div 2} = a^5$.

(Compare this with $(a^5)^2 = a^{5 \times 2} = a^{10}$.)

Example 11 $\sqrt[3]{b^{21}} = \sqrt[3]{b^7 \times b^7 \times b^7}$
$= b^7$

or $\sqrt[3]{b^{21}} = b^{21 \div 3}$
$= b^7$.

Example 12 $\sqrt[3]{-8m^{15}n^3} = -2m^{15 \div 3}n^{3 \div 3}$
$= -2m^5n^1$
$= -2m^5n$.

Notice the minus sign, since $(-2)^3 = -8$.

Exercise 1d

Simplify

1 $\sqrt{x^4}$ 2 $\sqrt{m^{12}}$ 3 $\sqrt{n^8}$ 4 $\sqrt[3]{u^6}$

5 $\sqrt[3]{v^{15}}$ 6 $\sqrt[3]{-a^{12}}$ 7 $\sqrt{9b^6}$ 8 $\sqrt{16c^{16}}$

9 $\sqrt[3]{d^{18}}$ 10 $\sqrt[3]{-e^{18}}$ 11 $-\sqrt[3]{x^{18}}$ 12 $\sqrt[4]{y^{12}}$

13 $\sqrt[4]{a^{20}}$ 14 $\sqrt[3]{27b^{12}}$ 15 $\sqrt[3]{125c^6}$ 16 $\sqrt[4]{16d^{16}}$

17 $\sqrt[5]{m^{15}}$ 18 $\sqrt[5]{32n^{25}}$ 19 $\sqrt{a^4x^6}$ 20 $\sqrt[3]{b^6y^{12}}$

21 $\sqrt[3]{-c^9m^6}$ 22 $\sqrt[4]{a^4m^{12}x^8}$ 23 $\sqrt[3]{-b^3c^9}$ 24 $\sqrt[4]{81d^8e^4}$

25 $\sqrt[5]{-m^{10}n^{15}}$ 26 $\sqrt[5]{a^5b^{15}c^5}$ 27 $\sqrt[5]{-32m^5u^{20}}$

28 $\sqrt{a^2x^4} \times \sqrt{a^6x^2}$ 29 $\sqrt[3]{a^9m^6u^3} \div \sqrt[3]{a^3m^6}$

30 $\sqrt{d^4e^6v^2} \times \sqrt[3]{-d^3e^6}$

Example 13 *Multiply* $3d^2m - 5dm^2 + dm$ *by* $4d^2$.

Each term has to be multiplied by $4d^2$.

$$\begin{array}{r} 3d^2m - 5dm^2 + dm \\ +4d^2 \\ \hline 12d^4m - 20d^3m^2 + 4d^3m \\ \hline \end{array}$$

Example 14 *Multiply* $4x^2 + 7xy - y^2$ *by* $-xy$.

$$\begin{array}{r} 4x^2 + 7xy - y^2 \\ -xy \\ \hline -4x^3y - 7x^2y^2 + xy^3 \\ \hline \end{array}$$

Exercise 1e

Multiply

1	$3a + 5b - 2c$	by 3
2	$6p - 4q + 7r$	,, 2
3	$2m - 5n - 3$	,, -4
4	$a - 6b + 5c$	,, m
5	$3x + 5y + 2z$	,, a
6	$c - 5d - 3e$	,, $3a$
7	$4a + 3b - 2c$	,, $-4m$
8	$x^2 - 3x + 2$	,, -5
9	$3x^2 + 4x - 3$	,, $2x$
10	$a^2 + ab - b^2$	,, $3a$
11	$2a^2 + ab + 3b^2$	,, $-ab$
12	$d^2 - 2dm + m^2$	,, $3dm$
13	$a^2 + 3am - 2m^2$	,, $-3am$
14	$b^2 - 2bn - 5n^2$	,, $-2bn$
15	$-3x^2 - 4xy + 2y^2$	,, $5xy$
16	$2ab - 5bc - cd + 3ad$	,, $3a$
17	$3abc - 2bcd + 4cda$	,, $-2c$
18	$x^3 - x^2 - x + 1$	,, $-x$

19	$a^3 - 3a^2 + 5a - 2$	by $3a$
20	$2a^3d + 4ad^3 - a^2d^2 - 3d^4$	„ $4d$
21	$2m^3 - 5m^2 + 3m - 4$	„ $-3m$
22	$m^2 - 5mn - 3n^2$	„ $-4mn^2$
23	$a^3 + 4a^2x - ax^2 - 3x^3$	„ $-5a^2x$
24	$2ab^2c - 3a^2cd + 5bcd^2$	„ $3a^2bc$
25	$3u^2v^2 - 2u^3v - 5v^4 + uv^3$	„ $-2u^3v^2$

Example 15 *Simplify* $3mn(4m^2 + mn - 2n^2)$.

Each term inside the bracket must be multiplied by $3mn$.

$$3mn(4m^2 + mn - 2n^2) = 12m^3n + 3m^2n^2 - 6mn^3.$$

Example 16

$$-2d^2f(3d^3 - 2df^2 + 4d^2f^2) = -6d^5f + 4d^3f^3 - 8d^4f^3.$$

Example 17

$$\begin{aligned} 2x(5x + y) - 4y(2x - 3y) &= 10x^2 + 2xy - 8xy + 12y^2 \\ &= 10x^2 - 6xy + 12y^2. \end{aligned}$$

Exercise 1f

Simplify

1 $4x(a + b + 2c)$

2 $3m(x - 3y + 2z)$

3 $-2a(p - q - r + s)$

4 $x(x^2 + 3x - 2)$

5 $-3m(m^2 - 2m + 4)$

6 $-2a(3a^2 + 4a - 2)$

7 $u^2(2u^3 + 5u^2 - 4u - 3)$

8 $3d^2(d^2 + 4d + 1)$

9 $-4m^2(m^2 - 2m - 3)$

10 $p^3(3p^2 - 5)$

11 $-4n^3(n^2 + 2n - 1)$

12 $am(3a - 7m)$

13 $-3ab(4a - b - 2)$

14 $-2uv(-3u^2 + 2v^2)$

15 $4m^3(-2m^2 + m - 3)$

16 $-5hk(h^2 - 3hk + 2k^2)$

17 $3p(2p^2 - p - q + 2q^2)$

18 $a^2m(5a + 7m - 2)$

19 $-4uv^2(-2u^2 - 3uv - v^2)$

20 $2a^2b^3c(-3a + b - 2c)$

21 $a(a - m) - m(a + m)$

22 $m(m + 2u) - u(2m - u)$

23 $b(2b - 3x) + x(4b - x)$

24 $2c(c + 2d) - 3d(c - 2d)$
25 $x^2(3x - 1) - 2x(x^2 - x + 2)$
26 $2a(a^2 + 3a) + 3a^2(a - 4)$
27 $5mn(m - 3n) - 2mn(m + 4n)$
28 $3u(u^2 - v^2) + 2uv(u - 2v)$
29 $3a^2(2a - b) - ab(a + 2b) + b^2(2a - 3b)$
30 $4x^2(x - 3y) + 2xy(6x + 3y) - 3y^2(2x - 3y)$

Example 18 *Divide* $6h^2k - 15h^3k^3 + 3h^4k^2$ *by* $-3h^2$.

Each term in the given expression must be divided by $-3h^2$.

$$-3h^2\,)\,\overline{6h^2k - 15h^3k^3 + 3h^4k^2}$$
$$-2k + 5hk^3 - h^2k^2$$

Example 19 *Simplify* $\dfrac{10c^2d + 6cd^2 - 8c^2d^2}{2cd}$.

$$\frac{10c^2d + 6cd^2 - 8c^2d^2}{2cd} = 5c + 3d - 4cd.$$

Exercise 1g

Divide

1 $6a + 8b + 4c$	by 2
2 $3b - 12c + 15d$	„ 3
3 $9p + 3q - 6r$	„ -3
4 $-8x - 12y + 20z$	„ -4
5 $15a - 20b - 5c + 10d$	„ 5
6 $6ax + 3bx - 15cx - 9dx$	„ $3x$
7 $4ah - 2ak - 10am + 6an$	„ $-2a$
8 $-x^3 + 3x^2 - 5x$	„ $-x$
9 $6m^3 - 9m^2 - 15m$	„ $3m$
10 $2u^4 - 6u^3 + 10u^2 - 4u$	„ $-2u$
11 $10abc + 5bcd - 15cde$	„ $5c$
12 $v^5 - 2v^4 - 3v^3 + 4v^2$	„ v^2

13 $4a^7 + 2a^5 - 4a^3$ by $-2a^2$
14 $3b^3m - 12b^2m + 6bm$ „ $3bm$
15 $4u^3v - 8u^2v^2 + 16uv^3$ „ $4uv$
16 $6m^4n - 2m^3n^2 - 8m^2n^3 + 4mn^4$ „ $-2mn$
17 $-3x^6 - 9x^5 + 6x^4 - 3x^3$ „ $-3x^2$
18 $-8a^4u^2 + 4a^3u^3 - 12a^2u^4$ „ $4a^2u$
19 $6p^4q^3 - 9p^3q^2 - 3p^2q^3 + 6p^3q^4$ „ $-3pq^2$
20 $-8h^3k^3 - 6h^2k^2 + 2h^2k^4 - 4h^4k^2$ „ $-2h^2k^2$

Simplify

21 $\dfrac{a^4 + 3a^3 - 2a^2 - 5a}{a}$ **22** $\dfrac{3d^5 - 9d^4 - 3d^3 + 6d^2}{-3d}$

23 $\dfrac{4ax - 10bx^2 + 6cx^3}{-2x}$ **24** $\dfrac{4m^2u + 8mu^2 - 12m^2u^2}{4mu}$

25 $\dfrac{n^5 + 3n^4 - 2n^3 - 4n^2}{n^2}$ **26** $\dfrac{6x^4 - 9x^3y + 3x^2y^2}{-3x^2}$

27 $\dfrac{-4c^3e - 12c^2e^2 + 8ce^3}{-4ce}$

28 $\dfrac{-a^5b^2 + 2a^4b^3 + 5a^3b^4 - a^2b^5}{a^2b}$

29 $\dfrac{3x^5y^2 - 9x^4y^3 + 3x^3y^4 - 6x^2y^5}{-3x^2y^2}$

30 $\dfrac{4a^2m^2u^2 + 6am^3u^2 - 2a^3m^2u - 4am^2u^3}{2am^2u}$

Chapter 2

H.C.F. Factors. L.C.M. Fractions

H.C.F.

Example 1 *Find the H.C.F. of* $8ab^2c^3$, $6a^2b^3$ *and* $10ab^2c^2$.

$$8ab^2c^3 = 2 \times 2 \times 2 \times a \times b \times b \times c \times c \times c$$
$$6a^2b^3 = 2 \times 3 \times a \times a \times b \times b \times b$$
$$10ab^2c^2 = 2 \times 5 \times a \times b \times b \times c \times c.$$

The biggest collection of factors that is contained in all three expressions is $2 \times a \times b \times b$.

Hence the H.C.F. is $2ab^2$.

With practice it will be found unnecessary to write out the expressions in their expanded form. The H.C.F. may be written down by inspection.

Exercise 2a

Find the H.C.F. of

1 $amxy$ and $bmdx$
2 $9hkl$ and $6ghk$
3 mn^2 and m^2n
4 $8d^2e$ and $6def$
5 $10lm^2n^3$ and $15l^3m^2n$
6 $24a^2b^4$ and $16a^3b^3$
7 uvw, vwx and wxy
8 $8ab^3$, $2a^2b^2$ and $6a^3b$
9 $3c^4d^3$, $9c^2d^5$ and $7c^3d^4$
10 $12ax^3y^2$, $4a^3y^4$ and $8a^2xy^3$
11 $15abm^2n$, $6cmp^2b$ and $12b^2dmp$
12 $4f^3gh^3$, $8g^2h^4k^3$ and fg^3h^2k
13 $18a^2bm^2n^3$, $24a^3b^2m^2$ and $12a^2mn^2$
14 $16uv^2m^3n^2$, $32u^3mn^3$ and $24v^3m^2n^2$
15 $16a^4b^3x^3$, $24b^2m^3x^4y$ and $20a^2b^3nx^3$

Example 2 *Complete the bracket in the statement*

$$15mx^2 + 5m^3x - 10m^2x^2 = 5mx(\qquad).$$

When the contents of the bracket are multiplied by $5mx$ the original expression should be obtained. Hence the contents of the bracket may be found by dividing the given expression by $5mx$.

$$5mx\ )\ \underline{15mx^2 + 5m^3x - 10m^2x^2}$$
$$\underline{3x \quad + \ m^2 \quad - \ 2mx}$$

$\therefore\ 15mx^2 + 5m^3x - 10m^2x^2 = 5mx(3x + m^2 - 2mx).$

The result may be checked mentally by multiplication.

$5mx$ and $(3x + m^2 - 2mx)$ are said to be the **factors** of $15mx^2 + 5m^3x - 10m^2x^2$, just as 2 and 7 are the factors of 14, since $14 = 2 \times 7$.

Example 3 *Factorise* $15a^3b^4c - 6a^2b^5c^2 - 9a^4b^3$.

The H.C.F. of the three terms is $3a^2b^3$.

$\therefore\ 15a^3b^4c - 6a^2b^5c^2 - 9a^4b^3 = 3a^2b^3(5abc - 2b^2c^2 - 3a^2).$

Check by multiplying out mentally.

Exercise 2b

Complete the brackets in the following statements:

1 $9x + 3y + 6z = 3(\qquad)$
2 $5a - 15b - 10c + 20d = 5(\qquad)$
3 $8cm + 12dm - 16em = 4m(\qquad)$
4 $8ap - 6aq - 2ar + 4as = -2a(\qquad)$
5 $6x^4 + 3x^3 - 12x^2 - 9x = 3x(\qquad)$
6 $-6m^4 + 2m^3 - 8m^2 = -2m^2(\qquad)$
7 $3abx - 5acx + 2a^2x^2 = -ax(\qquad)$
8 $10a^2b^2 - 15a^2b + 20ab^2 - 5ab = 5ab(\qquad)$
9 $a^3b^2c - ab^3c^2 - a^2bc^3 = abc(\qquad)$
10 $-2p^3q^3r^2 - 6p^2q^3r + 4p^3q^2r^2 + 2p^2q^2r^3 = -2p^2q^2r(\qquad)$

Factorise

11 $4a - 8b - 12c + 6d$ **12** $9x + 12y - 6z - 3$
13 $3ab - 6ac + 3ad - 9ae$ **14** $12lx + 8mx - 4nx + 8px$
15 $3m^3 - 2m^2 + m$ **16** $6n^4 - 2n^3 + 4n^2 - 2n$

17 $5ab + 4a^2b - 6ab^2 - 2a^2b^2$

18 $2abx + 7acx - 3a^2x - 4ax^2$

19 $4a^4 + 2a^3 - 10a^2$

20 $3c^6 - 6c^5 + 5c^4 - 2c^3$

21 $6e^2m + 3em^2 - 3e^2m^2$

22 $x^6 - 5x^4 - 3x^2$

23 $2x^7 - 4x^5 + 6x^3 - 3x$

24 $4by^2 + 8bz^2 - 2byz$

25 $5d^3u - 3d^2v + 5d^3uv$

26 $6a^3m + 3a^2m^2 - 3am^3$

27 $d^2ef - de^2f + def^2 - def$

28 $4l^2mn - 10lm^2n - 6lmn^2$

29 $6a^2bm - 9ab^2m - 3a^2bn + 6ab^2n$

30 $5u^3v - 15u^2v^2 + 5uv^3$

31 $4a^4b + 6a^3b^2 - 2a^2b^3$

32 $4abm^2 - 2acm^2 + 6adm^2 - 4a^2m^2$

33 $3x^2y^2 - 15x^3y^2 - 9x^2y^3$

34 $12a^2bc + 8ab^2c - 4a^2b^2$

35 $6a^2hk - 3ah^2k + 9h^2k^2$

36 $p^2q^2r^2 + p^3qr^2 - p^2qr^3$

37 $4fg^2h^2 - 6f^2gh^2 - 2f^2g^2h + 2fgh$

38 $3a^2bm^2 + 9a^2cm^2 - 6a^3dm$

39 $10m^3u^2v^3 - 15n^2u^3v^2 - 5mu^4v + 10nu^3v^3$

40 $24a^2b^2c + 30b^2c^2d - 18c^2d^2a - 4abcd$

L.C.M.

Example 4 *Find the L.C.M. of* $4a^2bc$, $6ac$ *and* $8bc^2$.

$$4a^2bc = 2 \times 2 \times a \times a \times b \times c$$
$$6ac = 2 \times 3 \times a \times c$$
$$8bc^2 = 2 \times 2 \times 2 \times b \times c \times c.$$

The smallest collection of factors that contains *all* the factors of the three expressions is $2 \times 2 \times 2 \times 3 \times a \times a \times b \times c \times c$.

Hence the L.C.M. is $24a^2bc^2$.

With practice the L.C.M. may be written down by inspection, without writing each expression in its expanded form.

Exercise 2c

Find the L.C.M. of

1 mnu and muv

2 $3abm$ and $2am^2$

3 ab, bc and cd

4 $4x^2y$ and $6xy^3$

5 $9u^2mn$ and $6vm^2n$

6 $3a^2b$, abc and $6b^2c$

7 m^3n^2, $5m$ and $10n$

8 $3a^2b^5$, $6a^3c^2$ and $2b^3c$

9 $3f^2g$, $6g^2h$ and $4h^2k$

10 $8pqr^3$, $6p^2qs$ and $12q^3rs^2$

Find the H.C.F. and L.C.M. of

11 a^2bm^3n, ab^3m and abn^2

12 $2cdu^2$, $3d^2uv$ and $6c^2uv^2$

13 $9c^2d^3$, $3bcd^2e$ and $6bde$

14 $6am^2x$, $4anx^2$ and $8am^2nx^2$

15 $3a^2uv^4$, $a^4mu^2v^3$ and $4a^3m^2v^3$

Fractions

Example 5 *Fill the blank in the statement* $\dfrac{3ab}{5c^2d} = \dfrac{\quad}{20ac^2d^2}$.

$20ac^2d^2$ is obtained by multiplying the denominator $5c^2d$ by $4ad$.
$\therefore$ the numerator $3ab$ must also be multiplied by $4ad$.

$$\therefore \frac{3ab}{5c^2d} = \frac{12a^2bd}{20ac^2d^2}$$

Example 6 *Simplify* $\dfrac{5}{2cd} + \dfrac{4}{3de}$.

The L.C.M. of $2cd$ and $3de$ is $6cde$.

$$\therefore \frac{5}{2cd} + \frac{4}{3de} = \frac{5 \times 3e}{6cde} + \frac{4 \times 2c}{6cde}$$

$$= \frac{5 \times 3e + 4 \times 2c}{6cde}$$

$$= \frac{15e + 8c}{6cde}.$$

Example 7 *Simplify* $\dfrac{3x}{ab^2} - \dfrac{2y}{a^2bc}$.

The L.C.M. of ab^2 and a^2bc is a^2b^2c.

$$\therefore \frac{3x}{ab^2} - \frac{2y}{a^2bc} = \frac{3x \times ac - 2y \times b}{a^2b^2c}$$

$$= \frac{3acx - 2by}{a^2b^2c}.$$

Example 8 *Simplify* $\frac{4}{ab} + 3m$.

$$\frac{4}{ab} + 3m = \frac{4 + 3mab}{ab}.$$

Example 9 *Simplify* $\frac{a + 2b}{ab} - \frac{b + 2c}{bc}$.

$$\frac{a + 2b}{ab} - \frac{b + 2c}{bc} = \frac{c(a + 2b) - a(b + 2c)}{abc}$$

$$= \frac{ac + 2bc - ab - 2ac}{abc}$$

$$= \frac{2bc - ab - ac}{abc}.$$

Exercise 2d

Fill up the blanks in the following:

1 $\frac{3x}{2y} = \frac{\quad}{8yz}$ **2** $\frac{2c}{ab} = \frac{6c^2}{\quad}$ **3** $\frac{2mu}{\quad} = \frac{m}{4nu}$

4 $\frac{\quad}{c^2d^2e} = \frac{3e}{cd^2}$ **5** $3u = \frac{\quad}{2d}$ **6** $2ac = \frac{6ace}{\quad}$

7 $5a^2b = \frac{\quad}{3bc}$ **8** $\frac{m + n}{m} = \frac{\quad}{mn}$ **9** $\frac{a - b}{3ab} = \frac{\quad}{6a^2b}$

10 $\frac{2u - 3v}{4u^2v} = \frac{\quad}{12u^2v^2}$

Simplify

11 $\frac{1}{3x} + \frac{1}{5x}$ **12** $\frac{1}{4a} - \frac{1}{6a}$ **13** $\frac{1}{2a} + \frac{1}{2b}$

14 $\frac{1}{bx} - \frac{1}{ax}$ **15** $\frac{c}{m} - \frac{d}{n}$ **16** $\frac{k}{x} + 1$

17 $2 - \frac{b}{a}$ **18** $\frac{3}{cd} - \frac{2}{de}$ **19** $\frac{5}{a} + \frac{2}{b} - \frac{4}{ab}$

20 $\frac{3d}{8} - \frac{5e}{6}$ **21** $\frac{m+n}{2} + \frac{3}{a}$ **22** $\frac{a-2d}{m} + 2$

23 $3 - \frac{h+k}{a}$ **24** $2 - \frac{b-2c}{x}$

25 $\frac{2m-u}{3} + \frac{m-2u}{2}$ **26** $\frac{3b+c}{4} - \frac{2b-c}{3}$

27 $\frac{a+m}{2} - \frac{a+2m}{3} + \frac{a-m}{4}$ **28** $\frac{a+b}{x} + \frac{a-b}{y}$

29 $\frac{m+n}{m} - \frac{m-n}{n}$ **30** $\frac{3+a}{a} - \frac{2+b}{b}$

31 $\frac{2b}{a} + \frac{a-b}{b}$ **32** $\frac{3m}{n} - \frac{m+n}{m}$

33 $\frac{3}{m} - \frac{2}{m^2} + \frac{4}{m^3}$ **34** $\frac{2m}{5x} - \frac{m+2}{2x} + \frac{1+m}{10x}$

35 $\frac{x}{uv} - \frac{y}{vw}$ **36** $\frac{5a}{2bc} + \frac{4b}{3ac}$ **37** $\frac{5}{4mn^2} + \frac{2}{3m^2n}$

38 $\frac{3}{4u^2w} - \frac{1}{2v^2w}$ **39** $\frac{m}{abc} + \frac{n}{bcd}$ **40** $\frac{3c}{2ab^2} - \frac{d}{5a^2b}$

41 $\frac{m}{x^2y} + \frac{n}{y^2z} + \frac{r}{xyz}$ **42** $\frac{2a}{3cd^2} - \frac{b}{2de^2} + \frac{5a}{6cde}$

43 $\frac{h-k}{2h} - \frac{h+k}{3k} + \frac{h^2-k^2}{6hk}$

44 $\frac{u^2+2v^2}{uv} - \frac{3uv-u^2}{v^2} + \frac{v}{u}$

45 $\frac{2a-3b}{4ab} - \frac{2b+3c}{6bc} + \frac{3c+a}{3ca}$

Chapter 3

Congruent triangles. Mapping

A triangle has three sides and three angles, but there is no need for all six of these measurements to be known before the triangle can be drawn. There are certain groups of **three** facts that are sufficient to fix the shape and size of a triangle. This means that with the information given it is possible to draw one, and **only one,** triangle.

Two sides and the included angle. A $\triangle ABC$ is to be drawn and the facts given are (i) the length of $\overline{AB}$, (ii) the length of $\overline{BC}$, (iii) the size of $A\hat{B}C$. $A\hat{B}C$ is called the **included angle** because it lies between (or is included between) the given sides $\overline{AB}$ and $\overline{BC}$.

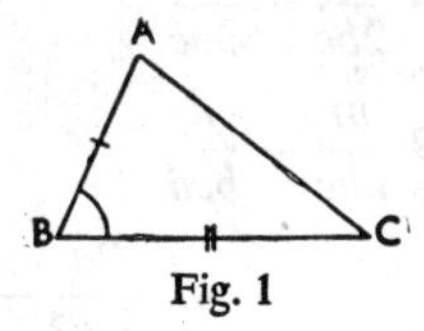

Fig. 1

First, the side $\overline{BC}$ is drawn of the given length. Then $A\hat{B}C$ is made, and the length for $\overline{BA}$ marked off. Finally A and C are joined and the triangle is complete. Any triangle drawn with these

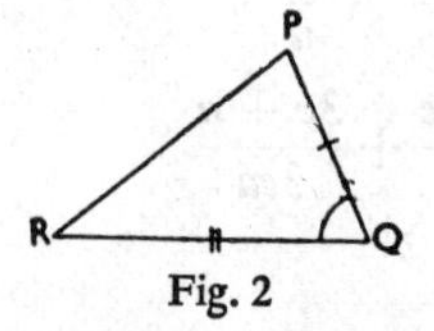

Fig. 2

three given facts is the same as $\triangle ABC$. The $\triangle PQR$ in which $PQ = AB$, $QR = BC$ and $P\hat{Q}R = A\hat{B}C$ may at first sight appear to be different, but if it were cut out and turned over it would be found to fit exactly over $\triangle ABC$. If two triangles LMN, XYZ are

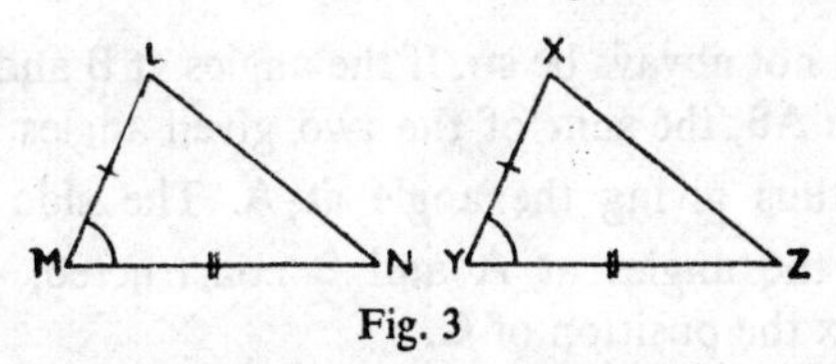

Fig. 3

drawn in which $LM = XY$, $MN = YZ$, $L\hat{M}N = X\hat{Y}Z$, the triangles are identical and are said to be **congruent,** or equal in all respects. It follows that $LN = XZ$, $M\hat{L}N = Y\hat{X}Z$, $L\hat{N}M = X\hat{Z}Y$.

If the given angle is **not included** between the two given sides, it is possible to draw two different triangles with the given information. In Fig. 4 the $\triangle$s A_1BC, A_2BC both have the same angle at

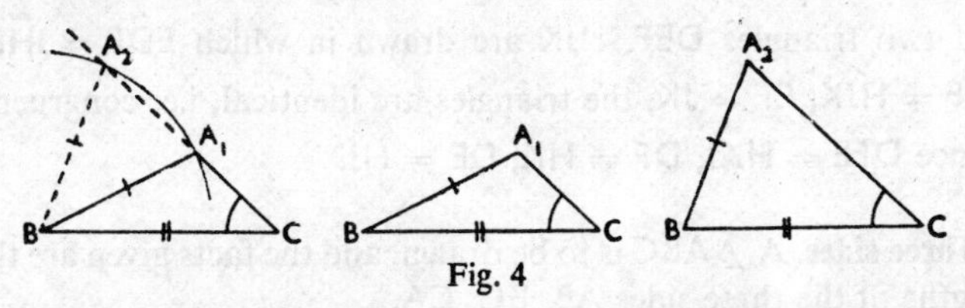

Fig. 4

C, the same side BC, and $A_1B = A_2B$. These two triangles are clearly not congruent. This is called the **ambiguous case.** If two triangles have two sides and a non-included angle of one equal respectively to two sides and the corresponding angle of the other, the triangles may be congruent, but are not necessarily so.

Two angles and corresponding side. A $\triangle ABC$ is to be drawn and the facts given are (i) the size of $A\hat{B}C$, (ii) the size of $A\hat{C}B$, (iii) the length of $\overline{BC}$.

First, the side $\overline{BC}$ is drawn of the given length. Then $C\hat{B}A$ and $B\hat{C}A$ are constructed according to the sizes given. $\overline{BA}$ and $\overline{CA}$ meet at A, thus fixing the third corner of the triangle. It is clear that no different triangle could result from the given facts.

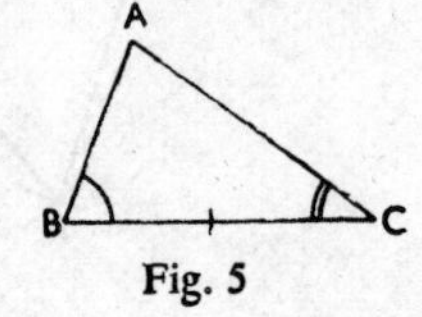

Fig. 5

It will be noticed that in this case the given side is between the two given angles, but this need not always be so. If the angles at B and C are given, together with AB, the sum of the two given angles is subtracted from 180°, thus giving the angle at A. The side $\overline{AB}$ is then drawn, and the angles at A and B constructed, $\overline{AC}$ and $\overline{BC}$ meeting to fix the position of C.

In fact, being given two angles of a triangle is virtually the same as being given all three angles. Hence it is immaterial which side is given.

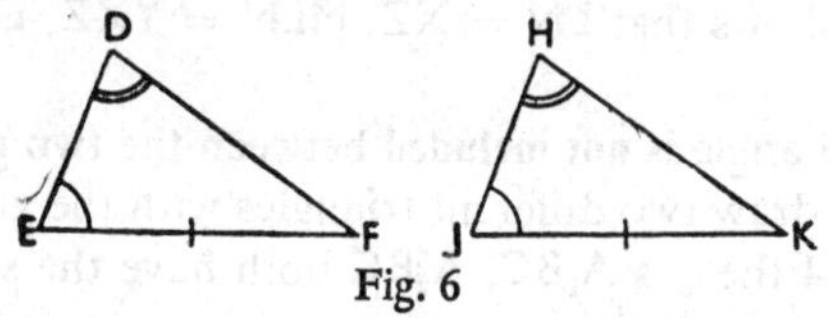

Fig. 6

If two triangles DEF, HJK are drawn in which $E\hat{D}F = J\hat{H}K$, $D\hat{E}F = H\hat{J}K$, EF = JK, the triangles are identical, i.e. congruent. Hence $D\hat{F}E = H\hat{K}J$, DF = HK, DE = HJ.

Three sides. A $\triangle ABC$ is to be drawn, and the facts given are the lengths of the three sides AB, BC, CA.

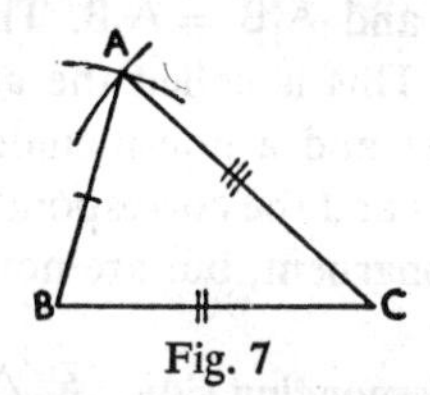

Fig. 7

First, the side $\overline{BC}$ is drawn of the given length. Then with centre B and radius AB an arc is drawn. Similarly with centre C and radius CA an arc is drawn. The two arcs meet at A, thus fixing the third corner of the triangle.

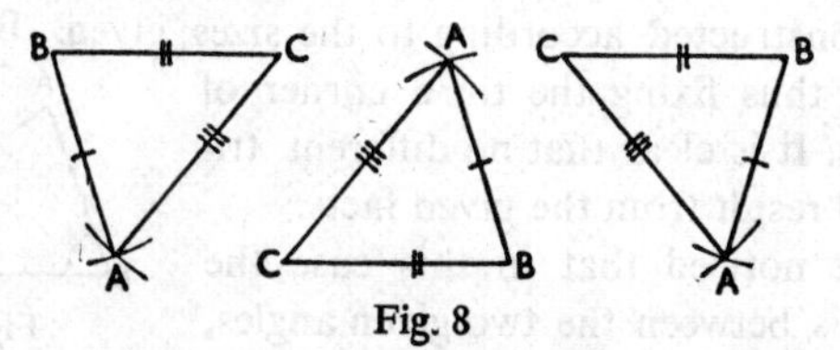

Fig. 8

No different triangle could result from this construction, although the triangle ABC could appear in different positions, or turned over, as in Fig. 8.

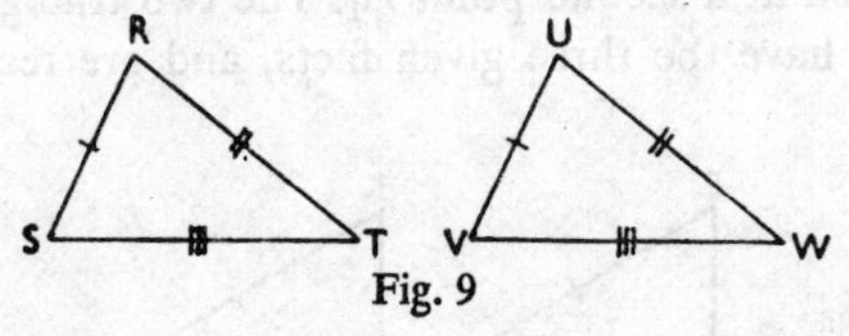

Fig. 9

If two triangles RST, UVW are drawn in which RS = UV, RT = UW, ST = VW, the triangles are congruent. Hence $R\hat{S}T = U\hat{V}W$, $R\hat{T}S = U\hat{W}V$, $S\hat{R}T = V\hat{U}W$.

Right angle, hypotenuse and one other side. A $\triangle$ABC is to be drawn, and the facts given are (i) $A\hat{C}B$ is a right angle, (ii) the length of the hypotenuse $\overline{AB}$, (iii) the length of $\overline{BC}$.

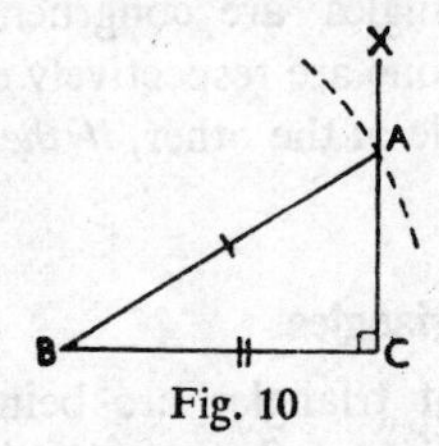

Fig. 10

The side $\overline{BC}$ is drawn of the given length. Through C a line $\overline{CX}$ is drawn at right angles to BC. Then with centre B and radius AB an arc is drawn to cut $\overline{CX}$ at A. $\triangle$ABC is then the required triangle.

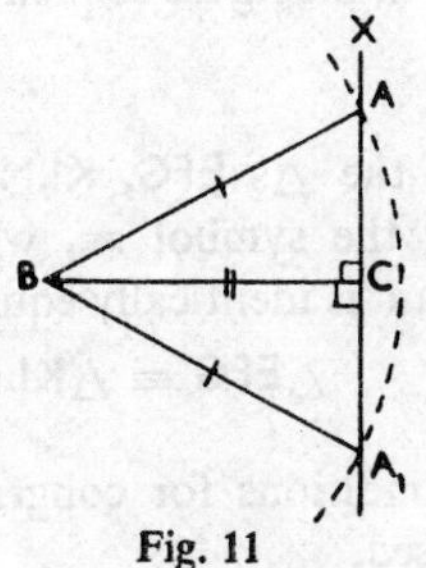

Fig. 11

No different triangle could result from this construction, although the arc with centre B could have been continued to cut $\overline{XC}$ produced at a second point A_1. The two triangles ABC and A_1BC both have the three given facts, and are really the same triangle.

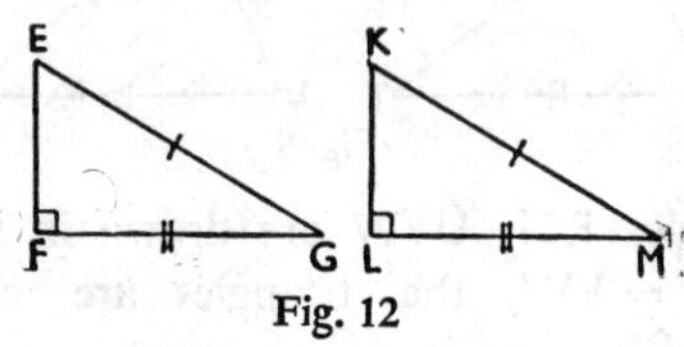

Fig. 12

If two triangles EFG, KLM are drawn in which $E\hat{F}G$ = a right angle = $K\hat{L}M$, EG = KM, FG = LM, the triangles are congruent. Hence EF = KL, $F\hat{E}G = L\hat{K}M$, $E\hat{G}F = K\hat{M}L$.

By comparing this with the ambiguous case in Fig. 4 it will be seen that two triangles are congruent if two sides and a **non-included** angle of one are respectively equal to two sides and the corresponding angle of the other, *if the non-included angle is a right angle.*

Naming of congruent triangles

Whenever congruent triangles are being named, the letters should be put in the right order, so that it is quite clear which letters of the two triangles correspond to each other. For example, in Fig. 12, △FGE is congruent to △LMK, not △KLM or △LKM etc. When congruent triangles are properly named in this way, it is unnecessary to look at the figure to pick out pairs of equal sides or equal angles.

The statement that the △s EFG, KLM are congruent can be abbreviated by using the symbol ≡, which has already been used in algebra to mean 'is identically equal to'.

Thus, $\triangle EFG \equiv \triangle KLM$.

The four sets of conditions for congruency of two triangles may now be summarised.

Two triangles are congruent if

(i) **two sides and the included angle** of one are respectively equal to two sides and the included angle of the other. (Abbreviation SAS)

(ii) **two angles and a side** of one are respectively equal to two angles and the **corresponding** side of the other. (ASA or AAS)

(iii) the **three sides** of one are respectively equal to the three sides of the other. (SSS)

(iv) they are **right-angled,** and have the **hypotenuse and another side** of one respectively equal to the hypotenuse and another side of the other. (RHS)

Similar triangles

If the **three angles** of one triangle are respectively equal to the three angles of another triangle, the two triangles are not neces-

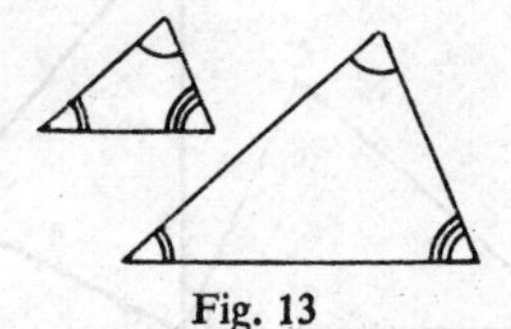

Fig. 13

sarily congruent, but are said to be **similar.** They are of the same *shape*, but may be unequal in *size*, as in Fig. 13. Similar triangles will be considered more fully in Chapter 16.

Mapping

Displacement. In Fig. 12 the triangle KLM can be considered as being the triangle EFG moved a distance GM in direction $\overline{GM}$ to the right. This is known as a **displacement** or **translation.** EK = FL = GM and $\overline{EK} \parallel \overline{FL} \parallel \overline{GM}$. In a displacement every point of one figure is moved the same distance in the same direction to form the new figure. △EFG is said to be **mapped** into △KLM by a displacement equal to $\overrightarrow{GM}$. The arrow over GM implies that the direction of the displacement is in the line from G to M and its magnitude is GM.

Reflection. In Fig. 11 the triangle A_1BC can be considered as the triangle ABC **reflected** in $\overline{BC}$ as in a mirror. $\overline{BC}$ is known as the **axis of reflection** for $\triangle ABC$, or **axis of symmetry** for the complete figure. Note that $\overline{BC}$ is the perpendicular bisector of the line joining any point in the original figure (the **object**) to the corresponding point in the reflected figure (the **image**). $\triangle ABC$ is said to be mapped into $\triangle A_1BC$ by reflection in $\overline{BC}$, and conversely.

Rotation. Fig. 14 shows two congruent triangles ABC and ADE. If $\triangle ABC$ were cut out and turned through 90° clockwise about the point A, it would fit exactly over $\triangle ADE$. $\triangle ABC$ is said to be mapped into $\triangle ADE$ by a **rotation** of 90° clockwise about A.

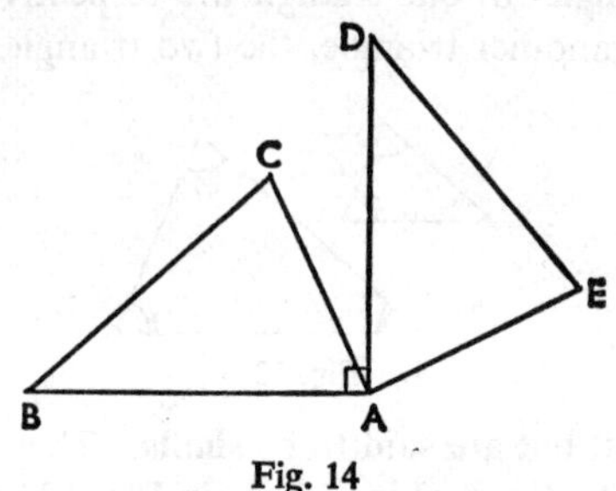

Fig. 14

Note that a rotation of 180° clockwise is the same as a rotation of 180° anticlockwise.

The ideas of displacement, reflection and rotation apply equally to figures other than triangles. In each of these three mappings any one point is mapped into one point, lines remain the same length, angles remain the same size, and areas are unchanged.

Fig. 15 shows a mapping involving both displacement and rotation. The triangle ABC can be considered as being displaced through $\overrightarrow{AD}$ to the dotted position DHG and then rotated about D into position DFE through an angle equal to $G\hat{D}E$ clockwise.

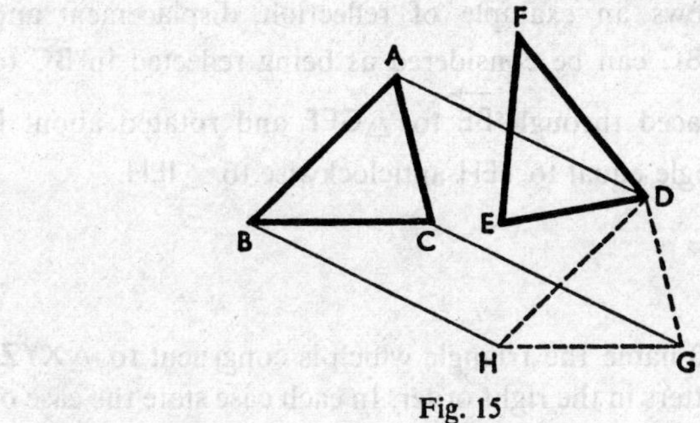

Fig. 15

Fig. 16 shows an example of displacement and reflection. $\triangle ABC$ can be considered as being reflected in $\overline{AC}$ to the dotted position AGC and displaced through $\overrightarrow{AD}$ to $\triangle DEF$.

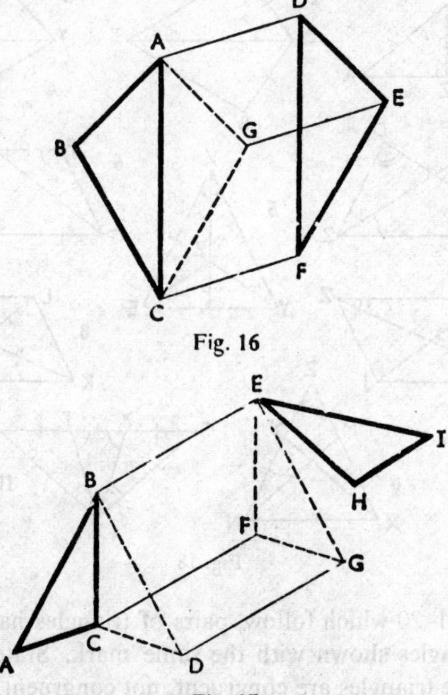

Fig. 16

Fig. 17

Fig. 17 shows an example of reflection, displacement and rotation. $\triangle ABC$ can be considered as being reflected in $\overline{BC}$ to $\triangle DBC$, displaced through $\overrightarrow{BE}$ to $\triangle GEF$ and rotated about E through an angle equal to $F\hat{E}H$ anticlockwise to $\triangle IEH$.

Exercise 3a

In nos. 1–10 name the triangle which is congruent to $\triangle XYZ$, keeping the letters in the right order. In each case state the case of congruency, using the following abbreviations: RHS, SSS, SAS, ASA or AAS. In each case sketch the diagram showing the axis of reflection or point of rotation.

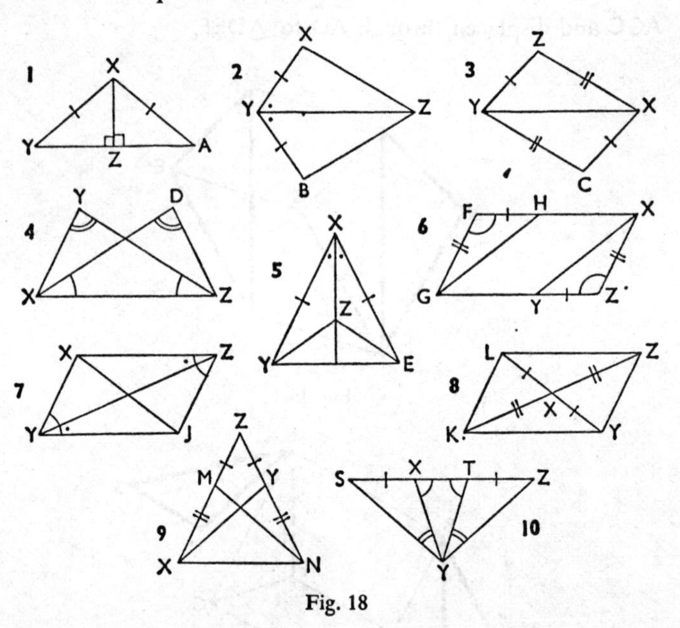

Fig. 18

In nos. 11–20 which follow, pairs of triangles have equal sides or equal angles shown with the same mark. State in each case whether the triangles are congruent, not congruent, or not necessarily congruent. Where appropriate state the case of congruency, and draw a sketch like Fig. 15, Fig. 16 or Fig. 17.

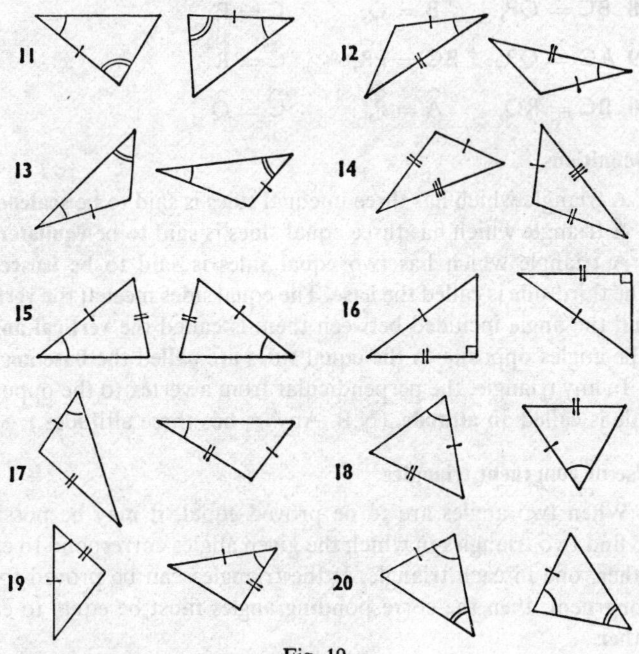

Fig. 19

In each of nos. 21–30 the statements refer to triangles ABC and PQR. In each case sketch the triangles and mark in what is given. If the triangles are congruent, state three other pairs of equal elements. Also give the case of congruency, and the appropriate mapping.

21 AB = PQ, BC = QR, $\hat{B} = \hat{Q}$

22 AB = RQ, $\hat{B} = \hat{Q}$, $\hat{C} = \hat{P}$

23 AC = PR $\hat{B} = \hat{R}$, $\hat{C} = \hat{Q}$

24 AB = QP, BC = PR, CA = RQ

25 AC = PQ BC = RQ, $\hat{A} = 90° = \hat{P}$

26 AB = RP, AC = RQ, $\hat{B} = \hat{P}$

27 AB = QR, AC = QP, $\hat{B} = \hat{P}$

28 BC = QP, $\hat{B} = \hat{Q}$, $\hat{C} = \hat{P}$

29 AC = QR, BC = PR, $\hat{C} = \hat{R}$

30 BC = RQ, $\hat{A} = \hat{P}$, $\hat{C} = \hat{Q}$

Definitions

A triangle which has three unequal sides is said to be **scalene.**

A triangle which has three equal sides is said to be **equilateral.**

A triangle which has two equal sides is said to be **isosceles.** The third side is called the **base.** The equal sides meet at the **vertex,** and the angle included between them is called the **vertical angle.** The angles opposite to the equal sides are called the **base angles.**

In any triangle, the perpendicular from a vertex to the opposite side is called an **altitude.** (N.B. Any $\triangle$ has three altitudes.)

Use of congruent triangles

When two angles are to be proved equal, it may be possible to find two triangles in which the given angles correspond to each other, one in each triangle. If the triangles can be proved to be congruent, then the corresponding angles must be equal to each other.

Similarly two lines will be equal in length if they are corresponding sides of two triangles which are proved to be congruent.

This use of congruent triangles is illustrated in Theorems 3 and 4 which follow.

Theorem 3

If two sides of a triangle are equal, then the angles opposite to those sides are equal.

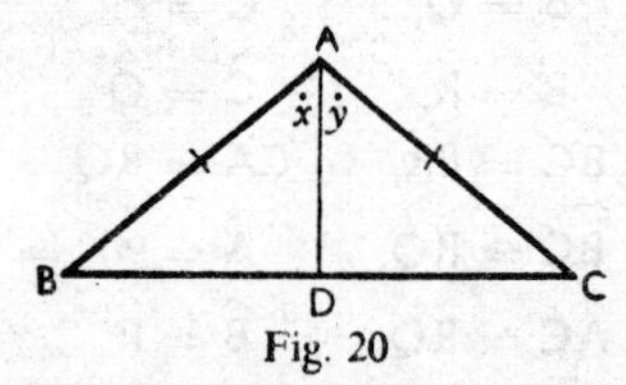

Fig. 20

This theorem may also be stated in the following way:

The base angles of an isosceles triangle are equal.

Given $\triangle ABC$ in which $AB = AC$.

To prove $\hat{B} = \hat{C}$.

Constr. Draw a line to bisect $B\hat{A}C$, and let it meet $\overline{BC}$ at D.

Proof. In $\triangle$s ABD, ACD

$AB = AC$	*given*
AD is common	
$x = y$	*constr.*
$\therefore \triangle ABD \equiv \triangle ACD$	*SAS*

$\triangle ACD$ is the reflection of $\triangle ABD$ in $\overline{AD}$

$\therefore \hat{B} = \hat{C}$. Q.E.D.

In the setting down of this theorem notice that

(i) in the first line of the proof, the order of the letters *does* matter; in the two $\triangle$s, A corresponds to A, B to C, D to D.

(ii) AB and x are put on the left of the = signs, because they are parts of $\triangle ABD$ which is mentioned first.

Theorem 4

If two angles of a triangle are equal, then the sides opposite to those angles are equal.

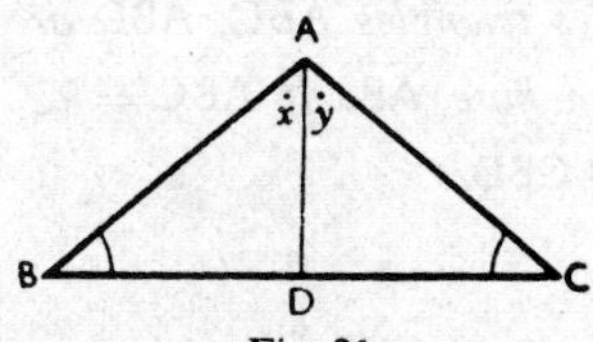

Fig. 21

Given $\triangle ABC$ in which $\hat{C} = \hat{B}$.

To prove $AB = AC$.

Constr. Draw a line to bisect $B\hat{A}C$, and let it meet $\overline{BC}$ at D.

Proof. In $\triangle$s ABD, ACD

$\hat{B} = \hat{C}$	*given*
$x = y$	*constr.*

$$\text{AD is common}$$

$$\therefore \triangle ABD \equiv \triangle ACD \qquad AAS$$

$$\triangle ACD \text{ is the reflection of } \triangle ABD \text{ in } \overline{AD}$$

$$\therefore AB = AC. \qquad \text{Q.E.D.}$$

It will be noticed that what is given in Theorem 3 is to be proved in Theorem 4, and vice versa. When this is true of two theorems, each is said to be the **converse** of the other.

For many statements the converse is true, but this is not always the case. For example, if two triangles are congruent their corresponding angles are equal; but if in two triangles the corresponding angles are equal, the triangles are not necessarily congruent.

The following important facts may be proved by taking a pair of congruent triangles as in Theorems 3 and 4. A formal proof of each should be written out in full.

1. In an isosceles triangle, the bisector of the vertical angle bisects the base at right angles.

2. In an isosceles triangle, the line joining the vertex to the mid-point of the base is at right angles to the base, and bisects the vertical angle.

3. In an isosceles triangle, the perpendicular from the vertex to the base bisects the base, and bisects the vertical angle.

Example 1 *Isosceles triangles* ABC, ABD *are drawn on opposite sides of a common base* $\overline{AB}$. *If* $A\hat{B}C = 72°$ *and* $A\hat{D}B = 118°$, *calculate* $A\hat{C}B$ *and* $C\hat{B}D$.

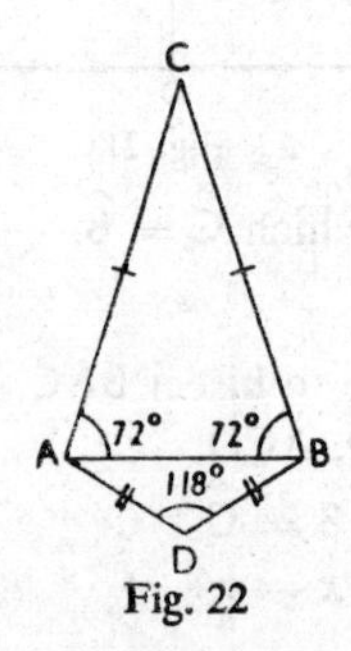

Fig. 22

In $\triangle ABC$, $A\hat{B}C = 72°$

$\therefore B\hat{A}C = 72°$ *base* $\angle$*s of isos.* $\triangle$ *are* =

$\therefore A\hat{C}B = 180° - 72° - 72°$ *sum of* $\angle$*s of* $\triangle = 180°$

$= 36°.$

In $\triangle ABD$, $A\hat{D}B = 118°$

$\therefore A\hat{B}D + B\hat{A}D = 180° - 118°$ *sum of* $\angle$*s of* $\triangle = 180°$

$= 62°$

$\therefore 2 \times A\hat{B}D = 62°$ *base* $\angle$*s of isos.* $\triangle$ *are* =

$\therefore A\hat{B}D = 31°$

$\therefore C\hat{B}D = C\hat{B}A + A\hat{B}D$

$= 72° + 31°$

$= 103°.$

Ans. $A\hat{C}B = 36°$ and $C\hat{B}D = 103°$.

Exercise 3b
Isosceles and equilateral triangles

In nos. 1–10, calculate the angles marked with letters.

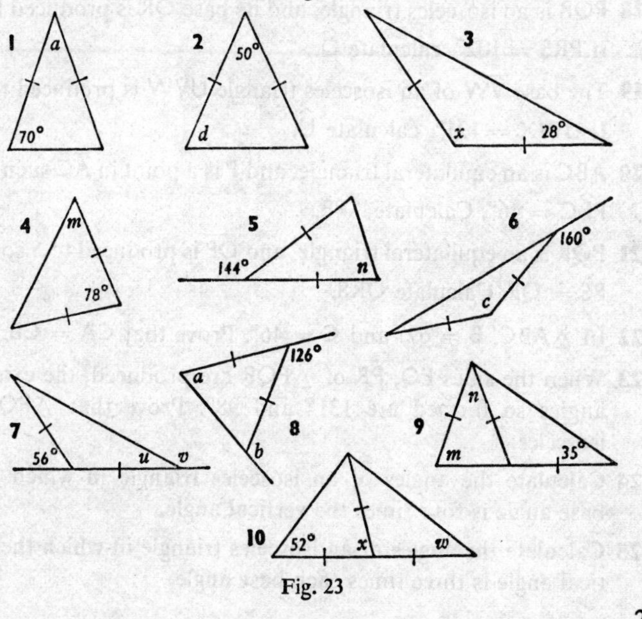

Fig. 23

11 Prove that the three angles of an equilateral triangle are equal. How many degrees are there in each?

12 Prove that if the vertical angle of an isosceles triangle is 60°, then the triangle is equilateral.

13 In the isosceles triangle ABC, AB = AC. If $\hat{B} = 55°$, calculate $\hat{A}$.

14 PQR is an isosceles triangle in which PQ = PR, and $\hat{P} = 58°$. Calculate $\hat{Q}$.

15 XYZ is an isosceles triangle with vertical angle X equal to 117°. Calculate $\hat{Z}$.

16 The base $\overline{JK}$ of an isosceles triangle HJK is produced to L. If $\hat{J} = 69°$, calculate $H\hat{K}L$.

17 ABC is an isosceles triangle with its base $\overline{BC}$ produced to D. If $\hat{A} = 75°$, calculate $A\hat{C}D$.

18 PQR is an isosceles triangle, and its base $\overline{QR}$ is produced to S. If $P\hat{R}S = 102°$, calculate $\hat{Q}$.

19 The base $\overline{VW}$ of an isosceles triangle UVW is produced to X. If $U\hat{W}X = 121°$, calculate $\hat{U}$.

20 ABC is an equilateral triangle, and P is a point in $\overline{AC}$ such that $P\hat{B}C = 46°$. Calculate $A\hat{P}B$.

21 PQR is an equilateral triangle, and $\overline{QP}$ is produced to S so that PS = QP. Calculate $Q\hat{R}S$.

22 In $\triangle ABC$, $\hat{B} = 67°$ and $\hat{C} = 46°$. Prove that CA = CB.

23 When the sides $\overline{PQ}$, $\overline{PR}$ of $\triangle PQR$ are produced, the exterior angles so formed are 131° and 98°. Prove that $\triangle PQR$ is isosceles.

24 Calculate the angles of an isosceles triangle in which each base angle is four times the vertical angle.

25 Calculate the angles of an isosceles triangle in which the vertical angle is three times each base angle.

26 XYZ is an equilateral triangle. The perpendicular from X to $\overline{YZ}$ meets $\overline{YZ}$ in M. The perpendicular from M to $\overline{XZ}$ meets $\overline{XZ}$ in N. Calculate $N\hat{M}X$.

27 ABCD is a square, and equilateral triangles ABX, BCY are drawn so that they lie outside the square. Calculate the angles of $\triangle BXY$.

28 ABCD is a quadrilateral in which $AD = BD = BC$, and $A\hat{D}B = B\hat{D}C = 62°$. Calculate $A\hat{B}C$.

29 ABC is a triangle in which $\hat{A} = 30°$ and $\hat{C} = 60°$. Q is a point in $\overline{AC}$ such that $QB = QC$. Prove that Q is the mid-point of $\overline{AC}$.

30 PQR is a triangle in which $\hat{Q} = 60°$, $\hat{R} = 90°$. Prove that $PQ = 2 \times QR$. (*Constr. Produce* $\overline{QR}$ *to* S *so that* $RS = QR$. *Join* $\overline{PS}$.)

In Theorems 3 and 4, one pair of congruent triangles was sufficient to prove what was needed. In Example 2 which follows, successive use is made of two pairs of congruent triangles. In order to prove that $OY = OZ$, $\triangle ONY$ must be proved congruent to $\triangle OMZ$. All that is known about these triangles is that $O\hat{N}Y = O\hat{M}Z$ (rt. $\angle$s) and $N\hat{O}Y = M\hat{O}Z$ (vert. opp.). In addition, a pair of equal sides is needed, such as NY and MZ, and these can be proved equal by first proving that $\triangle NYZ \equiv \triangle MZY$.

Example 2 XYZ *is an isosceles* $\triangle$ *having* $XY = XZ$. *The altitudes* $\overline{YM}$, $\overline{ZN}$ *intersect at* O. *Prove that* $OY = OZ$.

Given $\triangle XYZ$ in which $XY = XZ$. The altitudes $\overline{YM}$, $\overline{ZN}$ meet at O.

To prove $OY = OZ$.

Constr. None.

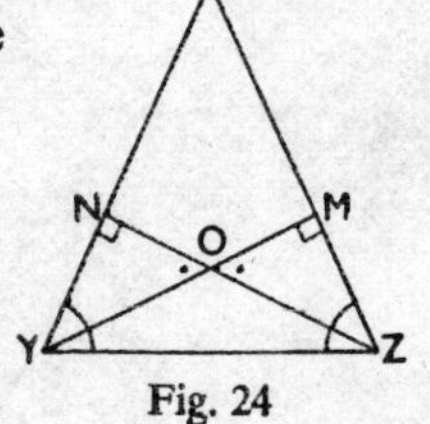

Fig. 24

Proof. In $\triangle$s NYZ, MZY

$\hat{YNZ} = \hat{ZMY}$ *rt. $\angle$s*

$\hat{NYZ} = \hat{MZY}$ *base $\angle$s of isos. $\triangle$*

YZ is common

$\therefore \triangle NYZ \equiv \triangle MZY$ *AAS*

$\triangle$NYZ is the reflection of $\triangle$MZY in $\overline{XO}$ produced

$\therefore NY = MZ$

In $\triangle$s ONY, OMZ

$\hat{ONY} = \hat{OMZ}$ *rt. $\angle$s*

$\hat{NOY} = \hat{MOZ}$ *vert. opp.*

$NY = MZ$ *proved*

$\therefore \triangle ONY \equiv \triangle OMZ$ *AAS*

$\triangle$ONY is the reflection of $\triangle$OMZ in $\overline{XO}$ produced

$\therefore OY = OZ.$

Q.E.D.

Another way of proving that OY = OZ is to start by proving that $\triangle$XMY is the reflection of $\triangle$ XNZ in $\overline{XO}$.

Hence $\hat{XYM} = \hat{XZN}$

But $\hat{XYZ} = \hat{XZY}$ *base $\angle$s of isos. $\triangle$*

$\therefore \hat{XYZ} - \hat{XYM} = \hat{XZY} - \hat{XZN}$

$\therefore \hat{MYZ} = \hat{NZY}$

$\therefore \triangle$OYZ is isosceles

$\therefore OY = OZ.$

Exercise 3c

1 $\overline{POQ}$, $\overline{XOY}$ are two straight lines which bisect each other at O. Prove that $\triangle POY \equiv \triangle QOX$.

2 Triangle ABC is isosceles with AB = AC. X, Y are points on $\overline{AB}$, $\overline{AC}$ respectively such that AX = AY. Prove that $\triangle ABY \equiv \triangle ACX$.

3 $\overline{AOB}$, $\overline{MON}$ are two straight lines which bisect each other at O. Prove that $\overline{AM}$ is parallel to $\overline{NB}$.

4 PQR is an isosceles triangle in which PQ = PR. M, N are points in $\overline{PQ}$, $\overline{PR}$ respectively such that PM = PN. Prove that MR = NQ.

5 ABC is an isosceles triangle. A line parallel to the base $\overline{BC}$ meets $\overline{AB}$ in D and $\overline{AC}$ in E. If AE = DE, prove that $\triangle ABC$ is equilateral.

6 PQRS is a quadrilateral in which PQ = PS, RQ = RS. Prove that $\overline{PR}$ bisects $S\hat{P}Q$.

7 ABCD is a quadrilateral in which $\overline{AB} \parallel \overline{DC}$ and $\overline{AD} \parallel \overline{BC}$. Prove that AB = DC and AD = BC.

8 Prove that the mid-point of a side of a square is equidistant from the ends of the opposite side.

9 PQRS is a quadrilateral and a line through P parallel to $\overline{QR}$ meets $\overline{SR}$ in X. If $\hat{S} = \hat{R}$, prove that $\triangle PSX$ is isosceles.

10 XYZ is an isosceles triangle and M is the mid-point of the base $\overline{YZ}$. A, B are points in $\overline{XY}$, $\overline{XZ}$ respectively such that XA = XB. Prove that AM = BM.

11 $\overline{OHM}$, $\overline{OKN}$ are two straight lines which meet at O. OM = ON and HM = KN. Prove that $O\hat{M}K = O\hat{N}H$.

12 ABC is an isosceles triangle in which AB = AC. $\overline{CA}$ is produced to D so that CA = AD. E is the mid-point of $\overline{BD}$. Prove that $\overline{AE}$ is perpendicular to $\overline{BD}$.

13 ABC is an isosceles triangle having AB = AC. The bisectors of the angles B, C meet the opposite sides in M, N respectively. Prove that BM = CN.

14 A is any point on the line which bisects $X\hat{O}Y$. Prove that the perpendiculars from A to $\overline{OX}$ and $\overline{OY}$ are equal.

15 PQR is a triangle in which PQ = PR. A is any point in $\overline{PQ}$, and through A a line is drawn perpendicular to $\overline{QR}$ to meet $\overline{RP}$ produced in B. Prove that PA = PB.

16 AMN, BMN are two triangles lying on the same side of $\overline{MN}$. AM = BN and AN = BM. $\overline{AN}$ and $\overline{BM}$ meet at X. Prove that MX = NX.

17 Two straight lines $\overline{AOB}$, $\overline{POQ}$ intersect at O, and the perpendiculars from P, Q to $\overline{AOB}$ are $\overline{PM}$, $\overline{QN}$ respectively. If PM = QN, prove that OM = ON.

18 P, Q are points on the base $\overline{BC}$ of an isosceles triangle ABC. If BP = CQ, prove that $\triangle$APQ is also isosceles.

19 M is the mid-point of the base $\overline{BC}$ of an isosceles triangle ABC, and P is any point on $\overline{AM}$. Prove that PB = PC.

20 $\overline{PQ}$, $\overline{RS}$ are parallel straight lines which are cut by a straight line in A, B respectively. The mid-point of $\overline{AB}$ is M, and another straight line through M meets $\overline{PQ}$, $\overline{RS}$ in X, Y respectively. Prove that XM = MY.

21 ABCD is a quadrilateral with all four sides equal. Prove that its diagonals meet at right angles.

22 M is the mid-point of the side $\overline{BC}$ of $\triangle$ABC. Prove that the perpendiculars from B and C to $\overline{AM}$ (or $\overline{AM}$ produced) are equal.

23 M is the mid-point of a straight line $\overline{XY}$, and P is any point on the straight line through M at right angles to XY. Prove that PX = PY.

24 XYZ is an isosceles triangle in which XY = XZ. Equilateral triangles AYZ, BZX, CXY are drawn so that they lie outside △XYZ. Prove that △ABC is isosceles.

25 O is a point in the side $\overline{BC}$ of △ABC such that OB = OC = OA. Prove that $B\hat{A}C = 90°$.

26 X, Y are points on the sides $\overline{AB}$, $\overline{CD}$ respectively of a square ABCD. If AX = CY, prove that AY = CX.

27 ABCD is a square and X, Y, Z are the mid-points of the sides $\overline{AB}$, $\overline{BC}$, $\overline{CD}$ respectively. Prove that △ABY ≡ △DCY and △XBY ≡ △ZCY. Hence prove that △AXY ≡ △DZY.

28 M is the mid-point of the side $\overline{PQ}$ of △PQR. The line through M parallel to $\overline{QR}$ meets $\overline{PR}$ in H. The line through M parallel to $\overline{PR}$ meets $\overline{QR}$ in K. Prove that MH = QK and MK = PH.

29 PQR is an equilateral triangle, and D, E, F are points in $\overline{PQ}$, $\overline{QR}$, $\overline{RP}$ respectively such that PD = QE = RF. Prove that △DEF is also equilateral.

30 ABC, DBC are isosceles triangles lying on opposite sides of a common base $\overline{BC}$. Prove that $\overline{AD}$ and $\overline{BC}$ meet at right angles.

31 PQR, TQR are isosceles triangles lying on the same side of a common base $\overline{QR}$, T lying within △PQR. Prove that $\overline{PT}$ produced bisects $\overline{QR}$.

32 PQR is any triangle, and squares PABQ, PCDR are drawn so that they lie outside the triangle. Prove that AR = CQ.

33 XYZ is any triangle, and equilateral triangles XAY, XBZ are drawn so that they lie outside the given triangle XYZ. Prove that AZ = BY.

34 PQRS is a quadrilateral in which $\overline{PQ}$ is parallel to $\overline{SR}$, and $\overline{PS}$ is parallel to $\overline{QR}$. Prove that $\overline{PR}$ and $\overline{QS}$ bisect each other.

35 ABCD is a quadrilateral in which AB = DC. X is a point within the quadrilateral such that AX = DX and BX = CX. Prove that if $\overline{BA}$ and $\overline{CD}$ are produced to meet at T, then △TBC is isosceles.

Chapter 4

Constructions

In their practical work, draughtsmen use instruments such as protractors, parallel rules, set-squares and so on, because by their use accurate figures can be constructed with comparative ease. The constructions in the present chapter will be done with only two instruments, namely compasses and ruler (used only as a straight-edge—no graduations needed). This is partly because it is good practice to be so restricted, and partly because these constructions are exercises in theoretical geometry—not aiming merely at a practical result.

The following points should be noted:

(i) All construction lines must be left visible, and nothing contributing to the final result should be rubbed out.

(ii) Great *care* is needed—drawing a line accurately through a point is not as simple as some may imagine.

(iii) A *hard* pencil with a *sharp* point must be used to enable lines and points to be as fine as possible.

(iv) Intersections of lines and arcs should be contrived so that the angle of intersection is as great (as near to 90°) as possible. In Fig. 25 there is a well-defined point of intersection at A; whereas at B there is quite a considerable 'area of intersection', because the angle is small and the lines are thick.

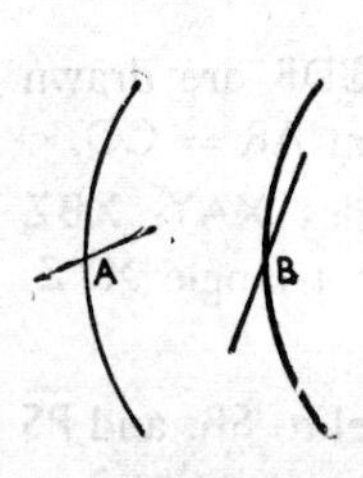

Fig. 25

(v) When a line is fixed by means of two constructed points, these points should be as far apart as possible. A small error in the relative position of two points close together may make a considerable error in the position of the line through them.

When a construction is stated formally it should be followed by a proof that the construction is correct.

It will be seen that the work is arranged in sections similar to those for a theorem, with 'To construct' instead of 'To prove'. The letters Q.E.F. (*quod erat faciendum*—which was to be done) at the end indicate that the construction has been completed successfully.

Construction 1

To bisect a given straight line.

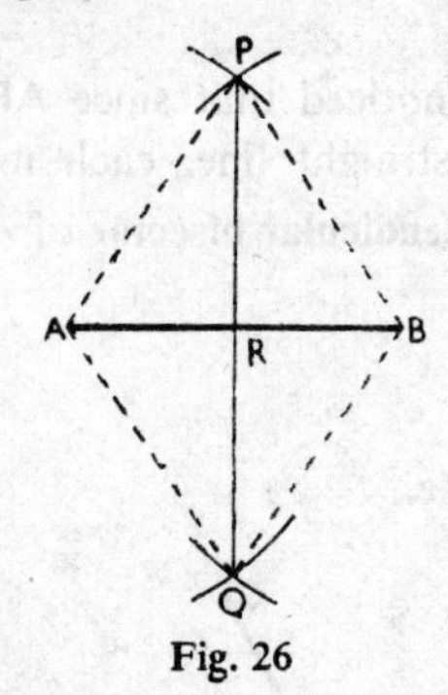

Fig. 26

Given a straight line $\overline{AB}$.

To construct the mid-point of $\overline{AB}$.

Construction. With centres A, B and equal radii draw arcs to cut each other at P, Q.

Join $\overline{PQ}$, cutting $\overline{AB}$ at R.

Then R is the required mid-point of $\overline{AB}$.

Proof. Join $\overline{AP}$, $\overline{BP}$, $\overline{AQ}$, $\overline{BQ}$.

In $\triangle$s APQ, BPQ

$AP = BP$ = *radii*

$AQ = BQ$ = *radii*

PQ is common

$\therefore \triangle APQ \equiv \triangle BPQ$ *SSS*

$\triangle BPQ$ is the reflection of $\triangle APQ$ in $\overline{PQ}$

$\therefore A\hat{P}Q = B\hat{P}Q$.

In $\triangle$s APR, BPR

$$AP = BP \quad = \textit{radii}$$
$$PR \text{ is common}$$
$$A\hat{P}R = B\hat{P}R \quad \textit{proved}$$
$$\therefore \triangle APR \equiv \triangle BPR \quad \textit{SAS}$$
$$\triangle BPR \text{ is the reflection of } \triangle APR \text{ in } \overline{PR}$$
$$\therefore AR = BR.$$

Q.E.F.

It should also be noticed that since $A\hat{R}P$ and $B\hat{R}P$ are equal and adjacent on a straight line, each must be a right angle. Hence $\overline{PQ}$ is the **perpendicular bisector** of AB.

Construction 2

To bisect a given angle.

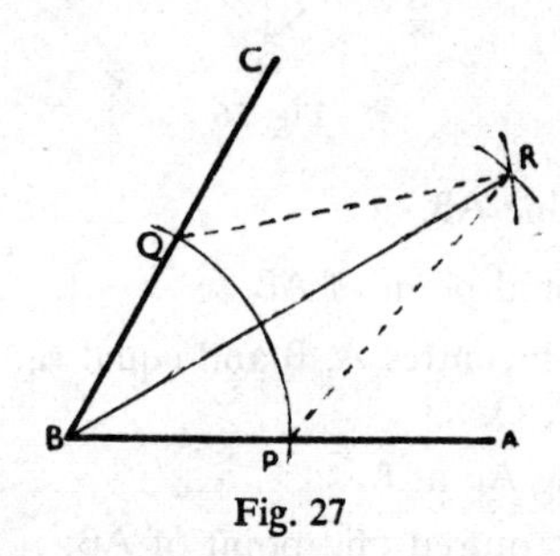

Fig. 27

Given an angle ABC.

To construct a line bisecting $A\hat{B}C$.

Construction. With centre B and any radius draw an arc cutting $\overline{BA}$, $\overline{BC}$ at P, Q.
With centres P, Q and equal radii draw arcs to cut each other at R.
Join $\overline{BR}$.
Then $\overline{BR}$ is the required bisector.

Proof. Join $\overline{PR}$, $\overline{QR}$.

In $\triangle$s PBR, QBR

$$BP = BQ \qquad = radii$$
$$PR = QR \qquad = radii$$
$$BR \text{ is common}$$
$$\therefore \triangle PBR \equiv \triangle QBR \qquad SSS$$

$\triangle QBR$ is the reflection of $\triangle PBR$ in $\overline{BR}$

$$\therefore P\hat{B}R = Q\hat{B}R$$
$$\therefore \overline{BR} \text{ bisects } A\hat{B}C.$$

Q.E.F.

Construction 3

To construct a perpendicular to a given straight line from a given point outside it.

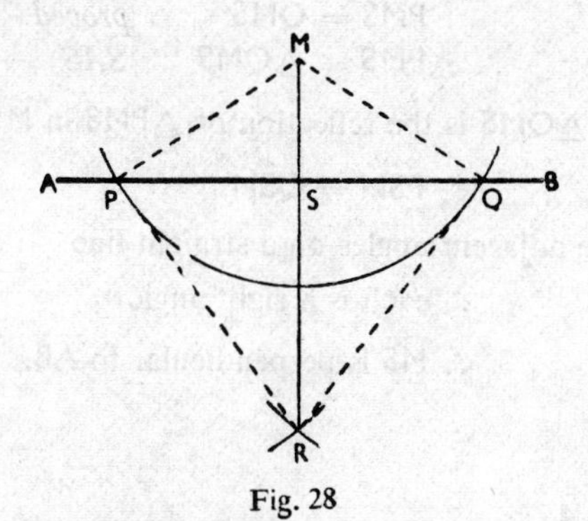

Fig. 28

Given a point M outside a line $\overline{AB}$.

To construct a line through M perpendicular to $\overline{AB}$.

Construction. With centre M and any radius draw an arc to cut $\overline{AB}$ at P, Q.

With centres P, Q and equal radii draw arcs to cut each other at R.

Join $\overline{MR}$ cutting $\overline{AB}$ at S.

Then $\overline{MS}$ is the required perpendicular.

Proof. Join $\overline{PM}$, $\overline{QM}$, $\overline{PR}$, $\overline{QR}$.

In $\triangle$s PMR, QMR

$$PM = QM \qquad = \textit{radii}$$
$$PR = QR \qquad = \textit{radii}$$
$$MR \text{ is common}$$
$$\therefore \triangle PMR \equiv \triangle QMR \qquad \textit{SSS}$$

$\triangle QMR$ is the reflection of $\triangle PMR$ in $\overline{MR}$

$$\therefore P\hat{M}R = Q\hat{M}R$$

In $\triangle$s PMS, QMS

$$PM = QM \qquad = \textit{radii}$$
$$MS \text{ is common}$$
$$P\hat{M}S = Q\hat{M}S \qquad \textit{proved}$$
$$\therefore \triangle PMS \equiv \triangle QMS \qquad \textit{SAS}$$

$\triangle QMS$ is the reflection of $\triangle PMS$ in $\overline{MS}$

$$\therefore P\hat{S}M = Q\hat{S}M$$

But these are adjacent angles on a straight line

$\therefore$ each is a right angle

$\therefore$ $\overline{MS}$ is perpendicular to $\overline{AB}$.

Q.E.F.

Construction 4

To construct a perpendicular to a given straight line at a given point on it.

Given a point M on a straight line $\overline{AB}$.

To construct a line through M perpendicular to $\overline{AB}$.

Construction. With centre M and any radius draw arcs to cut $\overline{AB}$ at P, Q.

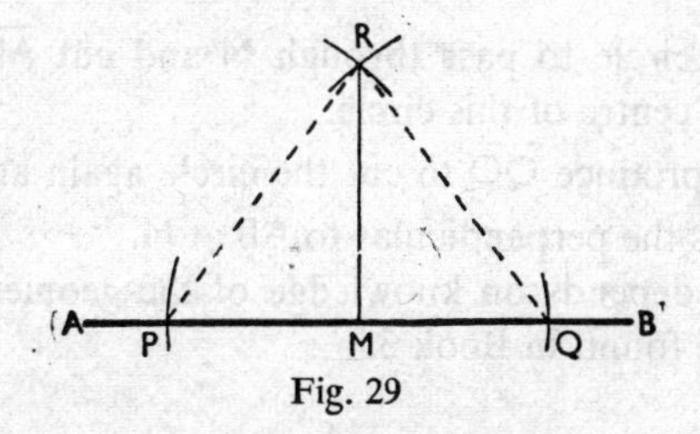

Fig. 29

With centres P, Q and equal radii draw arcs to cut each other at R.

Join $\overline{MR}$.

Then $\overline{MR}$ is the required perpendicular.

Proof. Join $\overline{PR}$, $\overline{QR}$.

In $\triangle$s PRM, QRM

$$PM = QM \qquad = \textit{radii}$$
$$PR = QR \qquad = \textit{radii}$$
$$MR \text{ is common}$$
$$\therefore \triangle PRM \equiv \triangle QRM \qquad \textit{SSS}$$

$\triangle QRM$ is the reflection of $\triangle PRM$ in $\overline{RM}$

$$\therefore P\hat{M}R = Q\hat{M}R$$

But these are adjacent angles on a straight line

$\therefore$ each is a right angle

$\therefore$ $\overline{MR}$ is perpendicular to $\overline{AB}$.

Q.E.F.

The following method is particularly useful if M happens to be near the edge of the paper.

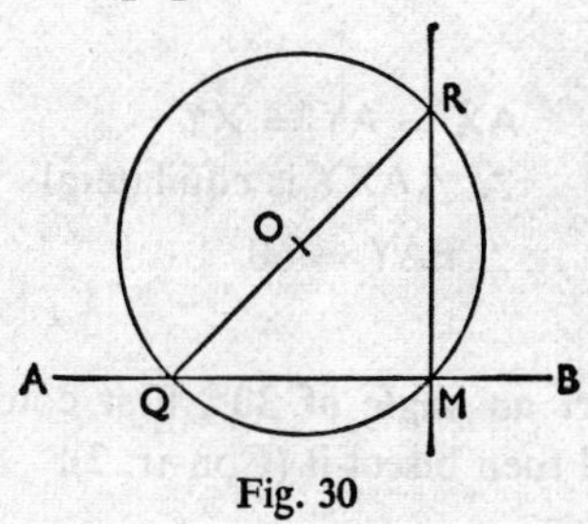

Fig. 30

Draw any circle to pass through M and cut $\overline{AB}$ again at Q. Let O be the centre of this circle.

Join $\overline{QO}$: produce $\overline{QO}$ to cut the circle again at R.

Then $\overline{MR}$ is the perpendicular to $\overline{AB}$ at M.

The proof depends on knowledge of the geometry of a circle which will be found in Book 3.

Construction 5. Some special angles.

(1) To construct an angle of 60°.

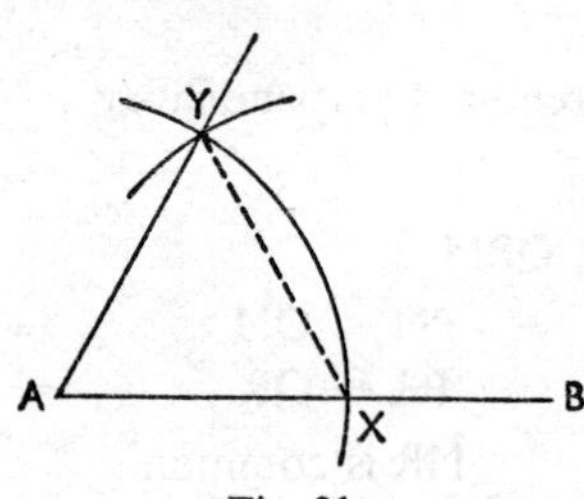

Fig. 31

Given a straight line $\overline{AB}$.

To construct an angle of 60° at A.

Construction. With centre A and any convenient radius draw an arc cutting $\overline{AB}$ at X.

With centre X and the same radius draw an arc cutting the first arc at Y.

Join $\overline{AY}$.

Then $B\hat{A}Y = 60°$.

Proof. Join $\overline{XY}$.

$AX = AY = XY$ = *radii*

$\therefore \triangle AXY$ is equilateral

$\therefore B\hat{A}Y = 60°$

Q.E.F.

(2) To construct an angle of 30°, first construct an angle of 60° as above, and then bisect it (Constr. 2).

(3) Angles of 15°, 7½°, etc. may be drawn by successive bisections as in (2).

(4) To construct an angle of 45°, first construct a right angle (Constrs. 3 or 4), and then bisect it.

Successive bisections will give **angles of 22½°,** etc.

By combining these angles together a large number of useful angles can be constructed without using a protractor.

Exercise 4a

Ruler and compasses only *to be used in this exercise.*

1 Construct angles of 60°, 30°, 75°, 90°, 120°, 37½°, 135°.

2 Construct an isosceles triangle with the equal sides 9 cm long and the angle between them 45°. Measure the third side.

3 Construct an isosceles △ABC so that AB = AC, BC = 75 mm and the length of the perpendicular from A to $\overline{BC}$ is 60 mm. Measure AB.

4 Draw a △ with sides 6, 7, 9 cm. Construct the three altitudes, which should meet at a point.

5 Draw a △ with sides 5, 6, 9 cm and construct the three altitudes (as in no. 4). Two of the sides will have to be produced.

6 Draw a triangle with sides 6, 8, 10 cm. Bisect the smallest angle and measure the two parts into which the bisector divides the side which it cuts.

7 Draw a circle of radius 75 mm. Draw two diameters at right angles. Construct two more diameters bisecting the angles between those drawn first. Join the ends of the diameters to form a regular polygon. What sort of polygon is it? What are the lengths of its sides?

8 By drawing radii at 60° intervals in a circle of radius 5 cm construct a regular hexagon. How long are its sides?

9 Construct a parallelogram with sides 6 cm and 9 cm, the angle between these sides being 60°. Measure the diagonals.

10 Construct a rhombus with sides 6 cm and one angle 75°. Measure the diagonals.

11 Draw a circle of radius 6 cm and any chord inside it. Bisect this chord at right angles. Does the bisector pass through any particular point? Do the same again with any other chord in the circle.

12 Draw a $\triangle ABC$ with sides 7, 8, 9 cm. Draw the perpendicular bisectors of all three sides: these should meet at one point O. With centre O and radius OA draw a circle. Does this circle pass through B and C? What is its radius?

13 Draw a $\triangle PQR$ with sides 69, 102, 135 mm. As in no. 12, construct the circle passing through P, Q and R. Measure its radius.

14 Draw a $\triangle$ with sides 6, 8 and 9 cm. Use Construction 1 to find the middle point of each side. Join each vertex to the mid-point of the opposite side. These three lines are called **medians.** Do the three medians meet at a point? By careful measurement find how this point divides the length of each median.

15 Do no. 14 again, using a triangle of any size. Do the three medians behave in the same way as before?

16 Draw a $\triangle ABC$ with sides 6, 8, 9 cm. Bisect all three angles of the triangle. The three bisectors should meet in one point: call this point I. Construct a perpendicular $\overline{IX}$ from I to $\overline{BC}$. Draw a circle with radius IX and centre I. Does this circle do anything special? Measure its radius.

17 Draw a $\triangle XYZ$ with sides 5, 7, 9 cm. By using the method of no. 16 construct a circle to touch all three sides of the triangle, and measure its radius.

18 Construct a quadrilateral ABCD with $\hat{D} = 90°$, AD = 6 cm, DC = 9 cm, BC = 8·4 cm, AB = 5·4 cm. Bisect angles D and A and let the bisectors meet at X. Construct the perpendicular $\overline{XP}$ to $\overline{DA}$. Draw the circle with centre X and radius XP. Does it touch all four sides or only three of them? Measure its radius.

19 Draw a circle of radius 5 cm. From any point P on the circumference draw chords PQ = 4 cm and PR = 6 cm. Complete the $\triangle$PQR. Take any point A on the circumference of the circle. Draw perpendiculars $\overline{AX}$, $\overline{AY}$, $\overline{AZ}$ from A to $\overline{QR}$, $\overline{RP}$, $\overline{PQ}$ respectively. Is there anything remarkable about the points X, Y, Z? Will this always be true? (Test by drawing another figure of any size which is convenient.)

20 Draw a circle, centre O, of radius 8 cm. From any point A on the circumference draw chords $\overline{AB}$, $\overline{AC}$ of lengths 14, 15 cm respectively.

Join $\overline{BC}$. Use Constr. 1 to find the mid-points of the sides of the triangle ABC: call these points D, E, F. Construct the three altitudes $\overline{AX}$, $\overline{BY}$, $\overline{CZ}$: let them meet at a point H. Find the mid-points of $\overline{AH}$, $\overline{BH}$, $\overline{CH}$: call them P, Q, R respectively.

Join $\overline{OH}$: find its mid-point N.

Then it should be possible to draw a circle with centre N which will pass through the nine points D, E, F, X, Y, Z, P, Q, R.

What is the radius of this circle?

Exercise 4b

In working the following examples draw a rough figure first, to give some idea of the shape of the final drawing. In nos. 1–15 *no explanation need be written, but all construction lines should be left in.*

1 Construct an equilateral triangle with sides of length 7·2 cm. Construct the perpendicular from a vertex to the opposite side and measure its length.

2 Construct a square with sides each 83 mm long. Measure the length of a diagonal.

3 Construct a rectangle measuring 7·4 cm by 10·3 cm. Measure the length of a diagonal.

4 Construct an isosceles triangle with base 8 cm long and the equal sides each 10 cm long. Construct two different altitudes and measure their lengths.

5 Construct a rectangle ABCD in which AB = 86 mm, BC = 58 mm. Construct the bisectors of $\hat{A}$ and $\hat{B}$, and let these bisectors meet at E. Construct the perpendicular from E to $\overline{AB}$ and measure its length.

6 Construct $\triangle$XYZ in which XY = 8·3 cm, YZ = 11·9 cm, $X\hat{Y}Z = 60°$. Construct M, the mid-point of $\overline{XZ}$, and measure YM.

7 Draw $\triangle$ABC having AB = 9 cm, BC = 12 cm, $A\hat{B}C = 60°$. Construct the bisector of $\hat{A}$ and let it meet $\overline{BC}$ at D. Measure DC.

8 Draw a line 10 cm long, and construct a square with this line as a diagonal. Measure a side of the square.

9 Construct $\triangle$LMN in which LM = 105 mm, $\hat{M} = 60°$, $\hat{N} = 90°$. Measure LN and MN.

10 Construct $\triangle$LMN in which LM = 7·6 cm, MN = LN = 9·7 cm. Through N construct a line parallel to $\overline{LM}$, and construct $\overline{MD}$ perpendicular to this line, meeting it at D. Measure MD.

11 Construct $\triangle$ABC with AB = 68 mm, AC = 102 mm, $\hat{B} = 120°$. Construct the perpendicular bisectors of $\overline{AB}$ and $\overline{BC}$, and let them meet at O. Measure OA, OB, OC.

12 Draw $\triangle$ABC in which AB = 99 mm, BC = 114 mm, CA = 126 mm. Through M, the mid-point of $\overline{BC}$, draw lines parallel to $\overline{AC}$, $\overline{AB}$ respectively, to meet $\overline{AB}$, $\overline{AC}$ in H, K. Measure HK.

13 Construct a parallelogram ABCD with BD = 104 mm, DC = 48 mm, $B\hat{D}C = 30°$. Measure AC.

14 Construct a trapezium PQRS in which $\overline{PQ}$ is parallel to $\overline{SR}$, PQ = 6 cm, PS = 5 cm, SR = 11 cm, QS = 9 cm. Measure QR.

15 Given that the diagonals of a parallelogram bisect each other, construct a parallelogram with one side 10 cm long, and diagonals 15 cm and 10 cm long. Measure the length of the side which is not given.

16 Draw $\triangle PQR$ such that $PQ = 66$ mm, $QR = 72$ mm, $RP = 84$ mm. Construct a point A in $\overline{PR}$ such that $AQ = AR$. State the steps of the construction and prove that it is correct.

17 Draw $\triangle ABC$ in which $AB = 5$ cm, $BC = 8$ cm, $CA = 7$ cm. Construct a point P in $\overline{BC}$ such that the perpendiculars from P to $\overline{AB}$ and $\overline{AC}$ are equal. State the steps of the construction and prove that it is correct.

18 Construct $\triangle ABC$ in which $BC = 8$ cm, $\hat{C} = 45°$, $AB + AC = 14$ cm. State the steps of the construction, and prove that it is correct.

Chapter 5

Percentages (2)

In Book 1 it was shown that a percentage is equivalent to a fraction with denominator 100,

$$\text{e.g. } 37\tfrac{1}{2}\% = \frac{37\frac{1}{2}}{100} = \frac{75}{200} = \tfrac{3}{8}.$$

Conversely, a fraction is converted to a percentage by multiplying by 100,

$$\text{e.g. } \tfrac{4}{5} = \tfrac{4}{5} \times 100\% = 80\%.$$

The worked example which follows illustrates the use of percentages for comparing increases or decreases of two or more varying quantities.

Example 1 *Two factories, A and B, produce bicycles at the rate of* 400 *and* 700 *per week respectively. If they increase their weekly outputs to* 424 *and* 735, *which increases at the greater rate per cent?*

For A, increase is 24 on 400,
which is 6 per 100, i.e. 6%.
For B, increase is 35 on 700,
which is 5 per 100, i.e. 5%

∴ factory A increases its output at the greater rate per cent.

Notice that B has the greater actual increase, but the smaller increase per cent.

Exercise 5a (Revision)

Express the following as fractions:

1 20%	**2** 30%	**3** 25%	**4** 10%	**5** 80%
6 70%	**7** 150%	**8** 120%	**9** 5%	**10** $33\frac{1}{3}\%$
11 $66\frac{2}{3}\%$	**12** 75%	**13** $12\frac{1}{2}\%$	**14** 15%	**15** $2\frac{1}{2}\%$
16 58%	**17** 230%	**18** 85%	**19** 118%	**20** $3\frac{1}{2}\%$

Express the following as percentages:

21 $\frac{1}{4}$	**22** $\frac{1}{3}$	**23** $\frac{1}{10}$	**24** $\frac{1}{8}$	**25** $\frac{3}{5}$
26 $\frac{9}{10}$	**27** $\frac{1}{6}$	**28** $\frac{5}{4}$	**29** $\frac{7}{8}$	**30** $\frac{2}{3}$
31 $\frac{1}{20}$	**32** $\frac{1}{25}$	**33** $\frac{13}{10}$	**34** $\frac{7}{5}$	**35** $\frac{9}{40}$
36 $\frac{7}{50}$	**37** $\frac{5}{6}$	**38** $\frac{17}{5}$	**39** $\frac{9}{25}$	**40** $\frac{11}{300}$

The following should be remembered:

$100\% = 1$	$10\% = \frac{1}{10}$	$5\% = \frac{1}{20}$	$2\frac{1}{2}\% = \frac{1}{40}$
$50\% = \frac{1}{2}$	$25\% = \frac{1}{4}$	$12\frac{1}{2}\% = \frac{1}{8}$	$75\% = \frac{3}{4}$
$33\frac{1}{3}\% = \frac{1}{3}$	$66\frac{2}{3}\% = \frac{2}{3}$		

Notice that 5% of £1 $= \frac{5}{100}$ of 100p $=$ 5p

Similarly 17% of £1 $=$ 17p

83% of £1 $=$ 83p, and so on.

Example 2 *Find the value of* 15% *of* 2·38 *kg.*

$$\begin{aligned} 15\% \text{ of } 2{\cdot}38 \text{ kg} &= \frac{15}{100} \times 2{\cdot}38 \text{ kg} \\ &= 15 \times 0{\cdot}0238 \text{ kg} \\ &= 0{\cdot}357 \text{ kg} \\ &= 357 \text{ g} \end{aligned}$$

Alternatively

$$\begin{aligned} 15\% \text{ of } 2{\cdot}38 \text{ kg} &= \frac{3}{20} \times 2{\cdot}38 \text{ kg} \\ &= 3 \times 0{\cdot}119 \text{ kg} \\ &= 0{\cdot}357 \text{ kg} \\ &= 357 \text{ g} \end{aligned}$$

Example 3 *Express* 3·3 *m as a percentage of* 7·5 *m.*

$$\begin{aligned} 3{\cdot}3 \text{ m} &= \frac{3{\cdot}3}{7{\cdot}5} \text{ of } 7{\cdot}5 \text{ m} \\ &= \frac{33}{75} \times 100\% \text{ of } 7{\cdot}5 \text{ m} \\ &= \frac{33 \times 4}{3}\% \text{ of } 7{\cdot}5 \text{ m} \\ &= 44\% \text{ of } 7{\cdot}5 \text{ m} \end{aligned}$$

Example 4 *Find the sum of money of which £6·46 is 85%.*

85% of the required sum is £6·46

$$\therefore 100\% \text{ ,, ,, ,, ,, ,, } £6{\cdot}46 \times \frac{100}{85}$$

$$= £\frac{646}{85}$$

$$= £\frac{38}{5}$$

$$= £7{\cdot}60$$

Alternatively

$$£6{\cdot}46 \times \frac{100}{85} = £6{\cdot}46 \times \frac{20}{17}$$

$$= £0{\cdot}38 \times 20$$

$$= £7{\cdot}60$$

Exercise 5b

Find the value of

1 25% of £10

2 75% of 30p

3 50% ,, 3·5 m

4 $33\frac{1}{3}$% ,, 8·16 l

5 $12\frac{1}{2}$% ,, £11·36

6 150% ,, 22 m

7 19% ,, 300

8 82% ,, £150

9 120% ,, 15 kg

10 $2\frac{1}{2}$% ,, 60 km

Express

11 37 as a percentage of 50

12 64 ,, ,, ,, ,, 400

13 13p ,, ,, ,, ,, £1

14 19p ,, ,, ,, ,, 57p

15 400 g ,, ,, ,, ,, 8 kg

16 1·5 m ,, ,, ,, ,, 2·5 m

17 25p ,, ,, ,, ,, 10p

18 850 mm ,, ,, ,, ,, 1 m

19 15p ,, ,, ,, ,, 24p

20 3·5 kg ,, ,, ,, ,, 2·8 kg

Find the quantity of which

21 8p is 20%

22 12 m is 75%

23 5 g „ $33\frac{1}{3}\%$

24 £9 „ 30%

25 £5·50 „ 5%

26 4·35 kg „ 150%

27 39 „ 78%

28 2·4 m „ $66\frac{2}{3}\%$

29 50p „ 250%

30 £2·21 „ 65%

31 Express 39p as a percentage of £3.

32 What is $37\frac{1}{2}\%$ of 2 metres?

33 Calculate the quantity of which 1·19 kg is 85%.

34 Find the value of 46% of $2\frac{1}{2}$ kg.

35 Express 4·2 m^2 as a percentage of 6 m^2.

36 Find the sum of money of which 56p is $17\frac{1}{2}\%$.

37 Find the value of $8\frac{1}{3}\%$ of 84 g.

38 Find the quantity of which 5·6 kg is 175%.

39 Find the value of 215% of 40 m.

40 Express £2·34 as a percentage of £1·80.

41 A school has 325 pupils, of whom 26 are absent. What percentage is absent? What percentage is present?

42 A mixed school has 575 pupils of whom 44% are boys. How many girls are there in the school?

43 A coil spring 7·5 cm long is stretched to a length of 9·75 cm. What percentage is this of the original length?

44 A farmer ploughs 96 hectares, which is $37\frac{1}{2}\%$ of his farm. How big is his farm?

45 Two villages, A and B, have populations of 875 and 1 175. A increases by 16% and B increases by 12%. Which has the greater numerical increase?

46 A man spends £18·70, which is 85% of his weekly wage. What is his weekly wage?

47 In an examination a girl obtains 336 marks out of 480. What percentage is this?

48 A man buys a suit costing £23·60 and pays a deposit of 15%. How much money does he still owe?

49 A farmer has a number of fruit trees, 65% apple and the remainder plum. If he has 936 apple trees, how many plum trees has he?

50 A man owes a certain sum of money, and pays off $62\frac{1}{2}$% of it. If he still owes £19·20, how much did he pay off?

When percentage increase or decrease is to be found, the percentage is reckoned on the **original value.** Profit and loss are calculated as a percentage of the **cost price,** unless there is a definite statement to the contrary.

There are two ways of finding the result of increasing or decreasing a given quantity by a given percentage. For example, suppose that the number 180 is to be increased by 40%.

(i) $40\% \text{ of } 180 = \frac{40}{100} \text{ of } 180 = 72$

$\therefore$ the required number $= 180 + 72 = 252$

(ii) The required number $= (1 + \frac{40}{100}) \text{ of } 180$

$$= \frac{140}{100} \text{ of } 180$$

$$= 252$$

The second method is generally preferable.

Similarly if 180 is to be decreased by 40%.

(i) $40\% \text{ of } 180 = 72.$

$\therefore$ the required number $= 180 - 72 = 108$

(ii) The required number $= (1 - \frac{40}{100}) \text{ of } 180$

$$= \frac{60}{100} \text{ of } 180$$

$$= 108$$

Example 5 *A mat is bought for* £1·40 *and sold at a profit of* 35%. *Find the selling price.*

First method

$$\text{Profit} = \frac{35}{100} \text{ of } £1{\cdot}40$$
$$= £1{\cdot}40 \times \frac{7}{20}$$
$$= £0{\cdot}07 \times 7$$
$$= £0{\cdot}49$$
$$\therefore \text{ selling price} = £1{\cdot}40 + £0{\cdot}49$$
$$= £1{\cdot}89$$

Second method

$$\text{Selling price} = \frac{135}{100} \text{ of } £1{\cdot}40$$
$$= £1{\cdot}40 \times \frac{27}{20}$$
$$= £0{\cdot}07 \times 27$$
$$= £1{\cdot}89$$

Example 6 368 *is the result of increasing a number by* 15%. *Find the number.*

115% of the number is 368

∴ 100% ,, ,, ,, ,, $368 \times \dfrac{100}{115}$

$$= 368 \times \frac{20}{23}$$
$$= 16 \times 20$$
$$= 320$$

Example 7 *A bicycle is sold for* £18·90 *at a loss of* 12½%. *Find the cost price.*

Since 100 − 12½ = 87½, the selling price is 87½% of the cost price.

∴ 87½% of the cost price is £18·90

$$\therefore 100\% \text{ of the cost price is } £18{\cdot}90 \times \frac{100}{87\frac{1}{2}}$$

$$= £18{\cdot}90 \times \frac{200}{175}$$

$$= £18{\cdot}90 \times \frac{8}{7}$$

$$= £2{\cdot}70 \times 8$$

$$= £21{\cdot}60$$

Alternatively The loss is $12\frac{1}{2}\%$, which is $\frac{1}{8}$, so that the selling price is $\frac{7}{8}$ of the cost price.

$\therefore \frac{7}{8}$ of the cost price is £18·90

$\therefore \frac{8}{8}$ " " " " " £18·90 × $\frac{8}{7}$

= etc. as before.

Example 8 *A lamp is sold for* £3·15 *and the profit is* 65p. *Find the profit per cent.*

The cost price was £3·15 − £0·65

= £2·50

$\therefore$ on 250p the profit is 65p

$\therefore$ " 100p " " is $65 \times \frac{100}{250}$ p

$= 65 \times \frac{2}{5}$ p

= 26p

$\therefore$ the profit is 26%.

Exercise 5c

1 By what fraction (uncancelled) should a quantity be multiplied to

(i) increase it by 20%, 50%, 37%, 6%, 130%?

(ii) decrease it by 20%, 50%, 37%, 6%, 82%?

Find the selling price of an article which is bought for

2 £1·25 and sold at a profit of 24%

3 75p „ „ „ „ „ „ 12%

4 £8·50 „ „ „ „ „ „ 46%

5 £340 „ „ „ „ loss „ 6%

6 £9·20 „ „ „ „ „ „ $7\frac{1}{2}$%

Find the gain or loss per cent when an article is bought for

7 30p and sold for 42p

8 £7·60 „ „ „ £6·65

9 £3·50 „ „ „ £4·34

10 £16·40 „ „ „ £19·27

11 £184 „ „ „ £101·20

Find the cost price of an article which is sold for

12 £77 at a profit of 10%

13 £5·85 „ „ „ „ 30%

14 £9·40 „ „ „ „ $17\frac{1}{2}$%

15 £15·75 „ „ loss „ 16%

16 £319·60 „ „ „ „ 6%

17 When a farm of 325 hectares is increased by 16%, what is its new area?

18 A man's income increases from £860 to £989. Find the increase per cent.

19 A boy spends 32% of his money and has 34p left. How much had he at first?

20 A girl takes an examination and gets 425 marks out of 625. What percentage is this?

21 A spring which was 35 cm long is stretched so that its length is increased by 16%. Find its new length.

22 Find a man's whole income if after paying 26% of it in taxes he has £725·20 left.

23 A tank contains 1 075 litres of water. If 387 litres are run off, what percentage of the original quantity remains?

24 A man buys a car for £350 and sells it for £374·50. His son buys a bicycle for £8 and sells it for £8·60. Which makes the greater profit per cent?

25 A tradesman has a capital of £760. If he increases it by $7\frac{1}{2}$%, how much will he then have?

26 When a tradesman increases his capital by $17\frac{1}{2}$% he has £1 363. How much had he at first?

27 A man's income is £1 024, and he has £793·60 left after paying his taxes. What percentage of his income does he pay in taxes?

28 A cricket team has scored 272 for 9 wickets. The last wicket increases this total by $6\frac{1}{4}$%. What is the final score?

29 Find the original contents of a tank if, after $8\frac{1}{3}$% has been run off, 528 litres remain.

30 A tailor allows a discount of $2\frac{1}{2}$% for a prompt cash payment. Find the reduced price of a suit listed at £27·20.

31 A factory increases its annual production of cars from 4 325 to 4 671. Find the increase per cent. How many cars would it have had to produce for an increase of 12%?

32 Find the profit per cent when an article is bought for £2·25 and sold for £2·52. Find also the price at which it should be sold to make a profit of 14%.

33 A man's salary is increased from £925 to £1 073. Find the increase per cent. What would have been his new salary if the increase had been 15%?

34 By selling an article for £21·75 a man makes a profit of 16%. What did it cost him? For how much should he have sold it in order to make a profit of 28%?

35 A business man had a certain amount of capital in 1960, and during the next 5 years he increased it by a total of 15%, so that he had £6 716 in 1965. What was his capital in 1960? Find also his capital in 1955 if it was $7\frac{1}{2}$% less than it was in 1960.

Chapter 6

Simple interest

A borrower usually pays a certain sum of money for the privilege of using something which belongs to the lender. For example, a rowing-boat or a punt may be hired at so much per hour or per day, and a tenant pays what is called rent for the hire of a house which belongs to somebody else. When money is borrowed, the price paid for its hire is called the interest. If this interest is paid at regular intervals, e.g. annually or half-yearly, it is called **simple interest.**

The money borrowed is called the **principal,** and it is usual to pay as interest a certain percentage of the principal for each year for which the money is borrowed. For example, if £100 is lent at 3% **per annum,** the interest which the £100 earns is £3 each year. The interest on other sums of money would be in proportion, e.g. £200 would earn £6 per year, £500 would earn £15 per year, and so on.

Example 1 *Find the simple interest on* £600 *for* 5 *years at* 4% *per annum.*

£100 in 1 year earns £4

∴ £600 in 5 years earns £4 × 6 × 5

= £120

∴ the simple interest is £120

Exercise 6a (Oral)

Find the simple interest on

1 £400 for 1 year at 2% per annum

2 £700 „ 1 „ „ 3% „ „

3 £100 „ 3 years „ 2% „ „

4 £100 „ 2 „ „ 6% „ „

5 £100 „ 4 „ „ 1½% „ „

6 £100 for $3\frac{1}{2}$ years at 4% per annum
7 £300 „ 2 „ „ 5% „ „
8 £200 „ 4 „ „ 3% „ „
9 £700 „ 3 „ „ 3% „ „
10 £600 „ $2\frac{1}{2}$ „ „ 1% „ „
11 £350 „ 4 „ „ 2% „ „
12 £250 „ 2 „ „ 6% „ „
13 £150 „ 3 „ „ 4% „ „
14 £550 „ 4 „ „ 3% „ „
15 £250 „ 3 „ „ 5% „ „

Find the number of years in which the interest on

16 £100 at 4% is £24
17 £300 „ 1% „ £15
18 £200 „ 3% „ £18
19 £350 „ 2% „ £21
20 £450 „ 6% „ £54

Find the rate per cent per annum at which the interest on

21 £100 for 4 years is £10
22 £800 „ 3 „ „ £48
23 £300 „ 7 „ „ £63
24 £250 „ 4 „ „ £60
25 £175 „ 3 „ „ £42

Example 2 *Find the simple interest on* £126·70 *for* $7\frac{1}{2}$ *years at* 4% *per annum.*

£100 in 1 year earns £4

$$\therefore \text{£}126{\cdot}70 \text{ in } 7\tfrac{1}{2} \text{ years earns } \text{£}4 \times \frac{126{\cdot}7}{100} \times 7\tfrac{1}{2}$$

$$= \text{£}1{\cdot}267 \times 30$$

$$= \text{£}38{\cdot}01$$

The **amount** is the sum of the principal and the interest.

Example 3 *Find the amount of £343·20 in 5 years at $6\frac{1}{4}$% per annum.*

$$\text{£100 in 1 year earns £}6\tfrac{1}{4}$$

$$\therefore \text{ £343·20 in 5 years earns £}6\tfrac{1}{4} \times \frac{343{\cdot}2}{100} \times 5$$

$$= \text{£}\frac{25 \times 343{\cdot}2 \times 5}{4 \times 100}$$

$$= \text{£}\frac{85{\cdot}8 \times 5}{4}$$

$$= \text{£}\frac{429{\cdot}0}{4}$$

$$= \text{£}107{\cdot}25$$

$\therefore$ simple interest = £107·25
and principal = £343·20
$\therefore$ amount = £450·45

Exercise 6b

Rates of interest given here are assumed to be per annum.

Find the simple interest on

1	£225	for	4	years at	7%
2	£530	,,	6	,, ,,	4%
3	£12·50	,,	8	,, ,,	3%
4	£162·50	,,	3	,, ,,	6%
5	£382·50	,,	4	,, ,,	$2\frac{1}{2}$%
6	£826	,,	3	,, ,,	$7\frac{1}{2}$%
7	£101·25	,,	5	,, ,,	4%
8	£15	,,	32	,, ,,	$4\frac{1}{2}$%
9	£212·10	,,	$3\frac{1}{3}$	,, ,,	4%
10	£475·20	,,	6	,, ,,	$1\frac{1}{4}$%
11	£68·80	,,	5	,, ,,	2%
12	£61·65	,,	5	,, ,,	4%
13	£292·75	,,	10	,, ,,	2%

14 £787 for 9 years at 3%

15 £131·70 for 6 yr 8 mth at $4\frac{1}{2}$%

Find the amount of

16 £145·60 in 15 years at 5%

17 £93·75 „ 9 „ „ 8%

18 £312·80 „ 15 „ „ $2\frac{1}{2}$%

19 £206·25 „ 8 „ „ $4\frac{1}{2}$%

20 £52·35 „ 10 „ „ $3\frac{1}{3}$%

Formula

From the examples already done it will be seen that the simple interest is found by multiplying the principal by the rate per cent and by the number of years, and dividing the product by 100. Therefore if the symbol P is used for the principal, T for the number of years, R for the rate per cent, and I for the interest,

$$\textbf{then} \quad \mathbf{I} = \frac{\mathbf{PTR}}{\mathbf{100}}$$

If numerical values are given for any three of these letters the value of the fourth may be found.

$$\text{Since} \qquad \frac{PTR}{100} = I$$

$$PTR = 100 \times I$$

$$\therefore \mathbf{P} = \frac{\mathbf{100\,I}}{\mathbf{TR}} \quad \text{or} \quad \mathbf{T} = \frac{\mathbf{100\,I}}{\mathbf{PR}} \quad \text{or} \quad \mathbf{R} = \frac{\mathbf{100\,I}}{\mathbf{PT}}$$

Example 4 *Find the principal that will earn* £29·19 *in 6 years 3 months at* $3\frac{1}{2}$% *per annum.*

$$P = \frac{100 \times I}{TR}$$

$$= £\frac{100 \times 29{\cdot}19}{6\frac{1}{4} \times 3\frac{1}{2}}$$

$$= £\frac{100 \times 29{\cdot}19 \times 4 \times 2}{25 \times 7}$$
$$= £4{\cdot}17 \times 32$$
$$= £133{\cdot}44$$

Example 5 *Find the time in which* £151·20 *will earn* £39·69 *at* $3\frac{1}{2}$% *per annum.*

$$T = \frac{100 \times I}{PR}$$
$$= \frac{100 \times 39{\cdot}69}{151{\cdot}20 \times 3\frac{1}{2}} \text{ years}$$
$$= \frac{100 \times 3\,969 \times 2}{15\,120 \times 7} \text{ years}$$
$$= \frac{15}{2} \text{ years}$$
$$= 7\tfrac{1}{2} \text{ years}$$

Exercise 6c

The rate per cent is assumed to be per annum.

Find by formula the simple interest on

1 £250 for 8 years at 3%
2 £28·20 „ 7 „ „ $1\frac{2}{3}$%
3 £74·40 „ 2 yr 7 mth at 5%
4 £108 „ 8 months at $4\frac{1}{2}$%
5 £221·40 „ 1 yr 4 mth at $8\frac{1}{3}$%

Find the principal that will earn

6 £27 in 12 years at $2\frac{1}{2}$%
7 £297·50 „ 7 „ „ 5%
8 £31·56 „ 10 „ „ $2\frac{2}{3}$%
9 £162·89 „ 4 yr 4 mth at 4%
10 £130·32 „ 9 years at $12\frac{1}{2}$%

Find the time in which

11 £250 will earn £26·25 at 3%

12 £216·25 „ „ £121·10 at $3\frac{1}{2}$%

13 £294·25 „ „ £58·85 at 4%

14 £258·30 will amount to £344·40 at $2\frac{1}{2}$%

15 £159·60 „ „ „ £191·52 „ 5%

Find the rate per cent at which

16 £412 will earn £61·80 in $4\frac{1}{2}$ years

17 £245 „ „ £58·80 „ 8 „

18 £162 „ „ £21·60 „ 4 „

19 £485·40 will amount to £558·21 in 6 years

20 £372·68 „ „ „ £465·85 „ 10 „

Find by formula the amount of

21 £213·28 in 10 years at 5%

22 £150 „ 20 „ „ $4\frac{1}{4}$%

23 £57·36 „ 5 „ „ $3\frac{1}{3}$%

24 £172·35 „ 3 yr 4 mth at 4%

25 £423·68 „ 6 yr 3 mth „ $2\frac{1}{2}$%

When the amount is given, with the time and rate, the principal may be found by proportion.

Example 6 *Find the principal that would amount to* £210·25 *in* 2 *yr* 8 *mth at* 6% *per annum.*

The interest on £100 would be £6 × $2\frac{2}{3}$ = £16

∴ £116 is the amount of £100

$$\therefore \text{£}210{\cdot}25 \text{ is the amount of } \text{£}100 \times \frac{210{\cdot}25}{116}$$

$$= \text{£}\frac{21\,025}{116}$$

$$= \text{£}181{\cdot}25$$

∴ the principal is £181·25

Exercise 6d

Find the principal that would amount to

1	£345	in	5 years	at	3%	per annum
2	£288	,,	7 ,,	,,	4%	,, ,,
3	£2 126·40	,,	16 ,,	,,	$1\frac{1}{4}$%	,, ,,
4	£480	,,	7 ,,	,,	4%	,, ,,
5	£1 264·45	,,	6 ,,	,,	$3\frac{1}{2}$%	,, ,,
6	£151·20	,,	8 ,,	,,	$1\frac{1}{2}$%	,, ,,
7	£251·26	,,	9 ,,	,,	4%	,, ,,
8	£536·30	,,	2 yr 8 mth	,,	9%	,, ,,
9	£104·30	,,	2 yr 5 mth	,,	10%	,, ,,
10	£133·95	,,	7 yr 6 mth	,,	$2\frac{1}{2}$%	,, ,,

Example 7 *Find, correct to the nearest penny, the simple interest on* £258·54 *for* 12 *years at* $3\frac{1}{2}$% *per annum.*

Using the formula,

$$\text{interest} = £\frac{258{\cdot}54 \times 12 \times 3\frac{1}{2}}{100}$$

$$= £2{\cdot}585\,4 \times 42$$

$$= £108{\cdot}586\,8$$

$$= £108{\cdot}59 \text{ to nearest penny}$$

Example 8 *Find the rate per cent per annum at which* £169 *will earn* £29·57 *in* 7 *years.*

Using the formula,

$$\text{rate} = \frac{100 \times 29{\cdot}57}{169 \times 7}\%$$

$$= \frac{2\,957}{1\,183}\%$$

$$= 2{\cdot}499...\%$$

$$\therefore \text{rate} = 2\tfrac{1}{2}\%$$

Exercise 6e

The rate per cent is assumed to be per annum.
Results should be given correct to the nearest penny where necessary.

Find the simple interest on

1 £92·64 for 5 years at 4%
2 £83·33 „ $3\frac{1}{2}$ „ „ 6%
3 £314·45 „ 6 „ „ $3\frac{1}{2}$%
4 £126·78 „ 8 „ „ $2\frac{1}{4}$%
5 £213·47 „ 11 „ „ 3%
6 £192·40 „ 3 yr 9 mth at $2\frac{1}{2}$%
7 £574·73 „ 6 months „ 5%
8 £164·67 „ 9 months „ $12\frac{1}{2}$%
9 £72·95 „ 8 months „ 9%
10 £362·18 „ 2 yr 11 mth „ 3%
11 £281·30 „ 4 yr 1 mth „ $1\frac{3}{4}$%

Find the amount of

12 £154·17 in 6 years at 4%
13 £91·35 „ 8 „ „ $2\frac{1}{2}$%
14 £64·13 „ 5 „ „ $7\frac{1}{2}$%
15 £7·50 „ 5 yr 4 mth at $2\frac{1}{2}$%
16 £152·22 „ 4 yr 2 mth „ 3%
17 £144·17 „ 4 yr 6 mth „ 4%
18 £86·67 „ 6 yr 9 mth „ $3\frac{3}{4}$%

Find the rate per cent at which

19 £95 will earn £31·35 in 11 years
20 £56·35 „ „ £42·26 „ 50 „
21 £15·21 will amount to £18·25 in 8 years
22 £252·48 „ „ „ £297·93 „ 4 „

Find the number of years in which

23 £90 will earn £13·50 at 3%

24 £173·95 „ „ £20·87 „ 2%

25 £59·27 will amount to £82·98 at 5%

26 £116·07 „ „ „ £123·32 „ 5%

Find the principal that will earn

27 £36·45 in 8 years at $2\frac{1}{2}$%

28 £16·38 „ 6 „ „ $4\frac{1}{4}$%

29 £48·25 „ 3 yr 8 mth at 6%

30 £82·50 „ 7 yr 4 mth „ $3\frac{1}{2}$%

31 Find the time in which £350·83 will earn £73·67 at 3%.

32 Find the rate per cent per annum at which £436·10 will earn £122·11 in 8 years.

33 Find, correct to the nearest penny, the simple interest on £127·40 for 12 years at $4\frac{1}{8}$%.

34 Find the time in which £89·50 will amount to £114·56 at 6%.

35 Find, correct to the nearest penny, the principal that will earn £4·97 in 12 years at $2\frac{1}{4}$%.

36 If £19·15 amounts to £22·02 in 6 years, find the rate per cent per annum.

37 Find, correct to the nearest penny, the simple interest on £256·32 for $7\frac{1}{2}$ years at $5\frac{1}{4}$%.

38 Find the number of years in which £155·75 will amount to £186·90 at 6%.

39 Find the rate per cent per annum at which £38·17 will amount to £48·48 in 12 years.

40 Find, correct to the nearest penny, the principal that will amount to £278·48 in $4\frac{1}{2}$ years at $2\frac{2}{3}$%.

When the interest is to be calculated for a number of days, the time includes *either* the day on which the money is lent *or* the day on which it is repaid, but not both. It is usually simpler to ignore the first day and to count the last.

Example 9 *A man borrows £146 on 7 March, and on 21 May he repays it, with interest at 11%. How much does he pay altogether to clear the debt?*

Days in March 24
April 30
May 21

$$\therefore \text{period of loan} = 75 \text{ days} = \frac{75}{365} \text{ yr} = \frac{15}{73} \text{ yr}$$

$$\therefore \text{interest} = £\frac{146 \times \frac{15}{73} \times 11}{100}$$

$$= £\frac{146 \times 15 \times 11}{73 \times 100}$$

$$= £\frac{33}{10}$$

$$= £3{\cdot}30$$

$\therefore$ he pays £149·30 altogether.

Exercise 6f

Miscellaneous simple interest

Give answers to the nearest penny where necessary.

1 If £160 increases by £60 in 5 years, find the rate per cent per annum.

2 Find the time in which £135 will amount to £167·40 at $1\frac{1}{2}$%.

3 Find the simple interest on £48·67 from 5 March to 19 May at 7%.

4 Find the principal which earns £750·75 in 11 years at 7%.

5 In how many years will a sum of money double itself at 4%?

6 At what rate per cent per annum will a sum of money double itself in 40 years?

7 Find the simple interest on £15·25 for 25 days at 12%.

8 Find the rate per cent per annum at which £36·50 will earn £1·64 in 131 days.

9 The Post Office Savings Bank pays interest at the rate of $2\frac{1}{2}\%$ per annum. What sum invested will earn interest at the rate of 5 pence per month?

10 Find the rate per cent at which a principal of £65 will earn £11·38 interest in 7 years.

11 If £1 095 is borrowed at 11%, what total payment will settle the debt after a fortnight?

12 A man finds that he will have to pay a bill of £49 in 10 months' time. To meet this expense he puts aside a certain sum now, and invests it in the Post Office Savings Bank so that it will increase at the rate of $2\frac{1}{2}\%$ per annum. How much does he put aside now?

13 Find the interest at $3\frac{1}{2}\%$ on £182·50 from 25 March to 21 September of the same year.

14 Find the amount of £14·60 borrowed on 16 July and repaid on the following 9 October with interest at $8\frac{1}{3}\%$.

15 A man wants to buy a refrigerator priced at £91. He can have it now and pay for it by monthly instalments for a year, in which case the price is increased by 8%. Alternatively, he can invest a certain sum now at 4%, which after one year will amount to £91, enabling him to buy the refrigerator then for cash. Find how much money he saves by waiting a year for his refrigerator.

16 Find the sum to which £252 will amount in 9 months if invested in a Building Society which pays $4\frac{1}{4}\%$ per annum.

17 If £730 is borrowed on 1 January, find the total sum owing on 15 February, with interest added at 9% per annum.

18 Find the time in which £36·11 amounts to £41·16 at 8%.

19 Find the rate per cent at which £760 will earn £85·50 in 7 years 6 months.

20 Find the interest at $3\frac{1}{3}\%$ on £45·62 from 21 November 1967 to 4 April 1968.

21 Find to the nearest penny the simple interest on £42·45 for 219 days at 7%.

22 Find the principal that will amount to £467·90 in 18 years at $2\frac{1}{2}\%$ per annum.

23 Find the total amount to be paid if £52·08 is borrowed on 19 April and repaid on 12 September of the same year, with interest at 12% per annum.

24 If £308·35 was borrowed on 12 November 1967 and repaid with interest at $7\frac{1}{2}\%$ per annum on 6 April 1968, what was the total sum repaid?

25 A man has £1 620 in a Building Society yielding $4\frac{1}{2}\%$ per annum, and £648 in a Bank yielding $2\frac{3}{4}\%$. What rate per cent per annum is he receiving on the two together?

Chapter 7

Travel graphs

Certain problems involving time and distance do not require an exact answer: for instance, in the two problems which follow, the time of arrival and the time of meeting are required, and for these the time to the nearest minute is sufficiently accurate. In Example 2 the speed is also required, and an answer to the nearest whole number of km/h is adequate.

For such problems a graphical solution is satisfactory, and will often be found far more quickly than an arithmetical one.

Note—For these questions paper ruled in 2-cm squares, subdivided into 2-mm squares, is recommended (or 1-inch squares, divided into tenths of an inch).

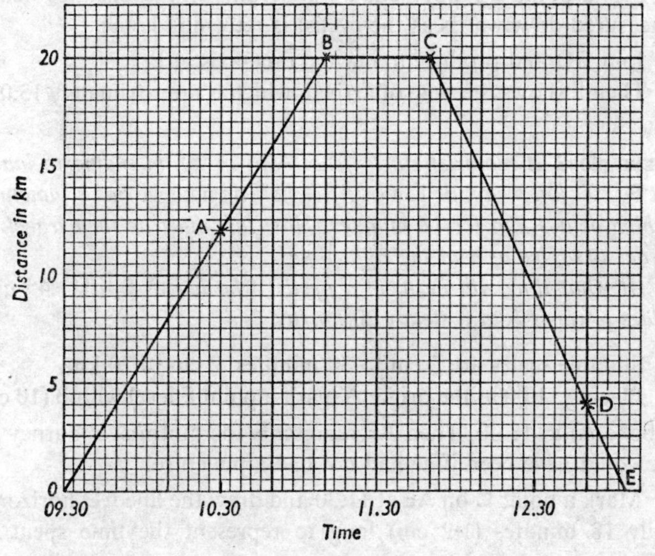

Fig. 32

Example 1 *A cyclist leaves his home at* 09.30 *and rides at a steady* 12 *km/h to a place* 20 *km away. He spends* 40 *minutes there, and returns at* 16 *km/h. At what time does he get home again?*

First choose convenient scales for both variables (time and distance): it is appropriate to take 3 cm for one hour, as this makes each small square represent exactly 4 minutes, and also allows enough space to cover the time occupied by the whole journey. 2 cm for 5 km is suitable for the vertical axis.

In time-distance graphs *time is always scaled horizontally.*

Mark in the scale on both axes, placing 09.30 at the origin.

In 1 hour the cyclist travels 12 km: plot the point A (10.30, 12 km).

Join $\overline{OA}$ and produce it to cut at B the horizontal line representing 20 km from home.

On the same horizontal line mark a point C 40 minutes beyond B. Then C represents the starting-point for the homeward journey. (*Note*—Between B and C time goes on but distance does not.)

Plot a point D 1 hour and 16 km from C, the distance being measured downwards as the cyclist is returning home.

Join $\overline{CD}$ and produce to cut the time-axis at E.

Then E shows the time of arrival, which is approximately 13.05.

Example 2 *A motorist starts from* A *at* 11.00, *intending to lunch at* B, 100 *km away, at* 13.00. *After half an hour he has a puncture which delays him for* 18 *minutes. How fast must he then travel in order to arrive at* B *at the right time?*

At what time will he meet a cyclist who leaves B *at* 11.45 *and rides towards* A *at a steady* 20 *km/h?*

Suitable scales are 2 cm to 30 minutes, 2 cm to 20 km.

Placing 11.00 at the origin A mark a point E level with B (10 cm above A) at 13.00. Then $\overline{AE}$ represents the motorist's journey as it would have been if he had not had a puncture.

Mark a point C on $\overline{AE}$ at 11.30 and draw the line $\overline{CD}$ horizontally 18 minutes (1·2 cm) long to represent the time spent in changing the wheel.

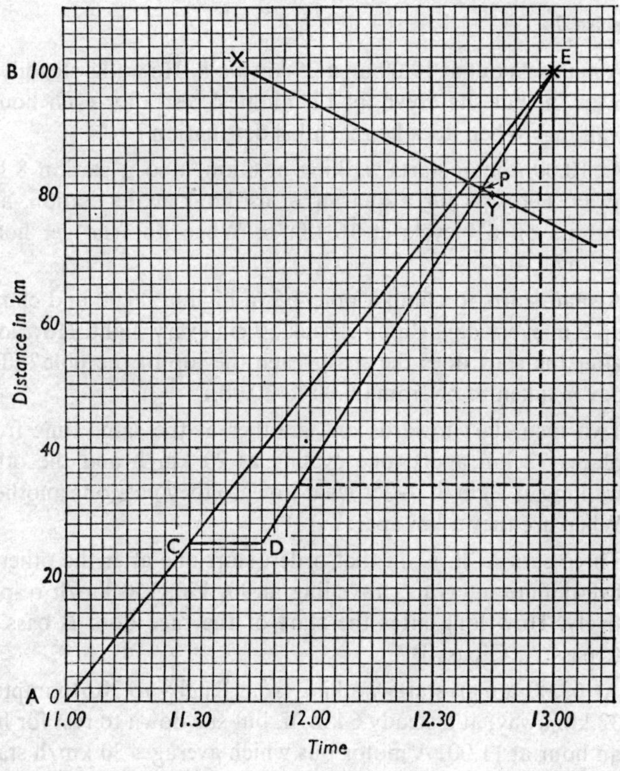

Fig. 33

Join $\overline{\text{DE}}$, which represents the actual journey from 11.48 to 13.00. To find the speed, draw a horizontal line one hour long at any convenient place and read off the corresponding vertical line (shown dotted in Fig. 33). This vertical line represents the distance travelled during the hour and is here $62\frac{1}{2}$ km: therefore the speed during this part of the journey is $62\frac{1}{2}$ km/h.

Mark the cyclist's start at X (from B at 11.45) and another point Y 20 km away at 12.45. Then $\overline{\text{XY}}$ shows the cyclist's journey.

The point P in which $\overline{\text{XY}}$ cuts $\overline{\text{DE}}$ shows the time at which the cyclist meets the motorist, which is approximately 12.42.

Exercise 7

1 A man sets out at 10.00 on a 25-km walk. He walks steadily at 6 km/h, but sits down for 12 minutes' rest after each hour's walking. When does he reach his destination?

2 At 10.00 a man starts walking at 6 km/h to a station 8 km away. He rests for a quarter of an hour at the station, and returns on a bicycle at 16 km/h. When does he get home again?

3 A snail starts to climb a pole 4·5 m high at 06.00 and climbs up 2 m every day, slipping back 50 cm every night. How long after the start does the snail reach the top of the pole? (The day is taken to be from 06.00 to 20.00.)

4 Two men start towards one another at the same time from places 32 km apart, one cycling at 20 km/h and the other walking at 5 km/h. After what time do they pass one another? When are they 5 km apart?

5 Three cars A, B, C, in that order, start one after the other at five-minute intervals, travelling at 90, 120, 150 km/h respectively. How long after the start of the race does B pass A, C pass A, C pass B?

6 At 09.00 a man starts walking from Rugby to Northampton, 32 km away, at a steady 6 km/h, but sits down to rest for half an hour at 11.00. A motor bus which averages 30 km/h starts from Rugby in the same direction at 11.15. At what time, and how far from Rugby, does the bus pass the man?

7 A short column of troops starts out on a route-march at 5 km/h with a rest of 10 minutes after each hour's marching. Half an hour later a car starts from the same place going in the same direction at an average speed of 40 km/h. The car, which does not have to slow down for the troops, stays for half an hour at a place 24 km away, and then comes back at the same average speed. How long an interval is there between the two meetings of the car and the column?

8 Which will be the first to reach a place 16 km away and by how many minutes: a man walking at 7 km/h who takes

15 minutes' rest after each hour's walking, or a man who starts ten minutes earlier and walks at 6 km/h without stopping?

9 A can run 100 m in 11·7 seconds and B can run the same distance in 12·3 seconds. How many metres' start should A give B in a 100-metre race if they are to finish together?

10 A bicyclist sets out at 09.15 to catch a train at a station 13 km away at 10.10. After 5 minutes he finds that he has left something at home, so he turns round and rides back at 16 km/h and then takes 2 minutes to find what he wants. How fast must he then ride if he is to catch the train? If his top speed is 17 km/h, by how many minutes will he miss the train?

11 Four hikers leave a hostel at 09.30 and walk together at 5 km/h until they reach a roundabout 8 km from the start. Here two of them sit down to rest, but get a lift in a car averaging 50 km/h after waiting at the roundabout for 40 minutes. The other two walk steadily until 11.30, when they catch a bus which averages 40 km/h. How far from the roundabout and at what time does the first pair catch up the second?

12 At 09.00 a man starts bicycling at a steady 16 km/h to meet a friend who leaves his home 20 km away at the same time and walks towards him at 6 km/h. At 09.30 the bicyclist has a puncture but, after waiting for 20 minutes, gets a lift in a farm cart going in the right direction at 7 km/h. At what time and how far from the second man's home do they meet, and when were they 2 km apart?

Revision examples

I

1 The cost of buying some books and having them sent to me was £21·15. If the books cost £1·15 each and the carriage was 45p, how many books did I buy?

2 Simplify (i) $3a^2b \times 2ab^3$ (ii) $(-mn) \times (-m^2n^2)$
(iii) $3x^4y^3 \div x^3y^3$ (iv) $(-cd^2e) \times (2ce^2)$
(v) $(8u^3v^2w) \div (-2uvw)$

3 Find the value of (i) 35% of 14·6 g
(ii) 85% of 27·4 km

4 In Fig. 34, find the angles marked with a letter.

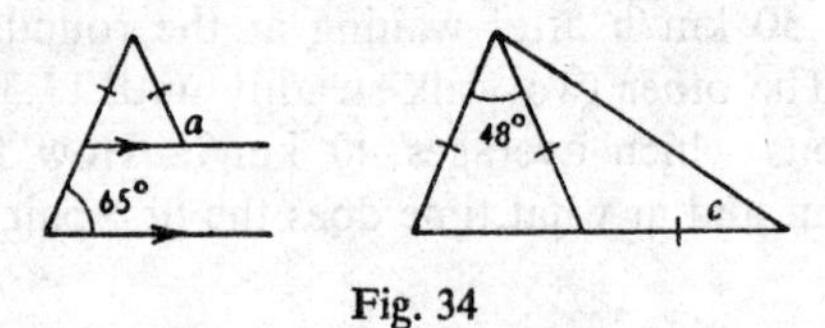

Fig. 34

5 Simplify $1\frac{3}{4} + \frac{2}{3}$ of $(4\frac{1}{4} - 3\frac{5}{8})$.

6 Find the H.C.F. of (i) a^3b^2 and ab^4
(ii) $8xy^2z^3$ and $4x^3y^2z$ (iii) $6am^2$, $9m^3n^2$ and $3a^2mn$

7 Find the simple interest on £17·50 in 6 years at 4%.

8 XYZ is an isosceles triangle having XY = XZ, and $\overline{\text{YM}}$, $\overline{\text{ZN}}$ are altitudes. Prove that YM = ZN.

9 Simplify (i) $2a - \{2(a - b) - 3(a + b)\}$

$$\text{(ii)}\ \frac{c + 2d}{3} - \frac{2c - 3d}{4} + \frac{c - 2d}{2}$$

10 Two cyclists are 69 km apart at A and B respectively. They cycle towards each other, the first at 14 km/h and the other at 16 km/h. By means of a graph find their distance from A when they meet, and the time taken.

II

1 I buy 6 things at £2·69 each, 3 at 43p each, 1 at £3·61, and a certain number at £1·28 each. If I spent £30 altogether, how many do I buy at £1·28?

2 Simplify (i) $(3a^3)^2$ (ii) $(b^2c)^3$ (iii) $(-u^2v^3)^2$ (iv) $(-2x^3)^3$ (v) $-(2m^2n)^4$

3 Find the cost price of a chair if a profit of $8\frac{1}{3}\%$ is made by selling it for £32·76.

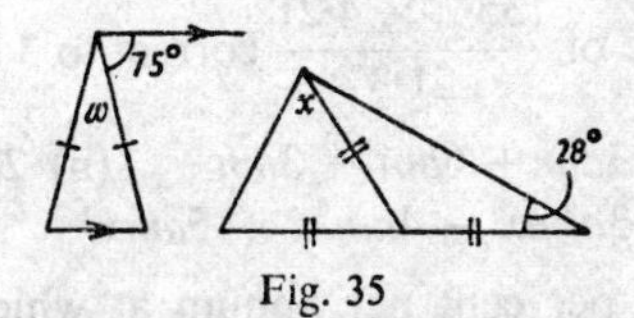

Fig. 35

4 In Fig. 35, find the angles marked with a letter.

5 Find the value of $\dfrac{22{\cdot}8 \times 0{\cdot}153}{48{\cdot}45}$.

6 Find the L.C.M. of (i) h^2k^3 and h^4k (ii) $3a^3b^2c$ and $6ab^2c^3$ (iii) $6u^2v$, $3vw^2$ and $4uvw$

7 Find the amount of £85·20 in 8 years at $7\frac{1}{2}\%$ per annum simple interest.

8 M is any point on the side $\overline{AB}$ of $\triangle ABC$. A line through M parallel to $\overline{BC}$ meets the bisector of $A\hat{B}C$ in P. Prove that BM = PM.

9 Solve the equations (i) $4(2x - 1) - 5(x - 2) = 1$

(ii) $\dfrac{x-2}{5} - \dfrac{x-3}{6} = \dfrac{3}{10}$

10 A rectangular tank contains 13 125 litres of water. If the tank is 3·5 m long and 2·5 m wide internally, find the depth of the water.

III

1 How many things at £1·35 each can I buy for £45, and how much shall I have left over?

2 Simplify (i) $\sqrt{4x^6}$ (ii) $\sqrt{m^2n^4}$ (iii) $\sqrt[3]{8a^6}$
(iv) $\sqrt[3]{-u^3v^9}$ (v) $\sqrt{16c^{16}}$

3 Find the quantity of which (i) 7·37 kg is 55%
(ii) 11·75 km is $62\frac{1}{2}$%

4 PXY, QXY are isosceles triangles lying on the same side of a common base $\overline{XY}$. If $P\hat{X}Y = 67°$ and $X\hat{Q}Y = 78°$, calculate $X\hat{P}Y$ and $P\hat{Y}Q$.

5 Find the value of $\dfrac{135{\cdot}2 \times 4{\cdot}21}{21{\cdot}3}$ correct to 3 significant figures.

6 Factorise (i) $3am + 6bm - 3mn$ (ii) $2a^3 - 6a^2 - 4a$
(iii) $3a^2mx - 4am^2x + 5amx^2$

7 Find the rate per cent per annum at which £175 will earn £110·25 simple interest in 9 years.

8 ABC is an isosceles triangle having AB = AC, and a line $\overline{BD}$ is drawn parallel to $\overline{AC}$. Prove that $\overline{BC}$ bisects $A\hat{B}D$.

9 If $a = 4$, $b = 3$, $c = -2$, find the value of
(i) $(a - b)^2 - 2(a - b)(b - c) + (b - c)^2$
(ii) $(a - 2b + c)^2$

10 A piece of string can be cut into 36 pieces each 1·95 m long. How many pieces would there be each 1·35 m long?

IV

1 A man leaves home at 13.00 and cycles to a place 30 km away, arriving there at 15.30. For the first 18 km he cycles at 12 km/h and then rests for 15 minutes. By means of a graph find his speed for the remainder of the journey.

2 (i) Multiply $2a^2m - 5am^2 + 3a^2m^2$ by $-3a^2m$
(ii) Divide $8u^3v^3 + 2u^2v^3 - 6u^3v^2$ by $2uv^2$

3 Find the result of (i) increasing £140 by 15%
(ii) decreasing £1·60 by 35%

4 In Fig. 36, find the angles marked with a letter.

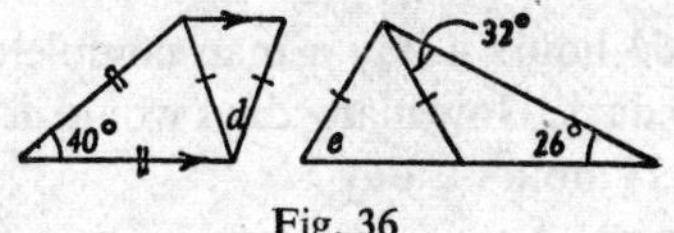

Fig. 36

5 Simplify $\dfrac{0{\cdot}105 \times 2{\cdot}52}{1{\cdot}26 \times 1{\cdot}68}$

6 Simplify

(i) $\dfrac{3}{m} + \dfrac{2}{mn} - \dfrac{1}{n}$ (ii) $\dfrac{4}{ac} - 3$ (iii) $\dfrac{3a - b}{4} - \dfrac{a + 2b}{3}$

7 Find the time in which £87·50 will earn £38·50 simple interest at 4% per annum.

8 From the mid-point of the base of an isosceles triangle perpendiculars are drawn to the other two sides. Prove that these perpendiculars are equal in length.

9 (i) Simplify the expression $\dfrac{5(2a - 1)}{6} - \dfrac{3(4a + 1)}{8} + \dfrac{11}{12}$

(ii) Solve the equation $\dfrac{5(2a - 1)}{6} + \dfrac{11}{12} = \dfrac{3(4a + 1)}{8}$

10 If a man works for $7\frac{1}{2}$ hours and is paid £7·20, how much should he receive for $3\frac{1}{2}$ hours' work at the same rate?

V

1 Find the total cost of travelling 96 km at $2\frac{1}{2}$p per km for a man, his wife, and three children at half fare.

2 Simplify (i) $2cd(-cd + 3c^2d - 2cd^2)$

(ii) $\dfrac{3m^2u - 9m^3u^2 - 6m^2u^3}{-3m^2u}$

3 Find the percentage profit when an article is bought for 75p and sold for 84p.

4 PQR is an isosceles triangle with its base $\overline{QR}$ produced to S so that RS = PR. If $P\hat{S}R = 39°$, calculate $Q\hat{P}R$.

5 By working $6\frac{3}{4}$ hours a day a man completes a certain piece of work in 20 days. How many days would it have taken if he had worked $7\frac{1}{2}$ hours a day?

6 Find the H.C.F. of (i) m^2uv^3 and u^3v^2
(ii) $4ad$, $6de$ and $2ae$ (iii) $3x^3y^3z^2$ and $4x^2y^3z^3$

7 Find the principal that will earn £31·50 simple interest in 7 years at 2% per annum.

8 $\overline{AB}$, $\overline{AC}$ are the equal sides of the isosceles triangle ABC, and BCD is an isosceles triangle with its base $\overline{BD}$ parallel to $\overline{AC}$. Prove that $B\hat{A}C = B\hat{C}D$.

9 Simplify (i) $2[3m - 2(3m - 1) + 3(2m + 1)]$
(ii) $2 - [(3p + 5) - (5p + 3)]$

10 Twelve books cost £8·20 altogether. Some were priced at 75p each, and the rest at 65p each. How many were there of each kind?

VI

1 How many tins of tobacco at 76p each can I buy for £19?

2 Simplify (i) $3(2a - b - c) - 2(3a - 2b + c)$
(ii) $2a(a - m) - 3m(a - 2m)$

3 Find the cost price of an article if a profit of 40% is made by selling it for £2·45.

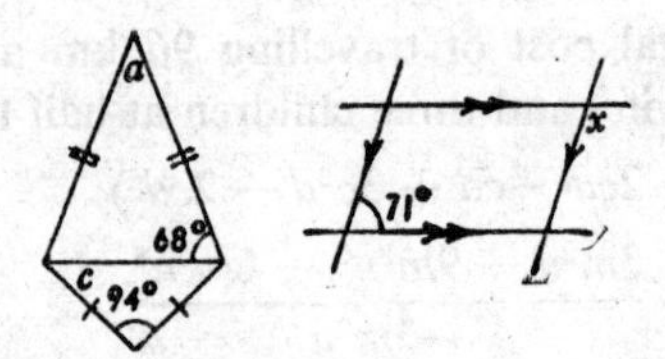

Fig. 37

4 In Fig. 37, find the angles marked with a letter.

5 Find the value of $\dfrac{152{\cdot}7 \times 0{\cdot}396}{19{\cdot}8}$

6 Find the L.C.M. of (i) $4a^2de$ and $6ad^2e^2$
(ii) ab^2c^2, a^2bc^2 and abc^3 (iii) $2mn$, $4m^2n$ and $6mn^3$

7 Find to the nearest penny the simple interest on £91·67 in 7 years at 3% per annum.

8 M, N are the mid-points of the sides $\overline{AB}$, $\overline{AC}$ of △ABC. A line through C parallel to $\overline{BA}$ meets $\overline{MN}$ produced in P. Prove that MN = NP.

9 Find the values of $2d^2 - 3d + 1$ when d has the values (i) 3, (ii) −3, (iii) 0, (iv) 1, (v) −1.

10 Two rectangles have the same area. One measures 2 m by 39 cm; the other is 65 cm wide. Find its length.

VII

1 A cyclist leaves a certain starting-point at 09.05 and travels at a steady 12 km/h. A second cyclist leaves the same starting-point at 09.55 and pursues the first cyclist at 16 km/h. By means of a graph find how far they have gone when the second cyclist overtakes the first, and at what time.

2 Simplify (i) $(-4mu^3) \times (2mu)$
(ii) $(-12a^2de^3) \div (-4ade)$
(iii) $(-2m^2n)^2$ (iv) $-(2ab^3)^2$ (v) $\sqrt{9u^4v^6}$

3 Find the selling price of an article which is bought for £27·50 and sold at a profit of 32%.

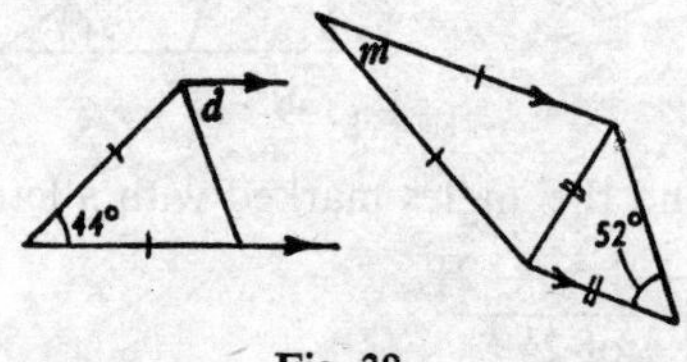

Fig. 38

4 In Fig. 38, find the angles marked with a letter.

5 If a gross of ties cost £46·80, how many can be bought for £26?

6 Factorise (i) $2a^2x - 8ax^2 + 6a^2x^2$
(ii) $a^2bc + ab^2d + a^2cd$
(iii) $6au^2 + 9u^2v - 3auv$

7 Find the amount of £215·75 in 8 years at $4\frac{1}{2}\%$ per annum simple interest.

8 PQR is an isosceles triangle in which PQ = PR. The bisectors of the angles Q, R meet at S. Prove that SQ = SR.

9 Solve the equations

(i) $4(5a + 2) - 5(3a + 1) = 2(a - 1)$

(ii) $\frac{6c + 5}{3} = \frac{4c + 1}{2} + \frac{5c}{6}$

10 A plot of land measures 101 m by 26 m. By how much does its area exceed a quarter of a hectare?

VIII

1 I order 27 copies of a book to be sent to me and the total cost is £18·10, including 55p for carriage. Find the price of one book.

2 (i) Multiply $x^2yz + 5y^2z^2 - 3xyz^2$ by $2yz^2$
(ii) Divide $-6a^3m^3 - 9a^4m^2 + 3a^2m^4$ by $-3a^2m$

3 Find the selling price of an article which is bought for £1·75 and sold at a loss of 16%.

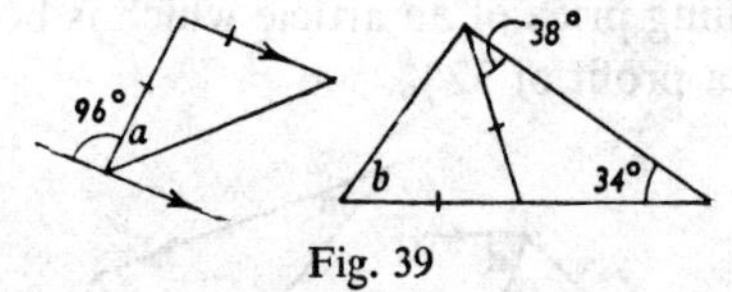

Fig. 39

4 In Fig. 39, find the angles marked with a letter.

5 Simplify $\frac{2\frac{3}{4} + 1\frac{5}{16} \div 2\frac{1}{4}}{\frac{2}{3} \text{ of } 2\frac{1}{7}}$

6 Simplify

(i) $\frac{u + v}{u} - \frac{u + v}{v}$ (ii) $\frac{m}{a^2b} + \frac{n}{ab^2}$ (iii) $\frac{1}{a^3} + \frac{1}{a^2} - \frac{1}{a}$

7 Find the rate per cent per annum at which £206·30 will amount to £268·19 in $7\frac{1}{2}$ years.

8 ABC is a triangle in which AB = AC. $\overline{BA}$ is produced to P, and $\overline{AQ}$ bisects $C\hat{A}P$. Prove that $\overline{AQ}$ is parallel to $\overline{BC}$.

9 Simplify

(i) $\dfrac{7(a-3)}{4} - \dfrac{5}{6} - \dfrac{5(a-4)}{3}$

(ii) $2[(m-n)-(3m+n)]-[(2m+n)-(m+2n)]$

10 A cyclist rides from one town to another at 20 km/h and returns at 16 km/h. If the return journey takes 18 minutes longer than the outward journey, find the distance between the towns.

IX

1 Find the total cost of 20 things at 13p each, 12 at 7p, 7 at £1·26, 29 at 11p, and 3 at £3·71.

2 Simplify (i) $\dfrac{4mu^2v - 8muv^2 - 2m^2uv}{-2muv}$

(ii) $3ax^2(4a^2x + a^2x^2 - 2ax^2)$

3 Find the cost price of an article if a loss of 12% is made by selling it for £1·54.

4 $\triangle$ABC is such that the length of the line joining A to the mid-point of $\overline{BC}$ is equal to $\frac{1}{2}$BC. If $A\hat{B}C = 57°$, calculate $A\hat{C}B$.

5 If $a = 1$, $b = 2$, $m = -2$, $n = 3$ find the values of

(i) $ab - mn$ (ii) $b^2 + m^2$ (iii) $(a-m)(b-n)$

6 Factorise (i) $3m - 9m^2 + 6m^3$

(ii) $4a^2x^2 + 6ax^2 - 4a^2x$

(iii) $u^2vw - 2uv^2w - 4uvw^2 - 2uvw$

7 Find the time in which £218·75 will amount to £341·25 at $3\frac{1}{2}$% simple interest.

8 AMN, BMN are isosceles triangles lying on the same side of a common base $\overline{MN}$. Prove that $\overline{AB}$ bisects $M\hat{A}N$.

9 Solve the equations (i) $2(5x + 7) - 3(3x + 2) = 4x$

(ii) $\frac{4(3a + 2)}{5} - \frac{3(4a - 1)}{10} = \frac{7a}{10}$

10 If 15 dogs eat 25 kg of biscuits in 20 days, how long would 22 kg of biscuits last for 12 dogs?

X

1 A man leaves home at 16.30 and cycles at a steady 16 km/h until 17.45. He rests for half an hour and then returns home, arriving at 19.35. By means of a graph find his speed on the return journey, assuming that it does not vary.

2 Simplify (i) $-2m(3m - n) - 3n(2m + n)$

(ii) $a(b - c) - b(c - a) - c(a - b)$

3 If $6\frac{2}{3}\%$ of the children in a school are absent when there are 322 present, how many children are there in the school?

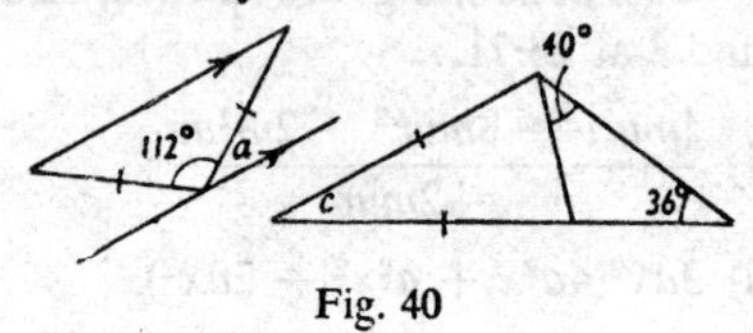

Fig. 40

4 In Fig. 40, find the angles marked with a letter.

5 Simplify $(2\frac{3}{4} - 1\frac{7}{8}) \times 7\frac{2}{3} \div 3\frac{5}{6}$.

6 Simplify

(i) $\frac{1}{mv} - \frac{2}{mu}$ (ii) $3 + \frac{1}{2x}$ (iii) $1 - \frac{d + e}{3a}$

7 Find the principal that will earn £151·50 simple interest in $5\frac{1}{3}$ years at $4\frac{1}{2}\%$ per annum.

8 ABCD is a square, and an equilateral triangle CDX is drawn so that it lies within the square. The diagonal $\overline{AC}$ cuts $\overline{DX}$ at Y. Prove that $X\hat{Y}C$ = 7 times $X\hat{C}Y$.

9 (i) Solve the equation $\frac{4(2a - 3)}{3} = \frac{3(2a - 5)}{4} + \frac{5a}{6}$.

(ii) Simplify the expression $\frac{4(2a-3)}{3} - \frac{3(2a-5)}{4} - \frac{5a}{6}$.

10 If the petrol consumption of a car is a litre for every 12 km, and petrol costs 8p a litre, how far could the car travel on £3 worth of petrol?

Chapter 8

Expansions and factors

The expression $(x + 2)(x - 5)$ means that each term in the first bracket is to be multiplied by each term in the second. When $x + 2$ is multiplied by x the result is $x^2 + 2x$, and when $x + 2$ is multiplied by -5 the result is $-5x - 10$. When these two results are put together the final result is $x^2 + 2x - 5x - 10$, i.e. $x^2 - 3x - 10$, which is therefore the product of $(x + 2)$ and $(x - 5)$.

The working may be arranged in various ways, and the arrangement which will be given first is the one which most resembles the corresponding process in arithmetic, where no letters are involved.

The product 25×31, which is really (2 tens + 5 units) $\times$ (3 tens + 1 unit), is worked as follows:

$$\begin{array}{r} 25 \\ 31 \\ \hline 75 \\ 25 \\ \hline 775 \end{array}$$

and the units, tens and hundreds are kept in separate columns. The working for the expansion of $(x + 2)(x - 5)$ may be arranged in a similar way.

$$\begin{array}{llll} x & +2 & & \\ x & -5 & & \\ \hline x^2 & +2x & & \ldots \quad x \times (x + 2) \\ & -5x & -10 & \ldots -5 \times (x + 2) \\ \hline x^2 & -3x & -10 & \end{array}$$

Notice that like terms are kept in separate columns.

Example 1 *Expand* $(2c - 3m)(c - 4m)$.

$$\begin{array}{r} 2c - 3m \\ c - 4m \\ \hline 2c^2 - 3cm \\ - 8cm + 12m^2 \\ \hline 2c^2 - 11cm + 12m^2 \\ \hline \end{array}$$

In this product, $(2c - 3m) \times c = 2c^2 - 3cm$, which is the first partial product; $(2c - 3m) \times (-4m) = -8cm + 12m^2$, which is written under $2c^2 - 3cm$ so that the term $-8cm$ is under $-3cm$, and the term $+12m^2$ starts a fresh column.

Example 2 *Expand* $(x - 3)^2$.

$$\begin{array}{r} x - 3 \\ x - 3 \\ \hline x^2 - 3x \\ - 3x + 9 \\ \hline x^2 - 6x + 9 \\ \hline \end{array}$$

Exercise 8a

Expand

1 $(a + 3)(a + 4)$
2 $(b + 2)(b + 5)$
3 $(m + 3)(m - 2)$
4 $(n - 7)(n + 2)$
5 $(x + 2)^2$
6 $(y + 1)(y - 4)$
7 $(c - 2)(c + 5)$
8 $(d - 3)(d - 4)$
9 $(p - 2)(p - 5)$
10 $(x - 4)^2$
11 $(y + 1)(y + 7)$
12 $(a - 4)(a + 6)$
13 $(b - 3)(b - 7)$
14 $(c + 5)(c - 1)$
15 $(3 + d)(2 + d)$
16 $(5 - x)(2 + x)$
17 $(3 - y)(4 - y)$
18 $(m + 2n)(m + 3n)$
19 $(a - 3b)(a + 2b)$
20 $(x - 4y)(x - 3y)$
21 $(p + 2q)^2$
22 $(m + 5n)(m - 3n)$
23 $(a + 5)(2a - 3)$
24 $(3x + 4)(x - 2)$

25 $(2h - k)(3h + 2k)$ **26** $(5x + 2y)(3x + 4y)$
27 $(3a - 2b)^2$ **28** $(5h + k)^2$
29 $(5a - 2b)(2a - 3b)$ **30** $(7m - 5n)(5m + 3n)$

Corresponding to the foregoing type of product there is a process for division which follows closely the method for long division with numbers only. The important difference is that when a term is placed in the quotient it is the result of dividing the first term of the dividend *exactly* by the first term of the divisor.

For example, with numbers only,

$$\begin{array}{l} 23\,)\,958\,(\,4 \\ \underline{92} \\ \text{etc.} \end{array}$$

$9 \div 2$ is not 4 exactly.

To divide $x^2 - 6x + 8$ by $x - 4$ the process is as follows:

$$\begin{array}{rl} x - 4\,) & x^2 - 6x + 8\;(x - 2 \\ & \underline{x^2 - 4x} \\ & \quad - 2x + 8 \\ & \quad \underline{- 2x + 8} \\ & \quad \underline{\quad \cdot \qquad \cdot} \end{array}$$

The x in the quotient is the result of dividing x^2 by x
" -2 " " " " " " " " $-2x$ " x

As the quotient is obtained in this way it follows that in each subtraction there is *no remainder in the first column.*

(Reminder of rule for subtraction—*change the lower sign and add*—see Book 1, Chap. 22.)

Example 3 *Divide* $6c^2 - 11cm - 12m^2$ *by* $3c + 2m$.

$$\begin{array}{rl} 3c + 2m\,) & 6c^2 - 11cm - 12m^2\,(\,2c - 5m \\ & \underline{6c^2 + \;\;4cm} \\ & \qquad - 15cm - 12m^2 \\ & \qquad \underline{- 15cm - 10m^2} \\ & \qquad \qquad \quad \underline{- \;\; 2m^2} \end{array}$$

$\therefore$ the quotient is $2c - 5m$ and the remainder is $-2m^2$.

Exercise 8b

Divide

1 $a^2 + 6a + 8$ by $a + 2$

2 $b^2 - 5b + 6$ by $b - 3$

3 $c^2 + 2c - 8$ „ $c - 2$

4 $d^2 - 2d - 15$ „ $d + 3$

5 $e^2 + 5e + 9$ „ $e + 3$

6 $m^2 - 3m + 1$ „ $m - 4$

7 $n^2 + 2n - 9$ „ $n + 4$

8 $x^2 - 5x + 3$ „ $x - 3$

9 $2y^2 - y - 15$ „ $y - 3$

10 $3h^2 + 5h - 2$ „ $h + 2$

11 $2k^2 - 13k + 17$ by $k - 5$

12 $4u^2 + 15u - 4$ „ $u + 4$

13 $3a^2 + 14a + 12$ „ $a + 3$

14 $a^2 + 3ab + 2b^2$ „ $a + b$

15 $c^2 - 2cd + d^2$ „ $c - d$

16 $x^2 + 2xy - 2y^2$ „ $x + 3y$

17 $3u^2 + 7uv - 6v^2$ „ $3u - 2v$

18 $4h^2 + 4hk - 4k^2$ „ $2h + 3k$

19 $10d^2 - 2de - 10e^2$ „ $5d - 6e$

20 $9p^2 - 27pq + 24q^2$ „ $3p - 5q$

Simplify

21 $(2x^2 - 5x - 12) \div (x - 4)$

22 $(3y^2 - 7y - 6) \div (3y + 2)$

23 $\dfrac{6a^2 + 17a + 5}{2a + 5}$

24 $\dfrac{6d^2 - 13d + 6}{3d - 2}$

25 $(2a^2 + 7ab + 6b^2) \div (2a + b)$

26 $(3x^2 - 7xy + 4y^2) \div (3x - y)$

27 $\dfrac{4m^2 + 2mn - 4n^2}{2m + 3n}$

28 $\dfrac{15u^2 - uv - 5v^2}{5u - 2v}$

29 $\dfrac{24d^2 - 38de + 15e^2}{6d - 5e}$

30 $\dfrac{12a^2 - 5ac - 20c^2}{3a - 5c}$

The working for the expansion of $(x + 2)(x - 5)$ as on page 84 could have been arranged differently.

$(x + 2) \times x = x^2 + 2x$ and $(x + 2) \times (-5) = -5x - 10$,

and these partial products may be written on the same line.

Thus $\quad (x+2)(x-5) = x(x+2) - 5(x+2)$
$$= x^2 + 2x - 5x - 10$$
$$= x^2 - 3x - 10.$$

Example 4 $(2c - 3m)(c - 4m) = 2c^2 - 3cm - 8cm + 12m^2$
$$= 2c^2 - 11cm + 12m^2.$$

It will be noticed that the actual terms in the working are exactly the same as before, and that there is a saving of space rather than of time.

Example 5 $(3a+2)^2 = (3a+2)(3a+2)$
$$= 9a^2 + 6a + 6a + 4$$
$$= 9a^2 + 12a + 4.$$

Exercise 8c

Expand the following, arranging the working as in Example 4 or 5:

1 $(a+2)(a+3)$
2 $(c+6)(c-1)$
3 $(e-3)(e+2)$
4 $(d-6)(d+3)$
5 $(x-1)(x-2)$
6 $(a+3)^2$
7 $(b-5)^2$
8 $(m+4)(m-4)$
9 $(n+5)(n-4)$
10 $(d+3)(d-7)$
11 $(b-5)(b+6)$
12 $(p-3)(p-5)$
13 $(q-3)(q+3)$
14 $(u-9)(u+5)$
15 $(v-4)(v-9)$
16 $(2a+1)(a+3)$
17 $(b+4)(3b+2)$
18 $(2c-5)(c-3)$
19 $(d-9)(2d+3)$
20 $(2x+1)^2$
21 $(5x+2)(2x-3)$
22 $(3y-5)(2y+1)$
23 $(m+4n)^2$
24 $(u+2v)(u+3v)$
25 $(3d-2e)(3d+2e)$
26 $(3b+2c)(2b-c)$
27 $(2s-5t)(3s+t)$
28 $(2c-3d)^2$
29 $(4m-n)(3m-3n)$
30 $(2c-9e)(4c+5e)$

With practice it will be found unnecessary to write down all the working as in Exercise 8*c*, and the answer may be written down at once.

For example, in the product

$$(2c - 3m)(c - 4m) = 2c^2 - 3cm - 8cm + 12m^2,$$

the terms $-3cm$ and $-8cm$ may be combined mentally, and the answer $2c^2 - 11cm + 12m^2$ written down.

Example 6 $(d - 2)(3d + 5) = 3d^2 - d - 10.$

In the answer,

$3d^2$ is the product of d and $3d$
$-d$ is the result of combining $-2 \times 3d = -6d$
and $d \times 5 = 5d$
-10 is the product of -2 and 5.

Example 7 *Find the coefficient of ab in the expansion of* $(5a + 2b)(4a - 3b)$.

The terms containing ab are $2b \times 4a = 8ab$
and $5a \times (-3b) = -15ab$.

These terms combine into $-7ab$.

$\therefore$ the coefficient of ab in the expansion is -7.

This working should be done mentally, and the result written down at once.

Exercise 8d

Find the coefficient of d in the expansion of

1 $(d + 2)(d + 7)$ **2** $(d - 4)(d + 6)$ **3** $(d - 3)(d - 1)$
4 $(d - 8)(d + 3)$ **5** $(d + 7)^2$

Find the coefficient of u in the expansion of

6 $(u + 2)(2u + 3)$ **7** $(u - 4)(3u + 5)$
8 $(2u - 5)(3u + 5)$ **9** $(4u - 5)(2u - 7)$
10 $(3u - 4)^2$

Find the coefficient of ab in the expansion of

11 $(3a + b)(a + 2b)$
12 $(a - b)(3a - 2b)$
13 $(4a + 3b)(5a - 3b)$
14 $(5a + 2b)(5a - 2b)$
15 $(a - 3b)^2$

Find the coefficient of mn in the expansion of

16 $(m + 4n)^2$
17 $(3m - 4n)(3m + 4n)$
18 $(2m - 5n)(3m + 4n)$
19 $(3m - 5n)^2$
20 $(5m - 3n)(4m + 5n)$

Without showing any working, write down the expansion of

21 $(a + 1)(a + 2)$
22 $(a + 2)(a + 3)$
23 $(a + 3)(a + 4)$
24 $(b + 1)(b - 2)$
25 $(b + 2)(b - 3)$
26 $(b + 3)(b - 4)$
27 $(c - 3)(c - 4)$
28 $(d + 7)(d + 1)$
29 $(e + 2)(e + 9)$
30 $(f - 5)(f - 4)$
31 $(x - 7)(x - 1)$
32 $(y - 2)(y - 9)$
33 $(h + 6)^2$
34 $(k - 5)^2$
35 $(z + 2)(z - 9)$
36 $(a + 4)(a + 6)$
37 $(a - 4)(a - 6)$
38 $(a - 4)(a + 6)$
39 $(a + 4)(a - 6)$
40 $(b + 6)(b - 3)$
41 $(c - 1)(c - 2)$
42 $(m - 1)^2$
43 $(n + 1)^2$
44 $(f + 9)(f + 11)$
45 $(e - 3)(e - 5)$
46 $(d - 2)(d + 10)$
47 $(h + 3)(h - 8)$
48 $(a + 3)^2$
49 $(a - 3)^2$
50 $(a + 3)(a - 3)$
51 $(b - 5)(b + 5)$
52 $(c + 7)(c - 7)$
53 $(2d + 1)(3d + 1)$
54 $(4a - 1)(5a - 2)$
55 $(m - 5)(2m + 4)$
56 $(3n + 2)(2n - 1)$
57 $(3h + 4)(5h - 2)$
58 $(2k - 7)(4k + 5)$
59 $(2x + 3)^2$
60 $(3t - 2)^2$
61 $(3d - 2)(3d + 2)$
62 $(3e - 5)^2$
63 $(5a - 2)(2a + 7)$
64 $(2a + 3b)(3a + 4b)$
65 $(2a + 5b)(3a - 4b)$
66 $(6m + n)(5m + n)$
67 $(5x - y)(2x - 3y)$
68 $(3m + 4n)(2m - 3n)$
69 $(3h + 5k)^2$
70 $(5h - 3k)(5h + 3k)$
71 $(2x - 5y)^2$
72 $(5a + 2d)(3a - 8d)$

73 $(4r - 7s)(3r + 2s)$ **74** $(4u - 9v)(3u - 8v)$

75 $(2e - 7f)(5e + 6f)$

Since $5 \times 7 = 35$, 5 and 7 are said to be the **factors** of 35. Similarly, since $(x + 2)(x - 6) = x^2 - 4x - 12$, $(x + 2)$ and $(x - 6)$ are said to be the factors of $x^2 - 4x - 12$.

An algebraical expression of this kind does not necessarily have factors, just as in arithmetic a number such as 13 is said to be prime because it has no factors (other than itself and unity).

For example $x^2 + 2x - 6$ has no factors.

Example 8 *Factorise the expression* $x^2 + 7x + 10$.

The object is to fill in the brackets in the statement

$$x^2 + 7x + 10 = (\quad)(\quad).$$

The first term in the given expression is x^2, and this can be obtained only by putting x first in each bracket.

The next term to consider is the last in the given expression, i.e. 10. This number is the product of the last terms in the two brackets, and there is the choice of 10 and 1, -10 and -1, 5 and 2, or -5 and -2. The possibilities to be considered are therefore

(i) $(x + 10)(x + 1) = x^2 + 11x + 10$

(ii) $(x - 10)(x - 1) = x^2 - 11x + 10$

(iii) $(x + 5)(x + 2) = x^2 + 7x + 10$ (the given expression)

(iv) $(x - 5)(x - 2) = x^2 - 7x + 10$

Notice in these four statements that the coefficient of x on the right-hand side is the *sum* of the numbers coming last in the two brackets, i.e. $11 = 10 + 1$, $-11 = (-10) + (-1)$ and so on. Hence (ii) and (iv) might have been discarded at once as -10 and -1 or -5 and -2 cannot add up to $+11$.

The required result is $x^2 + 7x + 10 = (x + 5)(x + 2)$.

(It does not matter which bracket comes first as $(x + 2)(x + 5)$ is the same product.)

Example 9 *Factorise the expression* $x^2 - 9x + 8$.

As in Example 8, the first term in each bracket is x. The last term is $+8$, which is the product of $+4$ and $+2$, -4 and -2, $+8$ and $+1$, or -8 and -1. Of these pairs of numbers only -8 and -1 add up to -9 which is the coefficient for the middle term.

$$\therefore x^2 - 9x + 8 = (x - 8)(x - 1).$$

Example 10 *Factorise the expression* $x^2 - 4x - 12$.

The first term in each bracket is x.

-12 is the product of -12 and $+1$, $+12$ and -1, -6 and $+2$, $+6$ and -2, -4 and $+3$, or $+4$ and -3.

The only pair which will give -4 as the coefficient for the middle term is -6 and $+2$, because $-6 + 2 = -4$.

$$\therefore x^2 - 4x - 12 = (x - 6)(x + 2).$$

Example 11 *Factorise the expression* $x^2 + 2x - 15$.

The first term in each bracket is x.

-15 is the product of -15 and $+1$, $+15$ and -1, -5 and $+3$, or $+5$ and -3.

The only pair which will give $+2$ as the coefficient for the middle term is $+5$ and -3, because $+5 - 3 = +2$.

$$\therefore x^2 + 2x - 15 = (x + 5)(x - 3).$$

The general idea in Examples 8, 9, 10 and 11 has been to find two numbers such that their product is the absolute term in the given expression, and their sum is the coefficient of x in the given expression. It will be noticed that

(i) when the sign of the absolute term is $+$, the two numbers are of the same sign as each other, and numerically the coefficient of x is their sum;

(ii) when the sign of the absolute term is $-$, the two numbers are of opposite signs, so that numerically the coefficient of x is their difference.

When found, the factors should always be checked mentally by multiplication.

Exercise 8e

Factorise the following where possible. If there are no factors say so.

1 $a^2 + 4a + 3$
2 $b^2 + 5b + 6$
3 $c^2 + 3c + 2$
4 $d^2 + 7d + 10$
5 $e^2 + 7e + 12$
6 $f^2 - 6f + 5$
7 $g^2 - 3g + 2$
8 $h^2 - 8h + 15$
9 $m^2 - 7m + 12$
10 $n^2 - 8n + 7$
11 $p^2 + 2p - 3$
12 $q^2 - 2q - 3$
13 $r^2 + 3r - 10$
14 $s^2 - 3s - 10$
15 $t^2 - t - 6$
16 $u^2 + u - 6$
17 $v^2 + v + 1$
18 $w^2 - 5w - 14$
19 $x^2 + 5x - 14$
20 $y^2 + y + 14$
21 $z^2 + 5z - 6$
22 $z^2 - 5z - 6$
23 $m^2 + 13m + 12$
24 $n^2 + 11n - 12$
25 $a^2 + a - 12$
26 $d^2 + 4d + 5$
27 $b^2 - 8b + 12$
28 $x^2 - 4x - 12$
29 $u^2 + 3u - 2$
30 $d^2 - 2d + 4$
31 $b^2 - 9b + 20$
32 $a^2 - 12a + 20$
33 $e^2 - e - 20$
34 $w^2 + 7w - 20$
35 $x^2 + 8x - 20$
36 $y^2 + 21y + 20$
37 $z^2 + 6z + 9$
38 $m^2 - 8m + 16$
39 $n^2 - 3n + 16$
40 $p^2 + 6p - 16$
41 $q^2 + 3q - 18$
42 $b^2 - 7b - 18$
43 $c^2 + 10c + 25$
44 $a^2 - 14a + 49$
45 $f^2 - 10f + 21$
46 $x^2 - 9$
47 $y^2 - 25$
48 $h^2 - 2h - 35$
49 $l^2 - 7l - 7$
50 $u^2 - 12u + 32$
51 $v^2 + 13v + 36$
52 $w^2 + 8w + 9$
53 $a^2 - 6a + 4$
54 $b^2 - 16$
55 $c^2 - 36$
56 $d^2 + 14d + 40$

57 $e^2 + 13e + 40$ **58** $f^2 + 8f - 48$

59 $g^2 - 2g - 48$ **60** $h^2 - 26h + 48$

Example 12 *Expand* $(a^2 + 5a - 4)(3a - 2)$.

(i)

$$\begin{array}{r} a^2 + 5a - 4 \\ 3a - 2 \\ \hline 3a^3 + 15a^2 - 12a \\ - 2a^2 - 10a + 8 \\ \hline 3a^3 + 13a^2 - 22a + 8 \\ \hline \end{array}$$

(ii)

$$\begin{aligned}(a^2 + 5a - 4)(3a - 2) &= 3a(a^2 + 5a - 4) - 2(a^2 + 5a - 4) \\ &= 3a^3 + 15a^2 - 12a - 2a^2 - 10a + 8 \\ &= 3a^3 + 13a^2 - 22a + 8.\end{aligned}$$

(iii) By the method of picking out coefficients, the answer can be written down at once by inspection. See Example 13.

Example 13 *Find the coefficients of* b^2 *and of* b *in the expansion of* $(3b^2 - b + 4)(5b - 2)$. *Hence write down the expansion.*

The terms containing b^2 are $(-b) \times (5b)$ and $(3b^2) \times (-2)$,

i.e. $-5b^2$ and $-6b^2$,

$\therefore$ the coefficient of b^2 is -11.

The terms containing b are $(4) \times (5b)$ and $(-b) \times (-2)$,

i.e. $20b$ and $2b$,

$\therefore$ the coefficient of b is 22.

The other terms are $(3b^2) \times (5b)$, i.e. $15b^3$,

and $(4) \times (-2)$, i.e. -8,

$\therefore$ the expansion is $15b^3 - 11b^2 + 22b - 8$.

The reasoning in this example would normally be done mentally, and the answers written down by inspection.

Exercise 8f

Expand (using method (i) or (ii) above)

1 $(a^2 + a + 2)(a + 1)$ **2** $(x^2 - x + 1)(x - 1)$

3 $(m^2 + 2m - 1)(m + 2)$
4 $(y^2 + 3y + 2)(y - 3)$
5 $(a^2 - 3a - 4)(2a + 1)$
6 $(b^2 + 5b - 3)(2b + 3)$
7 $(c^2 - 4c - 1)(c + 4)$
8 $(d^2 + 6d + 2)(3d - 1)$
9 $(x^2 - 5x + 2)(4x - 3)$
10 $(y^2 - 6y + 4)(3y + 5)$
11 $(2a^2 + 4a + 1)(2a + 1)$
12 $(2n^2 + 3n - 2)(4n - 6)$
13 $(3b^2 - 6b - 2)(3b - 1)$
14 $(5x^2 - 3x + 3)(4x + 5)$
15 $(4d^2 - 7d - 1)(5d + 2)$

Write down the coefficients of m^2 and of m in the following products. Also, *by inspection*, write down the expansions.

16 $(m^2 + 3m + 1)(m + 1)$
17 $(m^2 - 2m + 1)(m - 3)$
18 $(m^2 - 5m + 2)(m + 3)$
19 $(m^2 + m - 4)(2m - 3)$
20 $(m^2 + 6m - 2)(3m + 1)$
21 $(2m^2 - 3m - 4)(3m + 5)$
22 $(3m^2 - m + 4)(2m - 3)$
23 $(3m^2 + 6m + 8)(3m - 4)$
24 $(4m^2 - 10m + 3)(2m + 5)$
25 $(2m^2 - 7m - 5)(3m + 5)$

Example 14 *Simplify* $3(c - 2d)^2 - (4c + d)(c - 3d) + 3c^2$.

$$
\begin{aligned}
3(c - 2d)^2 - (4c + d)(c - 3d) + 3c^2 \\
&= 3(c - 2d)(c - 2d) - (4c + d)(c - 3d) + 3c^2 \\
&= 3(c^2 - 4cd + 4d^2) - (4c^2 - 11cd - 3d^2) + 3c^2 \\
&= 3c^2 - 12cd + 12d^2 - 4c^2 + 11cd + 3d^2 + 3c^2 \\
&= 2c^2 - cd + 15d^2.
\end{aligned}
$$

Example 15 *Solve the equation*

$$5a^2 - 3(a - 2)(a + 4) = (a + 1)(2a - 3).$$

$$
\begin{aligned}
5a^2 - 3(a - 2)(a + 4) &= (a + 1)(2a - 3) \\
\therefore 5a^2 - 3(a^2 + 2a - 8) &= 2a^2 - a - 3 \\
\therefore 5a^2 - 3a^2 - 6a + 24 &= 2a^2 - a - 3 \\
\therefore 5a^2 - 3a^2 - 6a - 2a^2 + a &= -3 - 24 \\
\therefore -5a &= -27 \\
\therefore a &= \frac{-27}{-5} \\
&= 5\tfrac{2}{5}.
\end{aligned}
$$

Exercise 8g

Simplify

1 $(a - 3)(a - 4) + (a - 1)(a + 5)$

2 $(m + 6)(m - 2) - (m - 3)(m + 1)$

3 $(2x + 3)(x - 2) + 2x(x - 1)$

4 $3d(2d + 3) - (3d + 1)(2d + 1)$

5 $(3b - 1)^2 - (2b + 1)^2$

6 $(f + g)^2 + (f - 2g)^2$

7 $(3n + 1)(n + 3) - 3(n - 2)(n - 4)$

8 $7ab + (4a - b)(3a + 2b) - (2a + 3b)(5a - b)$

9 $(x - 1)(x + 1) - (x + 2)(x - 3) + (x - 2)(x - 5)$

10 $6(2m + n)(m - n) - 3(m + 2n)(m - 2n) - 2(2m - n)^2$

Solve

11 $(x + 5)(x - 2) = x(x + 1)$

12 $(a - 4)(2a - 5) = 2a(a - 7)$

13 $(m - 2)(m + 3) = (m - 5)(m + 2)$

14 $(2p + 1)(3p - 2) = (p + 1)(6p - 5)$

15 $(2a - 3)(2a + 4) - 4a(a - 1) = 12$

16 $5x^2 - (x + 1)(2x - 3) = 3(x - 2)(x - 1)$

17 $(y - 7)(y + 3) = (y - 4)^2$

18 $(4n + 3)(n - 5) - (2n - 3)^2 + 2 = 0$

19 $(3d - 1)(2d + 1) - (2d + 5)(d - 3) = 4d(d + 2)$

20 $(3c + 5)(4c - 1) - 4(2c + 3)^2 + 2c(2c + 13) = 4$

Chapter 9

Vectors

A **vector** is a set or **array** of numbers as for example (1,2) or (−1,3,−2). If one went to a bank and obtained 10 twopenny pieces, 6 fivepenny pieces and 2 tenpenny pieces, this set of coins could be expressed by the vector (10,6,2). If the next day one obtained 15 twopenny pieces, 20 fivepenny pieces and 4 tenpenny pieces the total would be 25 twopenny pieces, 26 fivepenny pieces and 6 tenpenny pieces. This can be represented in vector form as

$$(10,6,2) + (15,20,4) = (25,26,6).$$

In adding vectors each **element** of one vector is added to the corresponding element of the other. The order of the elements is important so that the corresponding elements of each vector represent the same things; thus in this case the first element represents a number of twopenny pieces, the second element a number of fivepenny pieces and the third a number of tenpenny pieces. The denary number 438 can be considered as a vector, the first digit being the number of hundreds, the second the number of tens and the third the number of units. Just as 438 is not the same as 348 so (10,6,2) is not the same as (6,10,2).

It is not possible to add two vectors containing different numbers of elements as one is not entitled to assume that the missing element or elements are zero. For example (2,3) could mean 2 twopenny pieces, 3 fivepenny pieces and no tenpenny pieces, or it could mean no twopenny pieces, 2 fivepenny pieces and 3 tenpenny pieces. Thus (10,6,2) + (2,3) does not give enough information to perform an addition, as it could mean either (10,6,2) + (2,3,0) or (10,6,2) + (0,2,3).

If after drawing the above sum of money from the bank one bought an article for 42p, paying for it with 2 tenpenny pieces, 4 fivepenny pieces and 1 twopenny piece, the money remaining can be calculated as follows:

$$(25,26,6) - (1,4,2) = (24,22,4).$$

If one obtained 10 twopenny pieces, 6 fivepenny pieces and 2 tenpenny pieces from the bank on each of three separate occasions the total could be calculated as follows:

$$(10,6,2) + (10,6,2) + (10,6,2) = (30,18,6).$$

or more simply $\quad 3 \times (10,6,2) = (30,18,6).$

In multiplying a vector by a number each element of the vector is multiplied by the number.

If the sum of money obtained on one occasion is divided equally into two piles, each pile would contain 5 twopenny pieces, 3 fivepenny pieces and 1 tenpenny piece. Thus

$$\tfrac{1}{2}(10,6,2) = (5,3,1).$$

In dividing a vector by a number each element of the vector is divided by the number.

Exercise 9a

Add together the following vectors where possible:

1 (1,2) and (4,7)
2 (3,1,2) and (4,1,−3)
3 (5·1,2·3,3·1) and (6·2, 7·1,11·3)
4 (6,2,3) and (2,1)
5 (7,1,4,−1) and (3,2,−2,0)
6 (1,2,3), (4,2,1) and (2,−1,−2)
7 (3,2,1), (6,1,2,1) and (4,1,−2)

Perform the following vector subtractions where possible:

8 (4,3) − (2,1)
9 (2,5) − (3,−1)
10 (2,4,5) − (1,0,6)
11 (4·1,6·3,−2·8) − (3·2,7·1,−3·2)
12 (3,5,6) − (3,4,0,1)
13 (12,45,−78,46) − (43,−46,37,89)

Evaluate the following:

14 4(3,4,2,1)

15 3(1·2,3·1,4·5)

16 $\frac{1}{2}$(11,13,15)

17 $\frac{1}{4}$(12·5,13·2)

18 2·5(6·1,7·2,4·2)

19 1·1(12,13,14·2,15·1)

20 $\frac{2}{3}$(8,27,6,17,19)

Co-ordinates

In plotting graphs the position of a point is fixed by a vector whose two elements represent the distances of the point from two fixed straight lines, called **axes,** which are normally at right angles to each other: these axes intersect at the **origin.** The two elements of the vector are known as the **co-ordinates** of the point, and may be negative or positive. The set of figures used for the first co-ordinate and the set of figures used for the second are the numerical values of the **variables.**

If the variables are x and y, as in Fig. 41, positive values of x are measured to the right of O and negative values to the left; positive values of y are measured upwards from O and negative values downwards.

The co-ordinates of the point are written down in the form (x,y): thus, in Fig. 41 the point P is (10,5) because the x of P is 10 and the y is 5; Q is (5,−6), R is (−7,−4), S is (−3,8).

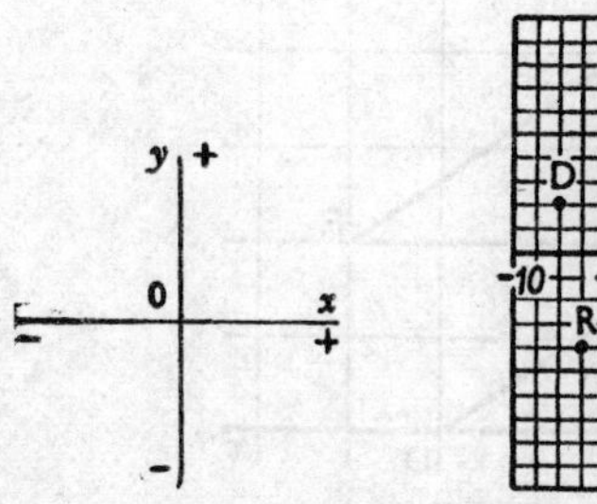

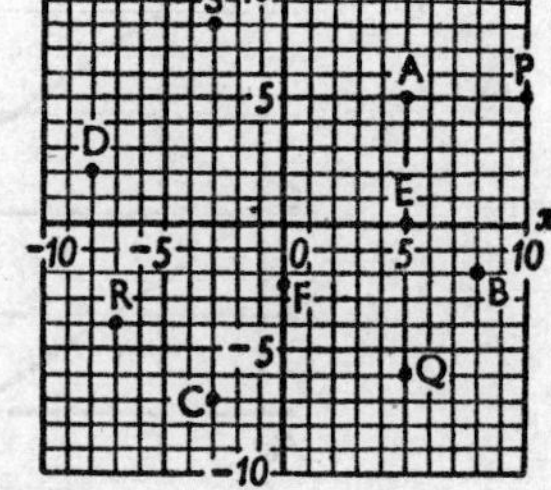

Fig. 41

Exercise 9b

1 Write down the co-ordinates of the points A, B, C, D, E, F given in Fig. 41.

2 Taking O in the middle of a piece of graph-paper and 2 cm as unit on both axes, mark in the points A (4,4), B (2,3), C (−2,1), D (−1,−3), E (3,−1), F (0,3), G ($2\frac{1}{2}$,0), H (0,−2), K (2,4).

What do you notice about the points (i) A, B, C? (ii) B, C, D, E?

What are the co-ordinates of the point in which $\overline{FG}$ cuts $\overline{HK}$?

3 As in no. 2, but on another piece of paper, mark in points P (4,3), Q (4,1), R (−1,1), S (−1,3), W (1,2), X (1,−1), Y (−2,−1), Z (−2,2).

Find the areas in cm² of rectangle PQRS, square WXYZ, triangle SXY, triangle PYZ.

Displacements

In Chapter 3 it was seen that one figure could be mapped into another by a displacement which could be expressed in terms of a directed line, for instance $\overrightarrow{AB}$. It should be noted that $\overline{AB}$ and $\overline{BA}$ mean the same thing, namely the line joining the points A and B, but $\overrightarrow{AB}$ and $\overrightarrow{BA}$ are exactly opposite as the first means a displacement from A to B and the second means a displacement from B to A.

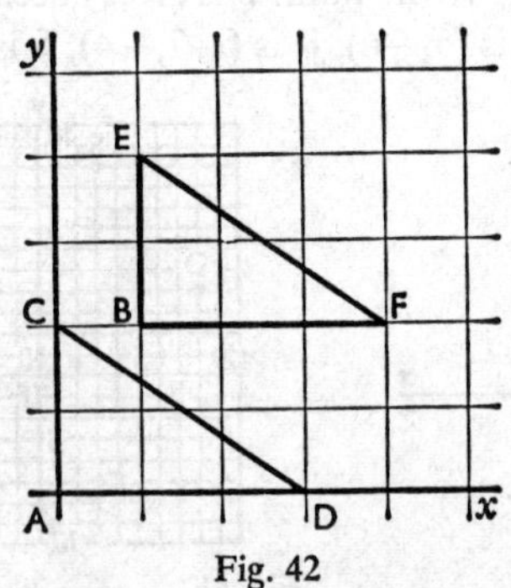

Fig. 42

If a triangle ACD has vertices A (0,0), C (0,2), D (3,0) and it is mapped into △BEF where B is (1,2), the co-ordinates of E and F are found by adding (1,2) to the vectors representing C and D.

Thus E is (0,2) + (1,2) = (1,4) and F is (3,0) + (1,2) = (4,2).

To find the co-ordinates of any point in a figure which is the displacement of another figure, the co-ordinates of the point into which the origin is mapped are added to the co-ordinates of the point in the original figure.

Example 1 *Find the co-ordinates of the corners of the square* EFGH *which is the result of displacing* ABCD, *where* A *is* (0,0), B *is* (3,0), C *is* (3,3), *and* D *is* (0,3), *and* $\overrightarrow{AE}$ *is represented by the vector* (2,4).

As A is the origin, and it is mapped into E,

E is (0,0) + (2,4) = (2,4).
∴ F is (3,0) + (2,4) = (5,4),
G is (3,3) + (2,4) = (5,7),
and H is (0,3) + (2,4) = (2,7).

Note that it is not necessary to draw a figure to answer this question.

Exercise 9c

1 Find the co-ordinates of the vertices of the triangle which is the displacement of △OAB, where O is (0,0), A is (4,2) and B is (2,5), given that O is displaced to (3,6). Illustrate your answer with a diagram.

2 What are the co-ordinates of the vertices of the triangle which is the displacement of △OAB in no. 1 through $\overrightarrow{OA}$?

3 What are the co-ordinates of the vertices of the triangle which is the displacement of △OAB of no. 1 through a vector (−1,2)?

4 Find the co-ordinates of the displacement of the rectangle ABCD, where A is (1,2), B is (1,5), C is (2,5) and D is (2,2), given that the origin is mapped into (−1,3).

5 Find the co-ordinates of the displacement of the rectangle ABCD of no. 4 when it is displaced through (3,1).

6 If a point A (3,1) is displaced to (4,5) what are the co-ordinates of the point into which the origin is displaced? What are the co-ordinates of the point displaced into (−1,2)?

7 Find the co-ordinates of the displacement of the rectangle ABCD of no. 4 when it is displaced through $\overrightarrow{AC}$.

8 Find the co-ordinates of the vertices of the triangle OAB of no. 1 when it is displaced through $\overrightarrow{AB}$.

9 What are the co-ordinates of the vertices of the triangle which is the displacement of △OAB through $\overrightarrow{BA}$?

10 PQRS is a rhombus where P is (1,4), Q is (5,7), R is (9,4) and S is (5,1). What are the co-ordinates of the vertices of the displacement of PQRS through (3,−1)?

11 What are the co-ordinates of the vertices of the displacement of the rhombus PQRS through (−5,−4)?

12 Find the co-ordinates of the displacement of PQRS through $\overrightarrow{PR}$.

Chapter 10

Functional graphs

In Chapter 25 of Book 1 the information which was necessary before a graph could be drawn was given in a 'table of values', from which points on the graph could be plotted. The connection between the two variables is in fact often given by an equation, and from this equation the table of values has to be calculated.

Example 1 *A wire of diameter d mm will support a load of w kg, where $w = 5d^2$. Draw a graph to show the load which can be supported by wires with diameters between zero and* 30 *mm. Read off (i) the loads which can be supported by wires of diameters* 7 *mm,* 28 *mm; (ii) the diameters necessary to carry loads of* 1 300 *kg,* 3 500 *kg.*

First draw up a table of values, finding w for convenient values of d.

When $d = 0$, $w = 5 \times (0)^2 = 0$
$d = 5$, $w = 5 \times (5)^2 = 125$
$d = 10$, $w = 5 \times (10)^2 = 500$, and so on.

d (mm)	0	5	10	15	20	25	30
w (kg)	0	125	500	1 125	2 000	3 125	4 500

d being the independent variable, values of d are ranged along the horizontal axis, taking a scale of 2 cm to represent 5 mm for d. On the vertical axis the scale is 2 cm to 1 000 kg.

Plot the points, marking them with a small × with a sharp pencil, and join them in a smooth freehand curve.

Copy the table of values on to the graph paper if there is room for it, read off the answers from the graph and write them down.

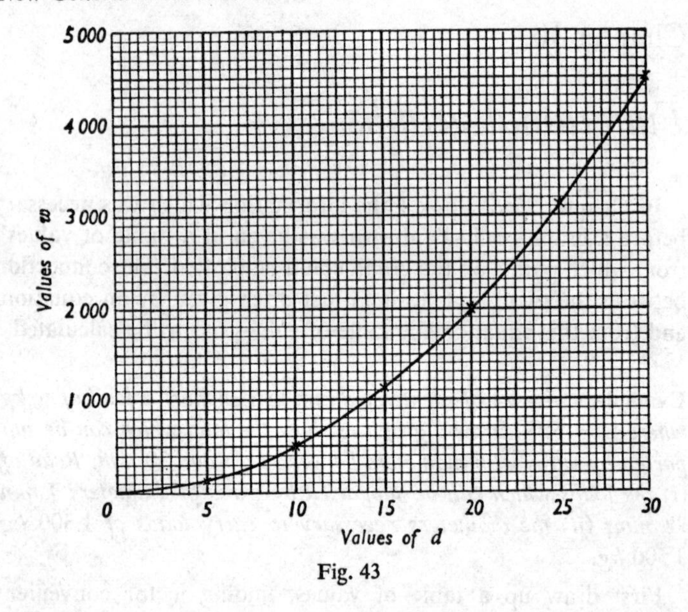

Fig. 43

This curve is said to be the **graph of the function $5d^2$** for values of d between zero and 30, the word function here meaning some expression involving d whose numerical values can be calculated for different values of d by substitution.

Alternatively the graph is that of the **equation $w = 5d^2$.**

In choosing the scales the object should be to create a curve which is easy to draw freehand, and also to use numbers whose subdivisions along the axes are quick to read.

If the graph occupies most of the space available on the paper the result is generally satisfactory.

Exercise 10a

1 The speed v km/h of a train drawing out of a station is given by the formula $v = 0{\cdot}5t$, where t is the time in seconds from the start. Draw a graph connecting v with t, taking values of t from 0 to 50 at 5-second intervals. Read off from the graph

(i) the speeds 13 seconds, 23 seconds from the start (ii) the times at which the speeds are 7 km/h, 22 km/h.

2 A mass W kg hanging at the end of a spiral spring stretches the spring to a length of l cm where $l = 12 + \frac{1}{4}W$. Draw a graph to show the length for masses of up to 20 kg. Read off (i) the lengths for masses of 7·4 kg, 15·5 kg (ii) the masses which will stretch the spring to lengths of 14·2 cm, 16·3 cm.

3 If F is the temperature on a Fahrenheit scale and C that on a celsius one, $C = \frac{5}{9}(F - 32)$. Taking values of F 40°, 80°, . . . 240°, plot C against F.

Change (i) 50° F, 100° F, 200° F into celsius
(ii) 10° C, 40° C, 75° C into Fahrenheit.

4 A stone falling freely drops s metres in t seconds, where $s = 4{\cdot}9t^2$. Show by means of a graph the distance fallen at any time up to 5 seconds from the start. When is the stone 10 m, 50 m, 100 m below the starting-point?

5 The distance to the horizon from a point h m above the ground is d km where $d = 3{\cdot}6\sqrt{h}$. Taking values 4, 16, 36, 64, 100 for h calculate the corresponding values of d and plot them on a graph. Hence find the distances visible from heights of 10 m and 80 m, and also how high the observer must be to see 15 km, 25 km.

6 The power output (W watts) of an electric fire with resistance 25 ohms connected to a voltage of V volts is given by the formula $W = V^2/25$. Calculate W for values 100, 150, 200, 250, 300 of V. Hence find graphically the power output when the voltage is 120 volts, 240 volts; find also the voltage required to produce 1 000 watts, 3 000 watts.

7 When circular discs of radius r mm are stamped out of brass sheet 8 mm thick, their masses are given by the formula $M = \frac{1}{5}r^2$, M being the mass in grammes. Draw a graph connecting M with r, and find from it the masses of discs of radius 15 mm, 74 mm. What radii will give discs of masses 100 g, 1 000 g?

8 The time (t s) of one complete swing of a pendulum l cm long is given by the equation $t = \frac{1}{5}\sqrt{l}$. Plot the graph connecting t with l, taking 0, 4, 16, 36, 64 as values of l. What length of pendulum beats $\frac{3}{4}$ s, 1 s, $1\frac{1}{2}$ s? What are the times of swing of pendulums 35 cm, 62 cm, 84 cm long?

9 The mass (M grammes) of a brass cube of edge x cm is given by the formula $M = 8x^3$. Draw a graph to show the masses of brass cubes with edges up to 10 cm long. What are the edges of cubes with masses 100 g, 1 000 g, 2 000 g, 5 000 g?

10 Boyle's law states that, for v cubic millimetres of gas compressed to p grammes per square millimetre, pv is constant. When this constant is 800 the law can be written in the form $v = \dfrac{800}{p}$. Calculate v for values of p between 20 and 100, and plot the graph connecting v with p. From the graph find (i) the volume when the pressure is 37 g/mm², 89 g/mm² (ii) the pressure when the volume is 27 mm³, 13 mm³.

11 After t seconds a marble rolling down a sloping groove has travelled s metres, where $s = 5t + t^2$. Draw a graph to show the distances covered in any time up to 6 seconds. Read off (i) the distance travelled after 2·3 s, 4·7 s (ii) the time taken to go 20 m, 60 m.

12 A stone slides x metres along the ice in t seconds, where $x = 10t - \frac{1}{2}t^2$. Draw the graph for values of t from 0 to 10. Find (i) how far the stone has gone in 5 s, 7 s (ii) the time after which the stone is 25 m, 45 m from the start.

13 The cost (C p) for silver-plating spoons l cm long is given by the formula $C = 3 + 4l^2$. Draw a graph to show the cost for spoons up to 10 cm long. What would be the cost for spoons 5·5 cm, 7·5 cm long?

14 According to the Highway Code the distance in which a car can be stopped by its brakes from different speeds is given by the formula $d = \frac{1}{5}v + \frac{1}{150}{}^2$, where v is the speed in km/h and d is the distance in metres. Plot d against v for values of v between 10 and 100. From what speeds can a car be stopped in 55 m, 20 m?

15 The cost £C of sending a liner across the Atlantic at various speeds is given by the formula $C = \frac{60\,000}{v} + 3v^2$, where v is the speed in knots. Find the cost at speeds between 12 and 30 knots, and deduce the most economical speed at which the crossing can be made.

Example 2 *Draw the graph of* $y = 3x - 4$ *for values of* x *from* -3 *to* $+3$, *and read off (i)* y *when* $x = 2{\cdot}5$ *(ii)* x *when* $y = -2$.

Begin, as in Example 1, by making a table of values:

x	-3	-2	-1	0	1	2	3
y	-13	-10	-7	-4	-1	2	5

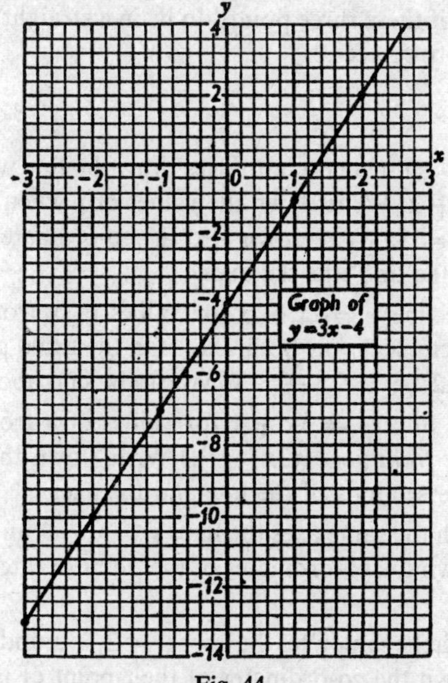

Fig. 44

Plot the seven points (Fig. 44), which will be found to lie in a straight line and may therefore be joined by using a ruler. Finally write down the equation, table of values and answers on the graph paper.

From the graph (i) when $x = 2{\cdot}5$, $y = 3{\cdot}5$
(ii) when $y = -2$, $x = 0{\cdot}67$

This line is the graph of the equation $y = 3x - 4$ or the graph of the function $3x - 4$, and $y = 3x - 4$ is called the equation of the line.

The line is the set of all points whose co-ordinates (x,y) satisfy the equation $y = 3x - 4$. If the line is called L, then in set language $L = \{(x,y) : y = 3x - 4\}$.

A **linear function of x** is one which contains no term in x of degree higher than the first. As the graph of such a function is a straight line it is unnecessary to plot more than two points to determine the line absolutely, but in practice it is better to plot three points: if these three points do lie in a straight line the working is probably correct.

Exercise 10b

1 Using a 2-cm scale on both axes draw the line whose equation is $y = x + 2$. Write down the values of y when $x = 3$, and of x when $y = 1$. Write down also the co-ordinates of the points in which the line cuts the axes.

2 Draw the line $y = 2x - 3$ for values of x from -1 to $+3$, taking 2-cm scale on both axes. On the same paper draw the lines $y = 2x$, $y = 2x + 1$. What can be said about these lines?

3 Draw the line $2y = 3x + 1$ for values of x from -2 to $+3$. (*Calculate from* $y = \frac{1}{2}(3x + 1)$.) Write down the co-ordinates of the intersections of the line and the axes.

4 Draw with the same axes the lines $y = x + 1$ and $y = 3x - 2$. Write down the co-ordinates of the point of intersection of the lines.

5 Draw with the same axes the lines $y = 2 - x$ and $2y = 4x + 5$. Write down the co-ordinates of their point of intersection.

6 Draw with the same axes the lines $2y = 3x + 5$ and $3y + 2x = 14$, taking a 1-cm scale on both axes. Write down

the co-ordinates of their point of intersection. What is the angle between the lines?

Find the points of intersection of the following pairs of lines:

7 $2x + 3y = 1$
$x - y = 3$

8 $2x - 3y = 7$
$4x - y = -2$

9 $2x + y = -1$
$3x - y = -10$

10 $3x + y = 6$
$x - 3y = 9$

11 $3x = 4y$
$5x - 2y = 7$

12 $2x + 3y = 2{\cdot}4$
$3x + 5y = 5$

Further examples on straight lines will be found in Chapter 14.

Example 3 *Draw the graph of* $y = x^2 + 2x - 3$ *for values of* x *from* -4 *to* $+2$. *Read off the values of (i)* y *when* $x = 1{\cdot}5$ *(ii)* y *when* $x = -1{\cdot}5$ *(iii)* x *when* $y = 1$ *(iv) the least value of* $x^2 + 2x - 3$ *(v) the value of* x *for which* y *is least.*

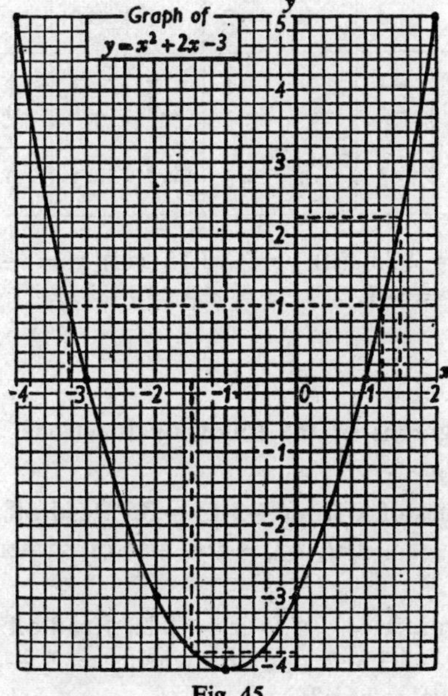

Fig. 45

The values of y are obtained by adding the values of x^2, of $2x$, and -3, setting out the table of values as follows:

x	-4	-3	-2	-1	0	1	2
x^2	16	9	4	1	0	1	4
$+2x$	-8	-6	-4	-2	0	2	4
-3	-3	-3	-3	-3	-3	-3	-3
y	5	0	-3	-4	-3	0	5

If the equation had been given in the form $y = (x + 3)(x - 1)$, the table of values might more conveniently have been set out as follows; y being obtained very quickly by multiplying together the values of $x + 3$ and $x - 1$.

x	-4	-3	-2	-1	0	1	2
$x + 3$	-1	0	1	2	3	4	5
$x - 1$	-5	-4	-3	-2	-1	0	1
y	5	0	-3	-4	-3	0	5

Ans. (i) $y = 2{\cdot}25$ (ii) $y = -3{\cdot}75$ (iii) $x = -3{\cdot}24$ or $1{\cdot}24$ (iv) -4 (v) $x = -1$.

Exercise 10c

Draw the graphs of the following functions, taking a 2-cm scale on both axes.

1 x^2 for values of x from -3 to $+3$. Read off the values of y when $x = 1{\cdot}5, -0{\cdot}7, 2{\cdot}3, -1{\cdot}4$; also of x when $y = 2, 7, 1{\cdot}9, 0{\cdot}8$.

2 $x^2 + 3x$ from $x = -4$ to $x = +1$. Read off the values of y when $x = -3{\cdot}3, 0{\cdot}2$, and of x when $y = 2, -1$. What is the minimum value of y?

3 $x^2 - 2x$ from $x = -2$ to $x = +4$. Read off the values of y when $x = 1{\cdot}3, -1{\cdot}6, 2{\cdot}4$; also of x when $y = 7, 2{\cdot}5, 0, -0{\cdot}5$. What is the minimum value of y?

4 $(x - 1)(x + 2)$ from $x = -3$ to $x = +2$. Read off the values of y when $x = 1{\cdot}5, -2{\cdot}3$; also of x when $y = 3{\cdot}5, -1{\cdot}3, 0$. What is the minimum value of y?

5 $x^2 + 2x - 4$ from $x = -4$ to $x = +2$. Read off the values of y when $x = -3{\cdot}1, -1{\cdot}3, 0{\cdot}3$; also of x when $y = 2, -2, 0$. What is the minimum value of y?

6 $x - x^2$ from $x = -2$ to $x = +3$. Read off the values of y when $x = -1{\cdot}5, 2{\cdot}2$; also of x when $y = -5, -3$. What is the maximum value of y?

7 $x(x - 3)$ from $x = -1$ to $x = +4$. Read off the values of y when $x = 2{\cdot}4, 3{\cdot}3$; also of x when $y = 3, 1{\cdot}3, -1{\cdot}3$. What is the minimum value of y?

8 $x^2 - 5x + 8$ from $x = 0$ to $x = 5$. Read off the values of y when $x = 0{\cdot}6, 3{\cdot}2$; also of x when $y = 3, 5$. What is the minimum value of y?

9 $(x + 2)^2$ from $x = -4$ to $x = 0$. Read off the values of y when $x = -0{\cdot}4, -2{\cdot}6$; also of x when $y = 2, 3$. What is the minimum value of y?

10 $4 + 3x - x^2$ from $x = -1$ to $x = +4$. Read off the values of y when $x = -0{\cdot}6, 2{\cdot}2$; also of x when $y = 3, 5{\cdot}5$. What is the maximum value of y?

Further examples on functions of this type will be found in Chapter 24.

Chapter 11

Parallelograms

Definitions

A **trapezium** is a quadrilateral which has one pair of opposite sides parallel.

A **parallelogram** is a quadrilateral which has both pairs of opposite sides parallel.

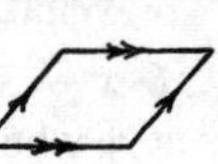

A **rhombus** is a quadrilateral which has all four sides equal.

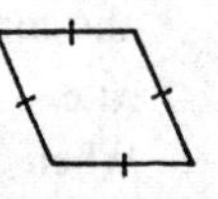

A **rectangle** is a quadrilateral which has all its angles right angles.

A **square** is a rectangle having all four sides equal.

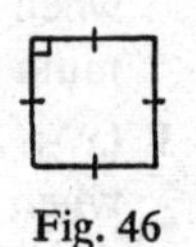

Fig. 46

Theorem 5

In a parallelogram the opposite sides are equal and the opposite angles are equal.

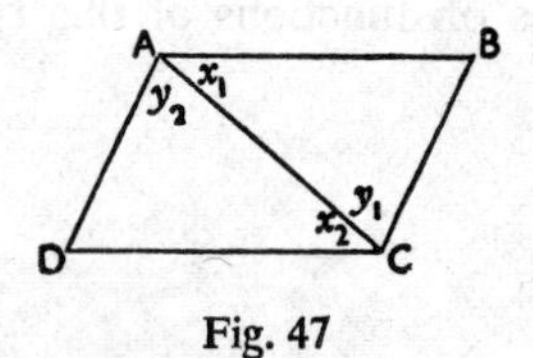

Fig. 47

Given a parallelogram ABCD.

To prove (i) AB = CD, BC = AD.

(ii) $\hat{B} = \hat{D}$, $\hat{A} = \hat{C}$.

Construction. Draw the diagonal $\overline{AC}$.

Proof. In the triangles ABC, CDA

$x_1 = x_2$ *alt.* $\angle s$, $\overline{AB} \parallel \overline{DC}$

$y_1 = y_2$ „ „ , $\overline{AD} \parallel \overline{BC}$

AC is common

$\therefore \triangle ABC \equiv \triangle CDA$ *ASA*

$\triangle CDA$ is the rotation of $\triangle ABC$ about the mid-point of $\overline{AC}$ through 180°

$\therefore$ (i) AB = CD, BC = AD

(ii) $\hat{B} = \hat{D}$

Also $\hat{A} = x_1 + y_2$

$= x_2 + y_1$

$= \hat{C}$.

Q.E.D.

Corollary. Since $\triangle ABC \equiv \triangle CDA$, these triangles are also equal in area.

Hence **a diagonal bisects a parallelogram.**

Theorem 6

The diagonals of a parallelogram bisect one another.

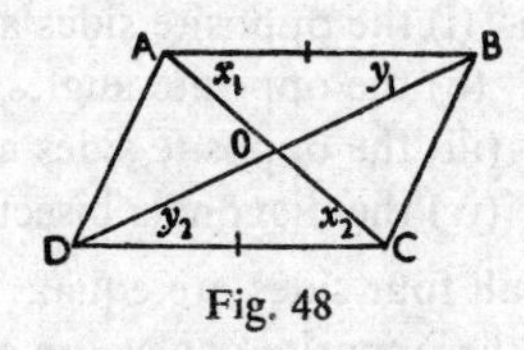

Fig. 48

Given a parallelogram ABCD, whose diagonals $\overline{AC}$, $\overline{BD}$ intersect at O.

To prove AO = OC, BO = OD.

Proof. In the triangles AOB, COD

$x_1 = x_2$ *alt.* $\angle s$, $\overline{AB} \parallel \overline{CD}$

$y_1 = y_2$ „ „ , „ „

$$AB = CD \qquad \textit{opp. sides of} \parallel \textit{gm.}$$
$$\therefore \triangle AOB \equiv \triangle COD \qquad ASA$$
$\triangle COD$ is the rotation of $\triangle AOB$ about O through 180°
$$\therefore AO = OC, BO = OD.$$

Q.E.D.

Exercise 11a

Prove formally the following theorems:

1 A quadrilateral having one pair of opposite sides equal and parallel is a parallelogram.

2 If both pairs of opposite sides of a quadrilateral are equal the quadrilateral is a parallelogram.

3 If both pairs of opposite angles in a quadrilateral are equal the quadrilateral is a parallelogram.

4 If the diagonals of a quadrilateral bisect one another the quadrilateral is a parallelogram.

5 The diagonals of a rhombus
(i) bisect one another at right angles,
(ii) bisect the angles of the rhombus.

Summary of facts

In a **parallelogram** (i) the opposite sides are parallel,
(ii) the opposite angles are equal,
(iii) the opposite sides are equal,
(iv) the diagonals bisect one another.

In a **rhombus** (i) all four sides are equal,
(ii) the opposite angles are equal,
(iii) the opposite sides are parallel,
(iv) the diagonals bisect one another at right angles,
(v) the diagonals bisect the angles.

In a **rectangle**, which is a particular case of a parallelogram, all four of the facts given for the parallelogram are true, with the additional one that all four angles are right angles.

A **square** is a particular case of a rhombus, with the additional fact that all four angles are right angles.

Exercise 11b

1 ABCD is a parallelogram and $\overline{CB}$ is produced to X so that BX = BC. Prove that AXBD is a parallelogram.

2 ABCD and ABXY are two parallelograms having the side $\overline{AB}$ in common. Prove that XYDC is a parallelogram.

3 ABC is a triangle and M the mid-point of $\overline{BC}$. The line through C parallel to $\overline{AB}$ cuts $\overline{AM}$ produced at X. Prove MX = MA.

4 ABCD is a trapezium having $\overline{AB}$ parallel to $\overline{DC}$: X is a point on $\overline{CD}$ such that CX = BA. Prove $\overline{AX} \parallel \overline{BC}$.

5 ABCD is a parallelogram. P and Q are points on $\overline{AB}$ and $\overline{CD}$ respectively such that BP = DQ. Prove that the mid-points of $\overline{AC}$, $\overline{BD}$ and $\overline{PQ}$ are coincident.

6 PQRS is a parallelogram. $\overline{SP}$ is produced to a point X so that PX = PS. $\overline{XR}$ cuts $\overline{PQ}$ at Y. Prove that Y is the mid-point of $\overline{PQ}$.

7 ABCD is a parallelogram. $\overline{DP}$, $\overline{BQ}$ are perpendiculars from D, B respectively to the diagonal $\overline{AC}$. Prove that BP = QD.

8 ABCD is a parallelogram. A line through C parallel to $\overline{BD}$ cuts $\overline{AD}$ produced at X and $\overline{AB}$ produced at Y. Prove that C is the mid-point of $\overline{XY}$.

9 ABCD is a parallelogram. Any line parallel to $\overline{AC}$ cuts $\overline{DA}$, $\overline{DC}$ at Q, R respectively, and $\overline{BA}$ produced, $\overline{BC}$ produced at P, S respectively. Prove PQ = RS.

10 ABCDEF is a regular hexagon with O its centre. Prove that (i) ABCO is a rhombus; (ii) ACDF is a rectangle.

11 If two sets of railway lines of the same gauge cut at an angle which is not a right angle, prove that the figure formed is a rhombus.

12 X and Y are points on the diagonal $\overline{BD}$ of a parallelogram ABCD such that BX = DY. Prove that $\overline{AC}$ bisects $\overline{XY}$.

13 In a parallelogram ABCD, $\overline{AB}$ is produced to E so that BE = AB, and $\overline{AD}$ is produced to F so that FD = AD. Prove that E, C and F lie in the same straight line.

14 The diagonals of a rectangle ABCD cut at O. Any line through O cuts $\overline{AB}$, $\overline{CD}$ at L, M respectively. Prove that AL = CM.

15 ABCD is a square whose diagonals cut at O. P and Q are points on $\overline{AB}$ such that AQ = BP = OA. By calculating numerical values of angles, show that $A\hat{O}P = \frac{1}{2}P\hat{O}Q = B\hat{O}Q$.

16 ABCD is a parallelogram. The bisectors of $\hat{A}$ and $\hat{B}$ meet $\overline{BC}$ and $\overline{AD}$ (produced if necessary) at X and Y respectively. Prove XY = CD.

17 In a parallelogram ABCD the bisectors of the angles at A and B meet at a point O on $\overline{CD}$. Prove that CD = 2CB.

18 ABCD is a parallelogram. P and Q are the mid-points of $\overline{AD}$ and $\overline{BC}$ respectively. BP and CD produced meet at X: $\overline{DQ}$ and $\overline{AB}$ produced meet at Y. Prove that BYDX is a parallelogram.

19 ABCD is a trapezium in which $\overline{AB}$ is parallel to $\overline{DC}$ and AD = BC. X is a point on $\overline{CD}$ such that BX = BC. Prove that ABXD is a parallelogram.

20 ABCD is a parallelogram and O the mid-point of $\overline{BD}$. Any line through O cuts $\overline{AB}$ in P and $\overline{CD}$ in Q. Prove that APCQ is a parallelogram.

Chapter 12

Averages

If you know that a batsman's 'average score' is 5·2 or that the 'average age' of a form in school is 16.3 you know immediately how good the batsman is or what kind of ages you may expect to find in the form.

In general the average of any set of numbers is a number which is typical of that set. There are various forms of average, which are used for sets of numbers of different kinds: in ordinary life the most usual form is the **mean value** or **arithmetic mean** (A.M.), which is equal to the sum of the numbers divided by the number of them.

Example 1 *In five successive innings a batsman's scores were* 3, 17, 30, 10, 6. *What was his average score?*

$$\text{Average score} = \frac{3 + 17 + 30 + 10 + 6}{5} = \frac{66}{5} = 13{\cdot}2.$$

Example 2 *A grocer bought* 20 *kilo of tea at* 60*p per kilo,* 50 *kilo at* 52*p and* 30 *kilo at* 44*p. If he mixed the three kinds together, what was the average cost of the mixture per kilo?*

20 kilo at 60p cost	1 200p
50 „ „ 52p „	2 600p
30 „ „ 44p „	1 320p
100 kilo of mixture cost	5 120p

$$\therefore \text{average cost per kilo} = \frac{5\,120\text{p}}{100} = 51{\cdot}20\text{p} \simeq 51\text{p}.$$

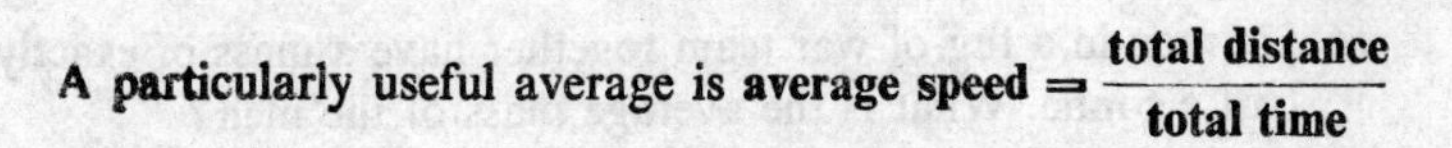

A particularly useful average is **average speed** $= \dfrac{\textbf{total distance}}{\textbf{total time}}$

Example 3 *A motorist travelled* 96 *km at an average speed of* 60 *km/h and returned at an average speed of* 48 *km/h. What was his average speed for the whole journey?*

$$96 \text{ km at } 60 \text{ km/h takes } \frac{96}{60} \text{ hours} = 1{\cdot}60 \text{ h}$$

$$96 \text{ km ,, } 48 \text{ ,, ,, } \frac{96}{48} \text{ ,, } = 2{\cdot}00 \text{ h}$$

$\therefore$ he has travelled altogether 192 km in 3·60 h

$$\therefore \text{ average speed} = \frac{192}{3{\cdot}60} \text{ km/h} = \frac{1\,920}{36} \text{ km/h} \simeq 53{\cdot}3 \text{ km/h.}$$

Exercise 12a

The first three examples are particularly suitable for class discussion.

1 During two successive half-hours in a car a man averaged 40 km/h and 60 km/h. What was his average speed for the whole time?

2 During two successive 30-kilometre runs in a car a man averaged 40 km/h and 60 km/h. What was his average speed for the whole distance?

3 After playing in a certain number of cricket matches, during which each had taken 16 wickets, A and B had the same average of 9 runs per wicket. In the next match A took 1 wicket for 26 runs, and B 4 for 56. What were their averages after this match? Does this result seem reasonable?

4 In six successive innings a batsman scored 21, 0, 11, 17, 2, 39, being out every time. What was his average score?

5 If the batsman in no. 4 scored 12 not out in his next innings, what was his average then?

6 Six men in a tug-of-war team together have a mass of exactly half a tonne. What is the average mass of the men?

7 In four successive days a beggar collected 68½p, 52p, 93½p and 64p. What were his average daily takings?

8 The temperatures at mid-day during a week in July were 29°, 33°, 31°, 31°, 21°, 23°, 28° C. What was the average mid-day temperature for the week?

9 In a day's fishing an angler caught four salmon of mass respectively 19·3 kg, 10·15 kg, 9·55 kg and 6·4 kg. What was the average mass of the fish?

10 In five successive years the amounts paid out by a charity were £208·10, £247·05, £184·20, £186·85 and £213·60. What was the average annual payment over the five years?

11 A blend of tea consists of 3 kilo at 86p mixed with 2 kilo at 76p. What is the cost per kilo of the blend?

12 The average age of 5 men is 20 yr 7 mth, and of four of them is 19 yr 11 mth. How old is the fifth man?

13 If the cox of a rowing eight is counted as a member of the crew the average mass of the nine men is 79 kg. Without him the average is 81·5 kg. What is the mass of the cox?

14 The average daily rainfall for a week in January was 5·5 mm. For the six weekdays of the same week the average was 1 mm. How much rain fell on the Sunday?

15 After 11 innings a batsman's average was 18 (and he had never been 'not out'). How much must he score in the next innings to bring his average up to 20?

16 The standard for throwing the cricket-ball is 55 m for a particular age-group: that is, competitors have to average at least 55 m in three throws. In his first two throws a boy gets 46 m and 58 m. How far must he throw the third time to get his standard?

17 In a year a man smokes about 2½ kilo of tobacco at 75p for 50 g and 6 000 cigarettes costing 31p for 20. What is his average weekly expenditure on smoking?

18 A bridge one and a quarter kilometres long cost seven and a half million pounds to build. What was the average cost per metre?

(19) In a year a motorist whose car does 100 km to 10 litres of petrol, costing 86p, covers 8 000 km. He also spends £1·50 on oil and £54 on taxation, insurance, etc. His garage costs him 35p per week. What is his average weekly expenditure on motoring, and what does his motoring cost him per kilometre, taking all expenses into account?

20 The ages of a family of six children are 16.4, 14.8, 13.6, 11.11, and the twins are 9.1. What is the average age of the family?

(21) In a test paper the marks of 15 boys were 6, 26, 18, 31, 36, 24, 23, 14, 29, 28, 32, 9, 11, 22, 21. What was the average mark for the form? By what percentages were the best and worst marks above and below this average?

(22) In an exam. set for three 'parallel' forms the average marks of the three forms were 74, 58 and 51. If the forms contained respectively 25, 22 and 23 boys, what was the average mark for the three forms together?

(23) Of a journey of 216 km, 56 km were in built-up areas, and in this part of the journey a motorist could average only 28 km/h. If his average speed for the whole journey was 48 km/h, how much did he average for the derestricted part of it?

(24) Over three consecutive 80-kilometre stretches of road a motorist averaged 40, 48 and 60 km/h respectively. What was his average speed for the whole distance?

When the average of a large set of numbers has to be found (e.g. when working out the average age of a form) it is convenient to guess the likely answer (called the **working mean**) and then work with the **deviations** of the successive numbers from this mean. This method is particularly useful when the numbers concerned are of roughly the same size.

Example 4 *The ages of the* 17 *pupils in a form, in years and months, are* 14.5, 15.2, 14.3, 13.9, 14.10, 14.11, 14.8, 15.3, 14.6, 15.6, 15.8, 16.1, 15.4, 14.4, 14.7, 14.9, 15.3. *Find the average age of the form.*

Take 15.0 as the working mean and write down two columns of numbers: the one marked + shows all the deviations for ages greater than 15.0 and the other (−) for those less than 15.0. The deviations are written in months.

Cancel the + and − figures as far as possible between the two columns and add up those not cancelled.

The result shows that the total deviation for the 17 pupils is 21 months less than 15.0.

15.0	
+	−
~~2~~	7
~~3~~	~~9~~
~~6~~	15
~~8~~	~~2~~
13	1
~~4~~	~~4~~
~~3~~	6
	~~8~~
	5
	~~3~~
13	34
	21

$\therefore$ average age is $\frac{21}{17}$ months ($\simeq$ 1·2 months) less than 15.0

$\therefore$ average age of form = 15 yr 0 mth − 1·2 mth
= 14 yr 10·8 mth
$\simeq$ 14.11

Exercise 12b

Use the method of Example 4 to find the average of each of the following sets of numbers:

1 223, 231, 229, 228, 222, 223, 230, 227, 222, 225.

2 18, 22, 23, 21, 17, 18, 18, 24, 21, 21, 19, 24, 16, 18, 19.

3 121, 128, 126, 118, 119, 122, 116, 113, 115, 121, 128, 119, 130, 118.

4 33·4, 33·6, 33·2, 33·1, 33·7, 33·8, 33·5, 33·5, 33·3, 33·7, 33·4, 33·8.

5 14.2, 14.5, 14.4, 14.0, 13.10, 13.11, 13.9, 14.1, 14.2, 15.1, 13.11, 14.3, 14.4, 13.3, 13.6, 14.1, these figures being ages in years and months.

6 £3·78, £3·82, £3·86, £3·89, £3·74, £3·81, £3·74, £3·76, £3·80, £3·88, £3·90, £3·75, £3·77, £3·85, £3·81.

Example 5 *A cyclist travels a km in x hours, and the next b km in y hours. What is his average speed for the whole journey?*

$$\text{Average speed} = \frac{\text{total distance}}{\text{total time}} = \frac{(a+b)\text{ km}}{(x+y)\text{ h}} = \frac{a+b}{x+y}\text{ km/h.}$$

Example 6 *In a mixed form of boys and girls the average age of the n boys is a years, and of the m girls b years. What is the average age of the whole form?*

$$\text{Total age of boys} = na \text{ years}$$
$$\text{Total age of girls} = mb \text{ years}$$
$$\text{Total number of children} = n + m$$

$$\therefore \text{ average age} = \frac{na + mb}{n + m} \text{ years.}$$

Exercise 12c

1 The ages of the four children in a family are a, b, c, d years. What is the average age of the family?

2 Three pieces of string are x cm, y cm, z cm long. What is the average length?

3 On seven successive days the rainfall was a, b, c, 0, d, 0, e mm. What was the average fall for the week?

4 In five successive innings a batsman scored p, q, r, s, t runs, and was out every time. What was his average score?

5 If in no. 4 the batsman had been not out once in the five innings, what would his average score have been then?

6 The standard distance for putting the shot is x m. In three successive puts a boy achieved $(x + 8)$ m, $(x - 5)$ m and $(x + 12)$ m. What was his average put?

7 The standard for throwing the cricket-ball is x m. In three successive throws a boy made distances of $(x - a)$ m, $(x + b)$ m and $(x + a)$ m. What was his average throw?

8 The average age of a form of n boys is x years. The form-master is y years old. What is the average age of the form if the master is included?

9 In an examination 10 boys averaged x marks, and 15 boys y marks. What was the average mark for the 25 boys?

10 After a number of matches a bowler had taken n wickets for a runs. In the next match he took 3 wickets for 28 runs. What was his new average (runs per wicket)?

11 a m^3 of gravel at £x per m^3 are mixed with b m^3 of sand at £y per m^3. What is the cost of the mixture per m^3?

12 The average mass of p children is x kg. The heaviest has a mass of exactly $14y$ kg. What is the average mass of the others?

13 A motorist averages x km/h for a hours, and then y km/h for b hours. What is his average speed for the whole journey?

14 A motorist's average speed (including stops) for a journey of x hours was v km/h. If in fact his stops added up to t hours, what was his average running speed?

15 A grocer wants to mix x kg of sugar at a p per kg with another grade at b p per kg so as to produce a mixture worth c p per kg. How many kg of the second kind will he need?

Chapter 13

Statistics (2)

The average of a set of numbers may be thought of as a number somewhere in the middle of the set and typical of the set as a whole. If, for instance, it is known that the average age of a class is 15 yr 3 mth, it is immediately obvious whereabouts in the school that class comes.

In Statistics there are three 'middle numbers' which are in common use: these are the mean, the median and the mode. (There are others, but their uses are beyond the scope of this book.)

The mean

The **mean** is the average or arithmetic mean (A.M.), already explained in Chapter 12, and is equal to the sum of all the numbers divided by the number of them.

It is convenient to write this fraction as $\frac{\Sigma x}{n}$. Σ (the Greek S) stands for 'the sum of' and x represents any one of the n numbers being considered, so that Σx means 'the sum of all the n numbers'.

The median

If a set of numbers is arranged in order of size, going either up or down, the middle term is called the **median.**

If there is an even number of terms the median is taken as the average (A.M.) of the two middle terms.

Example 1 *Find the median of* (*i*) 17, 34, 13, 22, 27, 44, 8, 31, 13
(*ii*) 8·3, 11·2, 9·4, 13·8, 12·9, 10·5.

(i) 8, 13, 13, 17, 22, 27, 31, 34, 44. Median is 22

(ii) 8·3, 9·4, 10·5, 11·2, 12·9, 13·8. Median $= \frac{10{\cdot}5 + 11{\cdot}2}{2} = 10{\cdot}85$

The mode

If a large array of numbers is being considered, any particular number is likely to occur more than once (as did 13 in Example 1 (i) above). When this happens, the number of times any particular number occurs is called its **frequency** (f), and the number which occurs most often (that is, which has the greatest frequency) is called the **mode**, because it is the most popular or the most 'fashionable' number in the whole array.

Example 2 *A pair of dice was thrown* 100 *times, and the score for each throw noted, also the number of times each score occurred (i.e. its frequency). The result is set out in the table below. Find the mode, median and mean of the scores.*

Score (x)	2	3	4	5	6	7	8	9	10	11	12
Frequency (f)	3	8	7	10	13	16	15	15	6	2	5

Here the greatest frequency is 16, and therefore the *mode* is 7.

In a distribution of this sort it is not really practicable to write down all the scores in order of size in order to pick out the median. There were 100 throws, so the middle one is the average of the 50th and 51st throws: if the scores were written down in order there would be three 2s, then eight 3s, then seven 4s, and so on: by the time all thirteen 6s had been written down, there would have been 41 throws recorded ($3 + 8 + 7 + 10 + 13$): the next sixteen throws, all 7s, brings the number of throws up to 57. The 50th and 51st throws come somewhere among the 7s, and 7 is therefore the *median* for this distribution.

The fact that the median is the same as the mode in this example happens only because the frequency figures rise and fall fairly smoothly. It is not always the case.

To obtain the *mean* the total score must first be found and, in order to do this, the frequencies must be taken into account.

2 was thrown 3 times, ∴ score in 2s was $3 \times 2 = 6$,
3 ,, ,, 8 ,, , ∴ ,, ,, 3s ,, $8 \times 3 = 24$, and so on.
The total score $= \Sigma(fx) = 3 \times 2 + 8 \times 3 + 7 \times 4 + \ldots = 695$
The number of throws $= \Sigma f = 100$

$$\therefore \text{ mean} = \frac{\Sigma(fx)}{\Sigma f} = \frac{695}{100} = 6{\cdot}95.$$

Exercise 13a

Find the mean, median and mode of the following sets of numbers:

1 4, 5, 5, 7, 8, 10
2 2, 3, 6, 6, 7, 7, 7, 8, 8, 9
3 15, 13, 13, 12, 11, 11, 10, 10, 10, 10, 9, 9, 8, 8, 7
4 6, 5, 3, 6, 3, 2, 4, 6, 4, 5, 6, 4

5

x	1	2	3	4	5	6
f	2	1	3	6	5	3

6

x	1	2	3	4	5	6	7	8	9	10
f	4	4	3	6	7	5	4	5	2	0

Histograms and frequency distributions

During a Physics 'practical' 21 boys in a form were asked to find the critical temperature, to three significant figures in degrees celsius, in an experiment. The recorded temperatures are set out in the table below, together with the number of boys who recorded each reading (i.e. the frequency):

Temperature °C (x)	70	71	72	73	74	75	76	82
Frequency (f)	1	2	3	6	4	2	2	1

Here the detailed readings have been grouped together in **classes**, so that the figure 70 includes all readings from 70·0 to 70·9 inclusive; 71 those from 71·0 to 71·9, and so on.

It is essential to do this grouping and to define the limits very clearly, or it may be difficult to decide whether the figure 72, for instance, is to be included at the end of the 71 group or at the beginning of the 72 group. It does not matter which alternative is chosen, but some decision must be made and clearly stated.

The **frequency distribution** is set out in a bar-chart called a **histogram**, shown in Fig. 49. Note that the reading for 82° C has not been included, as this is clearly a mistake, and its inclusion would falsify the result.

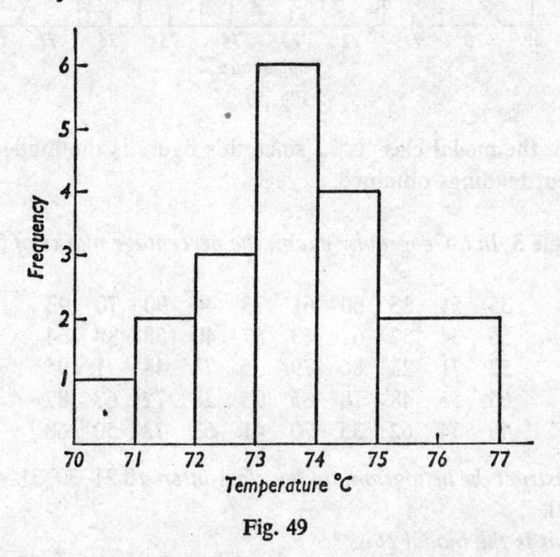

Fig. 49

In Fig. 50 the same information is presented in a **frequency-polygon.** Here the frequencies are plotted at the mid-points of successive class-intervals, and these points are joined by straight lines, the end points being joined to readings of $69\frac{1}{2}$ and $77\frac{1}{2}$ respectively on the base-line (since the frequency of these readings was zero).

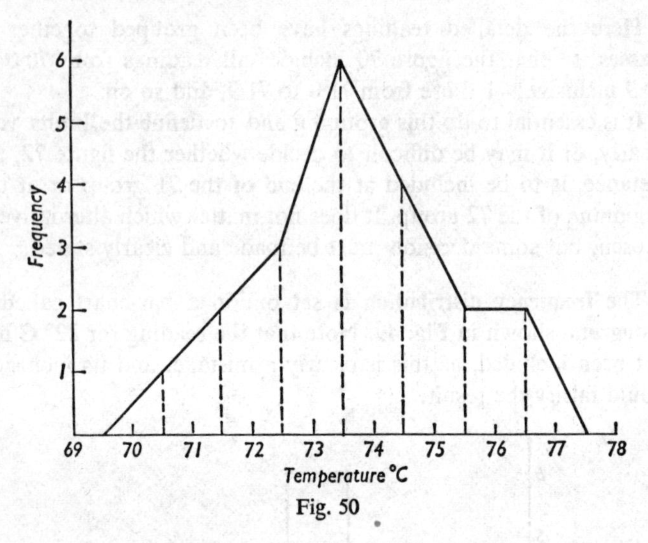

Fig. 50

Here the **modal class** is 73 since this figure is the mode of the different readings obtained.

Example 3 *In a Geography exam. the percentage marks of* 50 *boys were*

35	51	83	60	61	73	44	90	70	93
56	34	52	61	43	57	40	58	88	64
52	71	25	86	79	35	73	44	71	95
63	53	48	78	65	98	28	72	67	82
46	54	62	35	70	41	63	73	50	68

Construct the histogram, taking class-intervals 21–30, 31–40, . . ., 91–100.

What is the modal class?

Find the mean mark for the set.

To find the frequencies of the marks in the various classes, range them as shown below, marking each into its proper class with a vertical stroke, but making every fifth stroke horizontal, to cancel the previous four. The frequencies are thus arranged in groups of five and can quickly be totted up.

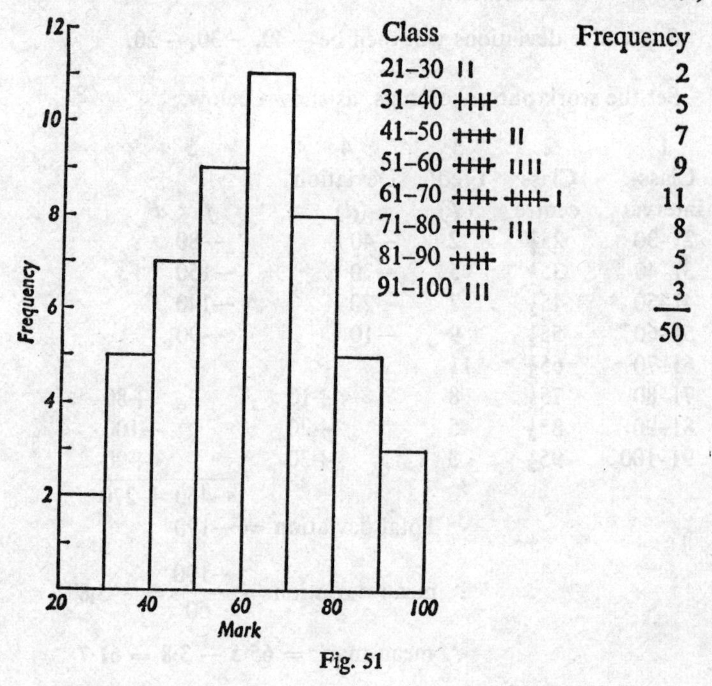

Class		Frequency
21–30	||	2
31–40	卌	5
41–50	卌 ||	7
51–60	卌 ||||	9
61–70	卌 卌 |	11
71–80	卌 |||	8
81–90	卌	5
91–100	|||	3
		50

Fig. 51

The modal class is 61–70, and the mode is taken to be the central value of this class, i.e. $65\frac{1}{2}$.

To find the mean mark (i.e. the average mark for the 50 boys) the method of Example 4 in Chapter 12 is used: a working mean is chosen and deviations from it are written down; the total deviation is calculated, then the average deviation, and finally the mean mark.

In this example $65\frac{1}{2}$ will be taken as the working mean, and all the marks in each class will be represented by the mid-mark of that class: for instance marks coming in the class 21–30 will be counted as $25\frac{1}{2}$, and so on.

Inevitably this assumption leads to some inaccuracy, but the error is so small that it makes a negligible difference to the final result, especially when the number of items being dealt with is large.

Successive deviations will then be −40, −30, −20. . . .

Set the work out in columns, as shown below.

1	2	3	4		5	
Class-interval	Class centre	Freqʸ. (f)	Deviation (d)		$f \times d$	
21–30	$25\frac{1}{2}$	2	−40		−80	
31–40	$35\frac{1}{2}$	5	−30		−150	
41–50	$45\frac{1}{2}$	7	−20		−140	
51–60	$55\frac{1}{2}$	9	−10		−90	
61–70	$65\frac{1}{2}$	11				
71–80	$75\frac{1}{2}$	8		+10		+80
81–90	$85\frac{1}{2}$	5		+20		+100
91–100	$95\frac{1}{2}$	3		+30		+90
					−460	+ 270

Total deviation = −190

$$\therefore \text{ mean deviation} = \frac{-190}{50} = -3{\cdot}8$$

$$\therefore \text{ mean mark} = 65{\cdot}5 - 3{\cdot}8 = 61{\cdot}7$$

If the median also is required, this would be the mark between boys numbered 25 and 26 in the ordered range of marks, and this would come somewhere in the 61–70 class (since 23 boys score 60 or less). In fact the 25th mark is 61 and the 26th is 62, so the median is 61·5.

It will be seen that, the larger the number of items being dealt with, the more tedious it becomes to pick out the median in this way. In such cases it is usual to construct what is called a **cumulative-frequency** table, derived from the previous frequency table, and then draw a curve called an **ogive** (Fig. 52), from which the median can be quickly deduced.

From the table it can be seen that 2 boys scored 30 or less; 7 (2 + 5) scored 40 or less, and so on, the successive figures being found by adding the next number in the list to the previous total: this is what is implied by the word cumulative.

Class	Freq^y.	Cum. freq^y.
21–30	2	2
31–40	5	$5 + 2 = 7$
41–50	7	$7 + 7 = 14$
51–60	9	$9 + 14 = 23$
61–70	11	$11 + 23 = 34$
71–80	8	$8 + 34 = 42$
81–90	5	$5 + 42 = 47$
91–100	3	$3 + 47 = 50$

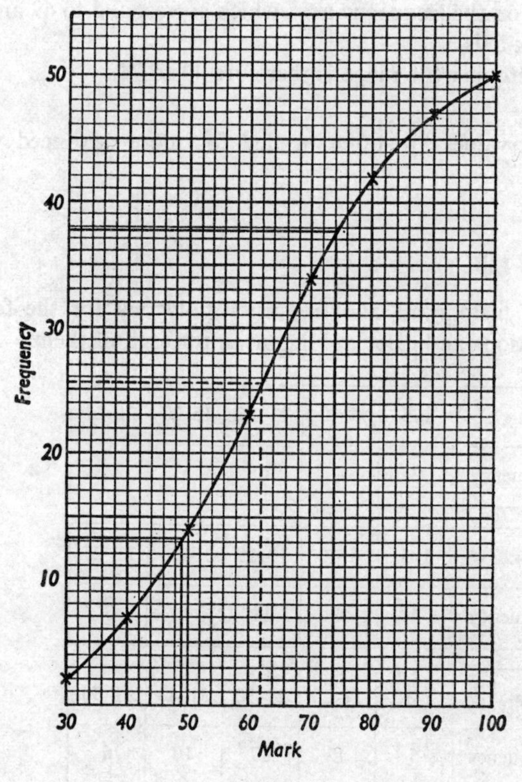

Fig. 52

The range is from boy number 1 to boy number 50, so that the middle of the range is the number $25\frac{1}{2}$: reading from this number to the mark-axis, the mark is 62, which is the required median, and agrees reasonably closely with the result obtained a few lines higher up.

Quartiles

The lower quartile is one-quarter of the way up the distribution, and the upper quartile three-quarters of the way up, the median coming halfway between them. These quartiles are respectively $13\frac{1}{4}$ and $37\frac{3}{4}$ on the frequency-axis, which correspond to 49 and 74 on the mark-axis.

The **interquartile range** is therefore 49 to 74.

These values are often needed for more advanced work in Statistics.

Exercise 13b

Draw histograms and frequency polygons for the following distributions and calculate the mean for each of them.

1

Class	1–5	6–10	11–15	16–20	21–25
Frequency	2	4	6	5	3

2

Class	1–5	6–10	11–15	16–20	21–25
Frequency	4	6	11	6	3

3

Class	1–10	11–20	21–30	31–40	41–50
Frequency	5	12	17	10	6

4

Class	8–14	15–21	22–28	29–35	36–42	43–49
Frequency	3	5	8	18	9	7

5–8 Draw the cumulative-frequency curves for the distributions in nos. 1–4 and read off the median and the interquartile range for each.

9 In a survey of 110 married couples in one parish enquiry was made into the number of children per family, with the following result:

Number of children	0	1	2	3	4	5	6	7	8 or more
Frequency	6	18	28	25	17	9	4	2	1

Draw the ogive: find the median and interquartile range.

10 Students taking a teacher-training course are grouped by age as follows:

Age group	19–20	20–21	21–22	22–23	23–24	over 24
Number in group	4	5	10	16	12	3

Find the average age of the students, and also the median and interquartile range.

11 During a school term the number of absentees is recorded daily:

Number absent	0–9	10–19	20–29	30–39	40–49	50–59
Frequency	5	18	23	17	14	3

Calculate the average daily number of absentees, and find the median of the distribution.

12 The percentage marks for 100 pupils in an O-Level examination are grouped as follows:

Percentage	0–9	10–19	20–29	30–39	40–49
Frequency	1	2	5	17	23

Percentage	50–59	60–69	70–79	80–89	90–99
Frequency	25	18	5	3	1

Find the average mark and the median.
If all candidates in the lower quartile are failed, at what mark is the pass-level fixed?
If only 10% gain distinctions, what mark is required for a distinction?

13 Some small nails are sold in packets which have printed on them 'Average contents 200 nails'. The contents of 100 packets, picked out at random, are counted and the results tabulated:

Nails per packet	185–189	190–194	195–199	200–204	205–209	210–214
Frequency	4	14	32	28	17	5

Is the statement on the packet true or not?
What is the median of the distribution, and what is the inter-quartile range?

14 The masses (in kg) of 30 new boys in a school were as follows:

43 45 50 47 51 58 52 47 42 54
61 50 45 55 57 41 46 49 51 50
59 44 53 57 49 40 48 52 51 48

Taking class-intervals 40–44, 45–49, . . . draw up a table of frequencies, as in Example 2, and find the average mass of the boys, and also the median of the distribution and the interquartile range.

15 The heights (in cm) of the same 30 boys as in no. 14 were

145	163	149	152	166	156	159	139	145	141
150	158	150	149	143	159	154	167	146	147
152	162	144	169	162	150	173	160	167	171

Take class-intervals 135–144, 145–154, . . . Draw up the table of frequencies. Find the average height of the boys, the median of the distribution and the interquartile range.

Chapter 14

Simultaneous linear equations (1)

Consider the equation $2x + y = 7$.

For any particular value of x there is a corresponding value of y: if $x = 0, y = 7$; if $x = 1, y = 5$; etc. These pairs of values can be arranged (as in Chapter 10),

x	0	1	2	3	4	5	...
y	7	5	3	1	−1	−3	...

and there is no limit to the number of possible pairs of values.

If the pairs of values for the equation $3x - 2y = 7$ are set out in the same way,

x	0	1	2	3	4	5	...
y	$-3\frac{1}{2}$	−2	$-\frac{1}{2}$	1	$2\frac{1}{2}$	4	...

it will be seen that the pair of values $x = 3, y = 1$ and *this pair only* occurs in both sets of numbers. This means that this pair satisfies both equations simultaneously (i.e. at the same time). Hence the solution of the **simultaneous equations** $2x + y = 7$, $3x - 2y = 7$ is $x = 3, y = 1$.

Notice how this result is illustrated by the graphs of the two lines (Fig. 53), which intersect at the point (3,1), this being the only point which is on both lines.

Reminder. When drawing the graphs of straight lines it is unnecessary to plot more than three points on each: see page 108.

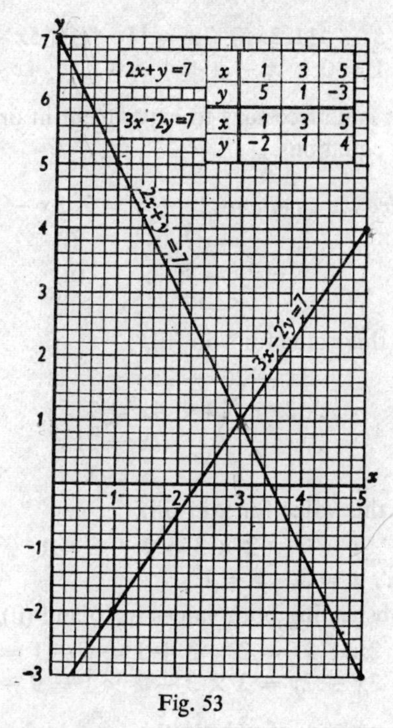

Fig. 53

If $L = \{(x,y): 2x + y = 7\}$ and $M = \{(x,y): 3x - 2y = 7\}$ then $L \cap M = (3,1)$; that is to say the intersection of the set of vectors defined by $2x + y = 7$ and the set of vectors defined by $3x - 2y = 7$ is the vector (3,1).

Exercise 14a

Solve graphically the following pairs of equations:

1 $x + y = 3$ $3x - y = 1$	**2** $x - y = 1$ $x + 2y = 7$	**3** $x - 2y = 1$ $2x + y = 2$
4 $y = 2x + 2$ $3x + 2y = 4$	**5** $3y = 2x + 8$ $x + y = 1$	**6** $x + 3y = 0$ $x - 3y = 6$
7 $x - y = 0$ $3x - y + 2 = 0$	**8** $4x - 2y = 7$ $x + 3y = 7$	**9** $x + y = 3$ $5x - 5y = 1$

10 $2x - 2y = 5$
$2x + 3y + 1 = 0$

11 $3x + 7y = 11$
$x - y + 4 = 0$

12 $5x - 2y = 1$
$4x + 3y = -10{\cdot}7$

In practice it is unnecessary to experiment in order to find the solution of the equations.

Example 1 *Solve the equations* $2x + y = 7$, $3x - 2y = 7$.

$$2x + y = 7 \qquad \text{(i)}$$
$$3x - 2y = 7 \qquad \text{(ii)}$$

From (i)
$$y = 7 - 2x \qquad \text{(iii)}$$

Substituting this value for y in (ii),

$$3x - 2(7 - 2x) = 7$$
$$\therefore\ 3x - 14 + 4x = 7$$
$$\therefore\ 7x = 21$$
$$\therefore\ x = 3$$

Substituting this value for x in (iii),

$$y = 7 - 2 \times 3 = 7 - 6 = 1$$
$$\therefore\ x = 3, \quad y = 1.$$

Check by substituting both values in (i) and (ii),

$$\text{(i)}\ 2x + y = 2 \times 3 + 1 = 6 + 1 = 7$$
$$\text{(ii)}\ 3x - 2y = 3 \times 3 - 2 \times 1 = 9 - 2 = 7.$$

The above method of **substitution** should be used only for cases in which one of the coefficients of x or y in one of the two equations is 1. When the numbers involved are larger, the following method is generally simpler: this is the method of **elimination,** which consists of getting rid of one letter by making its coefficients the same in both equations, and then adding or subtracting as may be necessary.

Example 2 *Solve the equations* $3x + 2y = 12$, $5x - 3y = 1$.

$$3x + 2y = 12 \qquad \text{(i)}$$
$$5x - 3y = 1 \qquad \text{(ii)}$$

$$\begin{array}{lrcl} \text{(i)} \times 3 & 9x + 6y & = & 36 \\ \text{(ii)} \times 2 & 10x - 6y & = & 2 \\ \hline \text{Add} & 19x & = & 38 \\ \therefore & x & = & 2 \end{array}$$

Substitute in (i), $3 \times 2 + 2y = 12$

$$\therefore 2y = 12 - 6 = 6$$
$$\therefore y = 3$$
$$\therefore x = 2, \quad y = 3.$$

Check in (i) $3x + 2y = 3 \times 2 + 2 \times 3 = 6 + 6 = 12$
(ii) $5x - 3y = 5 \times 2 - 3 \times 3 = 10 - 9 = 1$

Alternatively, instead of substituting $x = 2$ to find y, it may be simpler to start again with the original equations and eliminate x to find y: e.g.

$$\begin{array}{ll} \text{(i)} \times 5 & 15x + 10y = 60 \\ \text{(ii)} \times 3 & 15x - 9y = 3 \\ \hline \text{Subtract} & 19y = 57 \\ & \therefore y = 3. \end{array}$$

This alternative method is particularly useful when the value first found is a fraction, which may lead to complicated working when it is substituted.

Exercise 14b

A graphical method may be used as a check for the solutions of any of the following pairs of equations.

Use the method of substitution to solve:

1 $y = x + 1$, $x + y = 3$
2 $y = 2x - 4$, $3x + y = 11$
3 $2x + y = 0$, $x + 2y = 3$
4 $x + y = 4$, $2x - y = 5$
5 $y - 2x = 1$, $3x - 4y = 1$
6 $3x + 2y = 10$, $4x - y = 6$

Use the method of elimination to solve:

7 $x + 2y = 7$, $3x - 2y = -3$
8 $4x - 3y = 1$, $x - 2y = 4$
9 $5x + 2y = 2$, $2x + 3y = -8$
10 $4x + 3y = 9$, $2x + 5y = 15$
11 $3x - 2y = 4$, $2x + 3y = -6$
12 $2x - 5y = -6$, $4x - 3y = -12$

Solve the following pairs of equations:

13 $5x + y = 0$, $3x - 2y = 13$
14 $5x + 3y = 1$, $2x + 3y = -5$
15 $4a = 5b + 5$, $2a = 3b + 2$

16 $6h = 2k + 9$
$3h + 4k = 12$

17 $2p - 5q = 8$
$3p - 7q = 11$

18 $2r + 3s = 29$
$3r + 2s = 16$

19 $2x + 5y + 1 = 0$
$3x + 7y = 1$

20 $3a = 2b + 1$
$5a = 3b + 3$

21 $4x = y + 7$
$3x + 4y + 9 = 0$

22 $5v = 11 + 3u$
$2u + 7v = 3$

23 $5d = 2e - 14$
$5e = d + 12$

24 $6x - 5y = -7$
$3x + 4y = 16$

25 $3f - 4g = 1$
$6f - 6g = 5$

26 $4e + 3f = 4$
$2e = 5f + 15$

27 $4p + 2q + 8 = 0$
$6p = 2q - 27$

28 $4m = 3n$
$8m - 9n = 7$

29 $8y + 4z = 7$
$6y - 8z = 41$

30 $5h + 10k = 28$
$15h = 20k - 121$

Problems

In the sets of problems in Book 1 only one unknown was involved, and consequently only one equation was necessary to find it. When there are two unknown quantities to be found, two sets of facts must be given, from which two equations can be written down and solved.

Example 3 *Four knives and* 6 *forks cost* £1·36; 6 *knives and* 5 *forks cost* £1·64. *Find the cost of a knife and of a fork.*

Let one knife cost xp and one fork yp.
Then 4 knives cost $4x$p,
6 forks cost $6y$p,
and £1·36 = 136p.

$$\therefore 4x + 6y = 136 \quad \text{(i)}$$

Similarly $$6x + 5y = 164 \quad \text{(ii)}$$

(i) × 3 $$12x + 18y = 408$$

(ii) × 2 $$12x + 10y = 328$$

Subtract $$8y = 80$$

$$\therefore y = 10.$$

Substitute in (i), $4x + 60 = 136$

$$\therefore 4x = 136 - 60 = 76$$
$$\therefore x = 19.$$

$\therefore$ a knife costs 19p,
and a fork costs 10p.

Check.			
4 knives cost	£0·76	6 knives cost	£1·14
6 forks cost	£0·60	5 forks cost	£0·50
	£1·36		£1·64

Example 4 *Six years ago Alf was three times as old as Bert. Their combined ages now are* 24 *years. How old are they now?*

Let Alf's age now be a years, and Bert's b years.

Then $$a + b = 24 \quad \text{(i)}$$

Six years ago Alf was $a - 6$, and Bert was $b - 6$.

$$\therefore a - 6 = 3(b - 6)$$
$$\therefore a - 6 = 3b - 18$$
$$\therefore a - 3b = -12 \quad \text{(ii)}$$

Subtract (ii) from (i), $4b = 36$

$$\therefore b = 9.$$

Substitute in (i), $a + 9 = 24$

$$\therefore a = 15.$$

$\therefore$ Alf is 15 and Bert 9.

Check. Sum of ages $= 15 + 9 = 24$ years.
6 years ago Alf was 9 and Bert was 3; $9 = 3 \times 3$.

N.B. In both these examples the actual facts given are checked, and not the equations.

Exercise 14c

1 The sum of two numbers is 19 and their difference 5. Find the numbers.

2 The sum of two numbers is 17, and twice the larger exceeds three times the smaller by 4. Find the numbers.

3 Peter and John have 60p between them. Peter has 24p more than John. How much has each got?

4 Angela's and Cecily's ages add up to 25 years. 8 years ago Angela was twice as old as Cecily. How old are they now?

5 Six pencils and 3 rubbers cost 30p. 5 pencils and 2 rubbers cost 24p. How much does each cost?

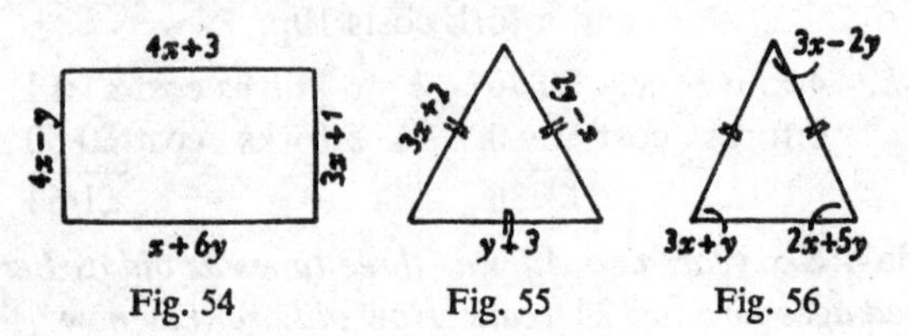

Fig. 54 Fig. 55 Fig. 56

6 The sides of the rectangle in Fig. 54 are given in centimetres. Find x and y, and the area of the rectangle.

7 The sides of the equilateral triangle in Fig. 55 are given in cm. Find x and y and the perimeter of the triangle.

8 In my pocket are x fivepenny pieces and y twopenny pieces. There are eight coins altogether, and their total value is 31p. How many of each sort have I?

9 Find the angles of the isosceles triangle in Fig. 56 above.

10 Three nuts and 6 bolts have a mass of 72 g; 4 nuts and 5 bolts have a mass of 66 g. Find the mass of a nut and of a bolt.

11 The average of two mixed numbers is 12, and one is 3 more than the other. Find the numbers.

12 A boy travels for x hours at 5 km/h and for y hours at 10 km/h. He travels 35 km altogether, and his average speed is 7 km/h. Find x and y.

13 In ten years' time a father will be twice as old as his son: ten years ago he was six times as old. How old are they both now?

14 Four tins of tobacco and 2 boxes of matches cost £1·56. A tin of tobacco costs 30p more than 4 boxes of matches. Find the cost of a tin of tobacco.

15 The tobacco I grow in my garden costs 99p less per 100 g than what I buy from the shop. If I mix 200 g of home-grown with 100 g of shop tobacco, the mixture works out at exactly half the price of the latter. What does the mixture cost per 100 g?

16 Two patrols of scouts competed in collecting money during National Scout Job Week. The patrol with six scouts collected altogether 6p more than the one with five scouts, but the average collection of the second patrol was 6p more than that of the first. How much did the two patrols collect between them?

Revision examples

XI

1 Divide $6x^2 - 7xy - 5y^2$ by $2x + y$.

2 On three successive Sundays the collections in a church were £6·95, £8·34, £7·53. After the next Sunday the average collection for the month was £7·69. What was the amount of the collection on the fourth Sunday?

3 A rough estimate of the number of boys at school (in thousands) in 1970 is as follows:

Age	14	15	16	17
Number	264	129	76	31

Represent these figures (i) in a pie-chart (ii) in a horizontal bar-chart.

4 Simplify (i) $1\frac{1}{5}(\frac{5}{12} - \frac{3}{8})$ (ii) $1\frac{1}{5} \times \frac{5}{12} - \frac{3}{8}$.

5 A man is 25 years older than his son. Eight years ago he was six times as old as his son. How old are they now?

6 Add together the following vectors:
(3·2, −1·2, −2·3), (4·2, 6·1, −3·1) and (7·3, 2·1, 8·1).

7 Solve the equations $3x + 2y = 12$, $5x - 3y = 1$.

8 Construct a parallelogram with diagonals 7·5 cm and 10·2 cm, and smaller sides 3·6 cm long. Measure the longer sides.

9 At what rate per cent does the simple interest on £57 for 5 years amount to £4·75?

10 In a parallelogram ABCD the bisectors of the angles at A and D meet at O. Prove that $\mathrm{A\hat{O}D}$ is a right angle.

XII

1 80 boys and 70 girls take an examination. 15% of the boys and 10% of the girls fail. What percentage of the whole number fails?

2 Solve graphically the equations $2y - x = 2$, $4y + 3x = 12$.

3 $\overline{ABCD}$ is a straight line such that AB = BC = CD. If ACXY is a parallelogram, prove that BDXY is also a parallelogram.

4 Factorise (i) $2ax^2 - 6bx + 4cx^3$ (ii) $x^2 - 11x - 26$.

5 In 1969 the £ sterling was worth 2·40 U.S. dollars or 1 500 Italian lire. Draw a 'ready-reckoner' graph connecting dollars and lire for amounts up to $12. Read off the equivalent amounts in the other currency of
(i) $10, $5·40 (ii) 1 000 lire, 6 200 lire.

6 The marks of eleven boys in a test paper were 31, 43, 79, 64, 46, 49, 87, 55, 62, 68, 48 out of 100. What was the average percentage mark, to one decimal place?

7 Solve the equations $2a - 3b = 7$, $4a + 5b = 3$.

8 A steel girder with section as shown, the dimensions given being in centimetres, is 3 metres long. Find the mass of the girder if the mass of 1 cm^3 of steel is 7·3 g.

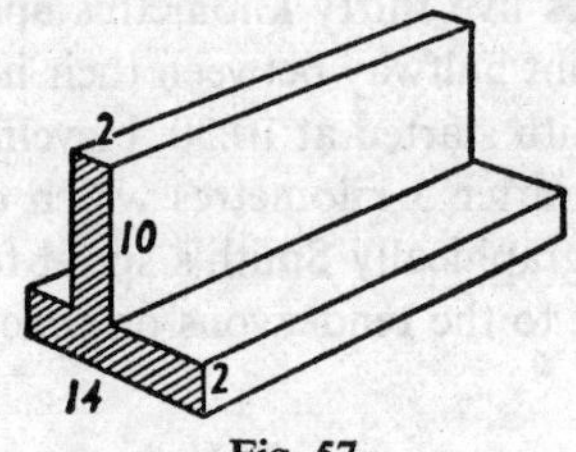

Fig. 57

9 A nut and a bolt together have a mass of 98 g. The mass of 4 bolts and 2 nuts is 336 g. Find the mass of a nut and of a bolt.

10 Draw a triangle with sides 6 cm, 8 cm, 9 cm. Find the length of the shortest altitude of the triangle by means of an accurate drawing.

XIII

1 Solve the equation

$$\tfrac{1}{4}(2x - 1) - \tfrac{1}{6}(x + 2) = \frac{x}{3} - \tfrac{1}{12}(2x - 3).$$

Check the answer.

2 Perform the following vector subtraction:

$$(3{\cdot}2, -5{\cdot}6, 7{\cdot}1, -6{\cdot}7) - (3{\cdot}6, 8{\cdot}9, -5{\cdot}7, -8{\cdot}5).$$

3 A yacht sails 4 km from A to B on a bearing of 060°; then 5 km from B to C on a bearing of 100°. Find by drawing the distance and bearing of A from C.

4 12 pencils and 6 rubbers cost 66p; 5 pencils and 3 rubbers cost 29p. How much does each cost?

5 After 12 innings a batsman's average was 18·5. What must he score in the next innings to raise his average to 20?

6 Solve the equations $6p - 5q + 7 = 0$, $3p + 4q = 16$.

7 In what time does £213·60 earn £33·64 interest at $4\frac{1}{2}\%$?

8 Simplify $(a + 5b)(a - 2b) + (a - 3b)(a - 4b)$.

9 In a parallelogram ABCD, AB = 2AD and M is the mid-point of $\overline{AB}$. Prove that $C\hat{M}D = 90°$.

10 Smith and Jones live thirty kilometres apart. They arranged to meet at a point halfway between their houses at 12.00 on a certain day. Smith started at 10.30, bicycling at 10 km/h, but had a puncture after 5 kilometres which delayed him for 10 minutes. Find graphically Smith's speed for the last 10 kilometres if he got to the rendezvous on time.

XIV

1 Solve graphically the equations $x + 2y = 4$, $3y - 5x = 15$.

2 A shop sends to the Post Office 6 parcels of 1·02 kg each, 4 of 0·87 kg each, 2 of 1·78 kg each and one of 2·05 kg. What is the average mass of the parcels?

3 In a parallelogram ABCD a point X is taken on $\overline{CD}$ such that $X\hat{A}B = \hat{B}$. Prove that AX = AD.

4 Arrange in order of size, largest first, $\frac{3}{16}$, 0·2, $\frac{7}{40}$, $\frac{11}{60}$.

5 Solve the equation $(x + 5)(x - 3) = x(x - 2)$.

6 Securities costing £75 are sold for £80·25. What percentage profit is this?

7 Solve the equations $3a - 4b = 1$, $1{\cdot}2a - 1{\cdot}2b = 1$.

8 Ten boys took a Mathematics test and a Physics test, both marked out of 50. The marks obtained by the individual boys were

M	8	10	16	20	22	26	30	32	38	44
P	12	18	22	24	30	32	34	42	44	48

Plot M against P. There seems to be a 'straight-line' relationship between the two subjects. Draw this line in. How many marks would a boy who scores 0 in Maths. expect to get in Physics?

9 Strawberry jam costs 2p per pot more than plum. 2 pots of strawberry and 3 of plum cost 59p altogether. How much does each sort cost?

10 Construct a rhombus of side 6 cm with the shorter diagonal 8·4 cm long. Measure the other diagonal.

XV

1 Expand $(3a^2 + 2a + 5)(2a - 3)$.

2 During one week in June the mid-day temperatures in degrees C were 22, 24, 24, 28, 23, 19, 21. What was the average mid-day temperature for the week, and what the greatest deviation from it, above and below?

3 Draw a triangle with sides 7·5 cm, 10·5 cm, 12 cm. Construct one of the altitudes. Hence calculate the area of the triangle. (Area $= \frac{1}{2}$ base $\times$ altitude.)

4 What principal earns £14·13 in 5 years at 3% per annum simple interest?

5 Bert is three years older than Alf: seven years ago he was twice as old. When will the sum of their ages be 35?

6 Solve the equations $\frac{3}{4}x + \frac{1}{2}y = 2$, $\frac{5}{2}x - y = -4$.

7 Evaluate the following:
(i) 4(6·2, 7·1, 3·2) (ii) $\frac{1}{3}$(12·6, 6·3, 7·2, 2·1).

8 In a parallelogram ABCD, X and Y are points on $\overline{BD}$ such that $\overline{AX}$ is parallel to $\overline{YC}$. Prove that AX = CY.

9 Simplify $1\frac{1}{4} \times (3\frac{1}{4} - 1\frac{1}{2}) \div \frac{5}{8}$.

10 Draw a graph from which the equivalents of amounts up to £1 in dollars may be read off. Take £1 = \$2·38 and use scales of 100 mm to £1 and 50 mm to \$1. Read off the values of \$1, \$2·26, \$1·64 in pence; and of 15p, 52p, 79p in dollars.

XVI

1 Factorise (i) $p^2 - 8p + 15$ (ii) $a^2 - 8a - 20$.

2 A motorist averages 48 km/h for the first 30 km of a journey, and 64 km/h for the next 120 km. What was his average speed for the whole journey?

3 ABCD is a parallelogram. Points P and Q are taken on $\overline{BD}$ such that BP = DQ. Prove that APCQ is a parallelogram.

4 The masses (M g) of metal discs of radius r cm are as follows:

M	50	100	150	200	250	300
r	1	1·41	1·73	2	2·24	2·45

Find graphically the mass of a disc of radius 1·5 cm, and the radius of a disc of mass 220 g.

5 Eight boys and 7 girls divide £2·26 between them, the boys taking 2p each more than the girls. How much does each get?

6 Construct a triangle ABC in which AB = 6 cm, BC = 12 cm, CA = 9 cm. The perpendicular bisector of $\overline{BC}$ cuts $\overline{AC}$ at Y. Measure CY.

7 Solve the equations $s = 2 - 2\frac{1}{2}t$, $t = 3\frac{1}{2} - 1\frac{3}{4}s$.

8 A bicycle bought for £12·60 is sold at a loss of 15%. What is the selling price?

9 Simplify $x - \{3 - [x - (2 - x) + 4]\}$. Check by putting $x = 1$.

10 Draw the graph of the function $x^2 - 3x$ for values of x from -1 to $+4$. What is the least value of the function? For what values of x does $x^2 - 3x = 2$? Read off the values of the function when $x = -0{\cdot}6$, $2{\cdot}7$.

XVII

1 Evaluate $\dfrac{5{\cdot}2 \times 2{\cdot}25}{0{\cdot}031\,2}$.

2 ABC is a triangle in which AB = 7 cm, BC = 8 cm, CA = 3 cm. Construct $\overline{\text{AP}}$, the perpendicular from A to $\overline{\text{BC}}$; also $\overline{\text{BX}}$ to bisect $\hat{\text{B}}$ and cut $\overline{\text{AP}}$ at X. Measure CX.

3 Write down the expansions of
(i) $(x - 3)(x - 4)$ (ii) $(a + 2b)(a - 3b)$ (iii) $(3p - 2q)^2$.

4 At what rate per cent simple interest does £650 amount to £767 in 3 years?

5 The average age of a class of 21 boys is 14 years 3 months. If the oldest boy is not counted in, the average drops to 14 years 2 months. How old is he?

6 A plate costs half as much again as a saucer. Two plates and three saucers cost 60p. How much does each cost?

7 Alice can run 100 metres in 15 seconds, and her young brother Bertie can run the same distance in 21 seconds. If she gives him 30 metres start in a 100-metres race, find by means of a graph who wins and by what distance.

8 Solve the equations $h = \frac{1}{3}k + 1\frac{1}{2}$, $\frac{1}{4}h + \frac{1}{3}k = 1$.

9 ABCD is a parallelogram whose diagonals meet at O. Any line through O cuts $\overline{\text{AB}}$ produced at X and $\overline{\text{CD}}$ produced at Y. Prove that AXCY is a parallelogram.

10 37 men each do 7 h 35 min work in a day. For what total working time, in a week of six days, does their employer have to pay wages?

XVIII

1 Solve the equations $8y + 4z = 7$, $6y - 8z = 41$.

2 Find the loss per cent if an article bought for £1·28 is sold for 80p.

3 Without using a protractor construct a parallelogram ABCD with AD = 6 cm, DC = 9 cm and $\hat{\text{D}} = 60°$. Find graphically a point P inside the parallelogram which is equidistant from $\overline{DA}$ and $\overline{DC}$, and is also 6 cm from B. Measure CP.

4 If a room is l metres long and b metres wide the cost, £c, of carpeting the floor is given by the formula $c = 3lb + 2$.

(i) Find the cost for a room 6 m long and 4 m wide.

(ii) Find the length of a room which is 5 m wide, and for which the cost of carpeting is £98.

5 A bankrupt whose debts amount to £2 107·50 can pay only 64p in the £. How much money has he?

6 A and B are two towns 40 km apart. A bus leaves A at 09.00, travels to B at a steady 50 km/h, waits for a quarter of an hour at B, and then returns to A at the same speed.

A cyclist leaves B at 09.20 and travels to A at a steady 20 km/h. Taking scales of 1 mm to represent one minute, and 2 mm for 1 km, represent the two journeys on a graph, and deduce from it the times at which the bus meets the cyclist and at which it overtakes him.

7 Divide 76 into two parts so that two-thirds of one part is equal to three-fifths of the other.

8 ABCD and BCXY are two parallelograms such that $\overline{AD}$ and $\overline{XY}$ are on opposite sides of $\overline{BC}$. Prove that $\overline{AX}$ bisects $\overline{DY}$.

9 Solve the equation

$$(4a + 3)(a - 2) - (2a - 3)(2a + 3) = 0.$$

10 A motorist had planned to reach a place 106 km away in two hours exactly. For the first 15 km he was able to average only 40 km/h. What average speed must he keep up for the rest of the journey if he is to arrive on time?

XIX

1 A is (2,3), B is (3,−2) and C is (2,1). Find the co-ordinates of the vertices of the triangle which is the displacement of △ABC through $\overrightarrow{AB}$.

2 ABCD is a parallelogram. Any line through D cuts $\overline{AB}$ at P and $\overline{CB}$ produced at Q: a line through B parallel to $\overline{DPQ}$ cuts $\overline{CD}$ at R and $\overline{AD}$ produced at S. Prove that PQ = RS.

3 Expand $(4x^2 - 3x + 1)(3x - 2)$.

4 A pedestrian leaves his house at A at 10.00 and starts walking to B, 15 kilometres away, at 6 km/h, taking ten minutes' rest at the end of each hour. A motorist leaves A at 11.00 also going towards B, and passes the pedestrian just as he is getting up to go on after his first rest. When does the motorist reach B, and when the pedestrian?

5 Archie had 6p more in his pocket than Bill, but after Archie had paid Bill 15p, Bill had twice as much as Archie. How much had each to begin with?

6 The average length of x pieces of string is 155 cm. Another y pieces have an average length of 160 cm. Find the average length of all the pieces of string taken together. If this average length is 158 cm, find the ratio $x : y$.

7 Find to the nearest penny the tax on £572·43 at 41p in the £.

8 Solve the equations $3(2x - y) = x + y + 5$,
$$5(3x - 2y) = 2(x - y) + 1.$$

9 Draw a triangle PQR with PQ = 5 cm, QR = 8 cm, RP = 6 cm. Find by construction a point X inside the triangle such that X is 2 cm from $\overline{QR}$, and also lies on the bisector of $Q\hat{P}R$. Measure $Q\hat{X}R$.

10 For a certain journey a man takes 1 h 51 min when he travels at 33 km/h. How long will he take to return at 37 km/h?

XX

1 Solve the equations $\frac{2}{x} - \frac{3}{y} = 1$, $\frac{8}{x} + \frac{9}{y} = \frac{1}{2}$.

2 Cubes are to be made of various materials, all the cubes being of the same mass. The relationship between the edge of the cube (x cm) and the density of the material (s g/cm³) is given in the table:

s	1	2	3	4	5	6	7	8
x	4·93	3·91	3·42	3·11	2·88	2·71	2·58	2·47

Find graphically (i) the density of a cube of edge 4 cm, 3 cm
(ii) the edge of a cube of density 2·8 g/cm³, 6·5 g/cm³.

3 ABCD is a parallelogram. Equilateral triangles BXC and AYD are drawn outside the parallelogram. Prove that $\overline{BD}$ bisects $\overline{XY}$.

4 Find the average of the following ages of 14 boys, given in years and months: 15.5, 15.0, 15.3, 14.5, 14.7, 15.4, 15.10, 14.9, 15.2, 13.11, 15.1, 16.1, 15.5, 14.11.

5 Draw a triangle with sides 12 cm, 8 cm and 10·5 cm. Bisect any two of the angles and let the bisectors meet at X. Construct the perpendicular from X to the longest side. Measure this perpendicular.

6 Factorise (i) $m^2 - 7m - 18$ (ii) $n^2 + 10n + 24$.

7 A is (1,2), B is (3,4), C is (−2,1) and D is (1,−2). Find the co-ordinates of the corners of the quadrilateral which is the displacement of ABCD through $\overrightarrow{AC}$.

8 Two cyclists are 66 km apart, and start out at the same time. If they approach one another they meet in 2 hours, but if they go in the same direction, it takes 7 h 20 min for the faster to overtake the slower. What are their speeds?

9 If the rates in a certain town are 73p in the £, what rate is paid on property of rateable value £113?

10 Draw the graph of the function $3x^2 + 5x - 6$ for values of x from −4 to +2. Read off the values of x when the function equals (i) 0 (ii) −5 (iii) 12.

Chapter 15

Intercept theorems

Theorem 7

The line joining the mid-points of two sides of a triangle is parallel to the third side and equal to half of it.

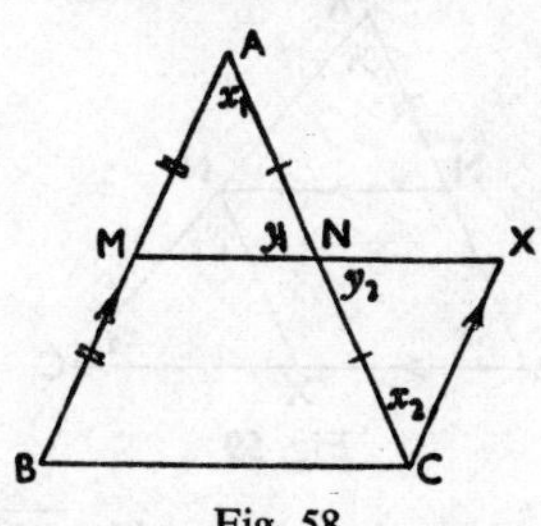

Fig. 58

Given triangle ABC with M, N the mid-points of $\overline{AB}$, $\overline{AC}$ respectively.

To prove (i) $\overline{MN} \parallel \overline{BC}$,

(ii) $MN = \frac{1}{2}BC$.

Construction. Draw $\overline{CX}$ parallel to $\overline{BA}$ to cut $\overline{MN}$ produced at X.

Proof. In $\triangle$s AMN, CXN

$x_1 = x_2$	*alt.* $\angle$*s*, $\overline{XC} \parallel \overline{AM}$
$y_1 = y_2$	*vert. opp.* $\angle$*s*
$AN = CN$	*given*
$\therefore \triangle AMN \equiv \triangle CXN$	*ASA*

$\triangle$CXN is the rotation of $\triangle$AMN about N through 180°

$\therefore AM = CX$ and $MN = XN$

But $AM = MB$	*given*
$\therefore XC = MB$	
Also $\overline{XC} \parallel \overline{MB}$	*construction*

∴ XCBM is a parallelogram *opp. sides = & ∥*

∴ (i) $\overline{MN} \parallel \overline{BC}$. Q.E.D.

Also BC = MX *opp. sides of ∥ gm.* XCBM

∴ (ii) MN = NX = ½MX = ½BC.

Q.E.D.

Corollary. A straight line drawn through the mid-point of one side of a triangle parallel to another side bisects the third side of the triangle.

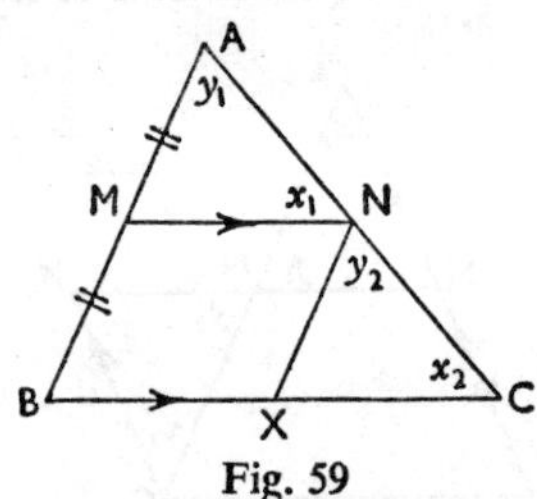

Fig. 59

Given that M is the mid-point of the side $\overline{AB}$ of a triangle ABC, and N a point on $\overline{AC}$ such that $\overline{MN} \parallel \overline{BC}$.

To prove that N is the mid-point of $\overline{AC}$.

Construction. Complete the ∥ gm. MNXB.

Proof. NX = MB *opp. sides of ∥ gm.* MNXB

MB = MA *given*

∴ NX = MA

In △s AMN, NXC

AM = NX *proved*

$x_1 = x_2$ *corr.* ∠*s*, $\overline{MN} \parallel \overline{BC}$

$y_1 = y_2$,, ,, , $\overline{NX} \parallel \overline{AM}$, *constr.*

∴ △AMN ≡ △NXC *AAS*

△NXC is the displacement of △AMN through $\overrightarrow{AN}$

∴ AN = NC

∴ N is the mid-point of $\overline{AC}$.

Q.E.D.

A **transversal** is any line which cuts other given lines.

If two lines cut a transversal, the part of the transversal cut off by them is called an **intercept.**

Theorem 8

If three or more parallel lines cut off equal intercepts on a transversal, then they cut off equal intercepts on any other transversal.

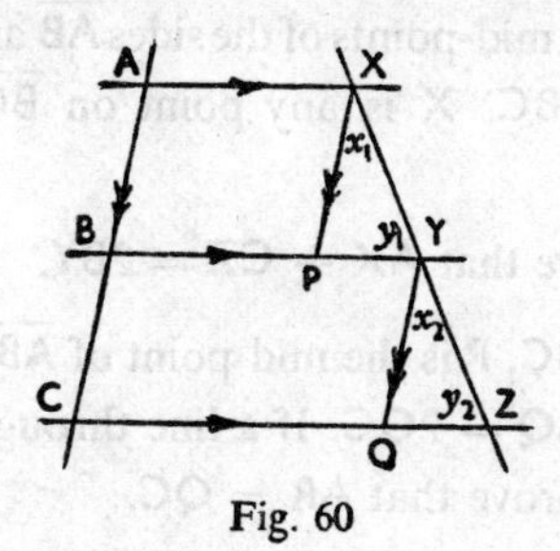

Fig. 60

Given three parallel lines cutting a fourth line at A, B, C so that AB = BC, and cutting another line at X, Y, Z respectively.

To prove XY = YZ.

Construction. Draw $\overline{XP}$, $\overline{YQ} \parallel \overline{ABC}$ to cut $\overline{BY}$, $\overline{CZ}$ at P, Q respectively.

Proof. AXPB is a ∥ gm. *opp. sides* ∥

∴ XP = AB *opp. sides equal*

Similarly YQ = BC *in* ∥ *gm.* YQCB

∴ XP = YQ. AB = BC, *given*

In △s XPY, YQZ

XP = YQ *proved*

$x_1 = x_2$ *corr.* ∠*s*, $\overline{XP} \parallel \overline{YQ}$

$y_1 = y_2$ „ „ , $\overline{BY} \parallel \overline{CZ}$

∴ △XPY ≡ △YQZ *AAS*

△YQZ is the displacement of △XPY through $\overrightarrow{XY}$

∴ XY = YZ. Q.E.D.

Exercise 15a

1 The diagonals of a parallelogram ABCD intersect at O, and P is the mid-point of $\overline{BC}$. Prove (i) $\overline{OP} \parallel \overline{DC}$ (ii) $OP = \frac{1}{2}DC$.

2 P and Q are the mid-points of the sides $\overline{BC}$ and $\overline{AD}$ respectively of a parallelogram ABCD. If the diagonals $\overline{AC}$ and $\overline{BD}$ meet at O, prove that POQ is a straight line.

3 M and N are the mid-points of the sides $\overline{AB}$ and $\overline{AC}$ respectively of a triangle ABC. X is any point on $\overline{BC}$. Prove that $\overline{MN}$ bisects $\overline{AX}$.

4 In Fig. 60, prove that $AX + CZ = 2BY$.

5 In a triangle ABC, P is the mid-point of $\overline{AB}$, and Q a point on $\overline{AC}$ such that $AQ = 2QC$. If a line through P parallel to $\overline{BQ}$ cuts $\overline{AC}$ at R, prove that $AR = QC$.

6 In a triangle ABC, X and Y are points on $\overline{AB}$ such that $AX = XY = YB$, and P and Q points on $\overline{AC}$ such that $AP = PQ = QC$. $\overline{XC}$ cuts $\overline{YQ}$ at Z. Prove that (i) Z is the mid-point of $\overline{XC}$ (ii) $YZ = 3ZQ$.

7 If the diagonals of a quadrilateral are at right angles prove that the figure formed by joining the mid-points of the sides of the quadrilateral is a rectangle.

8 ABCD is a quadrilateral: P, Q, R, S are the mid-points of its sides. Prove that PQRS is a parallelogram.

9 ABCD is a quadrilateral; X, Y are the mid-points of $\overline{AD}$, $\overline{BC}$; P, Q the mid-points of $\overline{BD}$, $\overline{AC}$ respectively. Prove that XPYQ is a parallelogram.

10 If the mid-points of the sides of an isosceles triangle ABC are joined, prove that the triangle thus formed is also isosceles.

11 In Fig. 59, p. 154, show that the area of the triangle AMN is one-quarter of that of the triangle ABC. (*Hint: join* $\overline{MX}$.)

12 ABC is a triangle right-angled at B, and X is the mid-point of $\overline{AC}$. Prove that $BX = \frac{1}{2}AC$. (*Hint: drop perpendicular* $\overline{XY}$ *to* $\overline{BC}$.)

13 In a parallelogram ABCD, X and Y are the mid-points of $\overline{AD}$ and $\overline{BC}$ respectively. Prove that $\overline{BX}$ and $\overline{DY}$ trisect $\overline{AC}$ (i.e. divide $\overline{AC}$ into three equal parts).

14 ABCD is a trapezium with $\overline{AB}$ parallel to $\overline{DC}$. If X and Y are the mid-points of $\overline{BD}$ and $\overline{AC}$ respectively, show that the line $\overline{XY}$, when produced, bisects both $\overline{AD}$ and $\overline{BC}$.

15 L and M are the mid-points of the sides $\overline{AB}$, $\overline{AC}$ of a triangle ABC. $\overline{LO}$ and $\overline{MN}$ are perpendiculars from L and M to $\overline{BC}$. $\overline{AO}$ and $\overline{AN}$ produced cut lines drawn through B and C at right angles to $\overline{BC}$ at P and Q respectively. Prove that PQCB is a rectangle.

16 P is the mid-point of the side $\overline{AB}$ of a triangle ABC, and Q a point on $\overline{AC}$ such that $AQ = 2QC$. $\overline{PQ}$ produced cuts $\overline{BC}$ produced at R. Prove that C is the mid-point of $\overline{BR}$.

17 ABCD is a parallelogram with M the mid-point of $\overline{AD}$, and X a point on $\overline{AC}$ such that $AX = \frac{2}{7}AC$. Prove that $\overline{MX}$ produced trisects $\overline{AB}$.

18 $\overline{AXYB}$ and $\overline{APQRC}$ are two straight lines through A such that $AX = XY = YB$ and $AP = PQ = QR = RC$. Prove that (i) $\overline{CX}$ is trisected at its intersections with $\overline{YQ}$ and $\overline{BR}$ (ii) $BZ = 8ZR$, where Z is the intersection of $\overline{CX}$ and $\overline{BR}$.

19 ABCD is a parallelogram and $\overline{LM}$ any line outside it. Parallel lines through A, B, C, D cut $\overline{LM}$ at P, Q, R, S respectively. Prove that $AP + CR = BQ + DS$.

20 ABCD is a trapezium with $\overline{AB}$ parallel to $\overline{DC}$. P, Q, R, S are the mid-points of $\overline{AD}$, $\overline{DB}$, $\overline{AC}$, $\overline{CB}$ respectively. Prove that (i) $\overline{PQRS}$ is a straight line (ii) $PQ = RS$.

Construction 6

To divide a given straight line into a given number of equal parts.

It is convenient, in explaining this construction, to consider division of a line into a specific number (say 5) of equal parts: the method is similar for any other number.

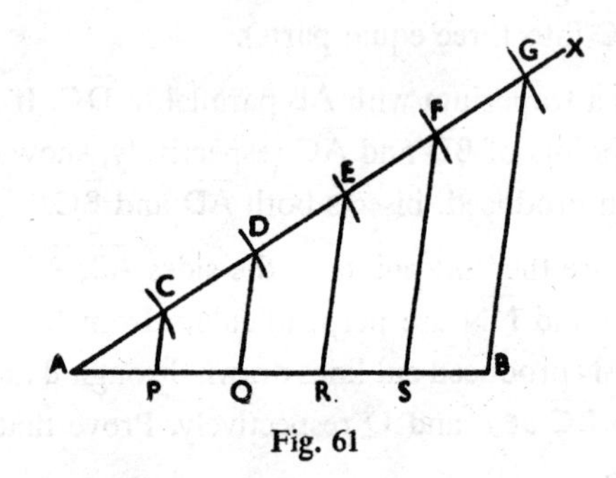

Fig. 61

Given a line $\overline{AB}$, to divide it into 5 equal parts.

Construction. Draw through A any line $\overline{AX}$ and step off on it from A (with compasses set to any convenient radius) 5 equal lengths AC, CD, DE, EF, FG.

Join $\overline{GB}$.

Through C, D, E, F draw lines parallel to $\overline{GB}$ to cut $\overline{AB}$ in P, Q, R, S respectively.

Then AP = PQ = QR = RS = SB.

The proof of this construction follows immediately from Theorem 8.

Exercise 15b

Use Construction 6 in all the examples which follow.

1 Draw a line 8 cm long and divide it into 3 equal parts. Measure one part.

2 Draw a line 7 cm long and divide it into 5 equal parts. Measure one part.

3 Draw a line $\overline{AB}$ 8 cm long. Find, by drawing, a point P on $\overline{AB}$ such that AP : PB = 2 : 3. Measure AP.

4 Draw a line $\overline{LM}$ 8 cm long. Find a point P on $\overline{LM}$ such that LP = $\frac{3}{7}$LM. Measure LP.

5 Draw a line $\overline{PQ}$ 9 cm long. Find a point X on $\overline{PQ}$ produced such that PX : QX = 4 : 1. Measure QX. (The point X is said to **divide $\overline{PQ}$ externally in the ratio of 4 : 1.)**

6 Draw a line $\overline{XY}$ 5 cm long. Divide it externally at Z in the ratio 7 : 3. Measure YZ.

Chapter 16

Similar triangles numerically. Enlargement

In Chapter 3 it was found that two triangles (other than right-angled triangles) are congruent if

(i) three sides
(ii) two sides and the included angle
(iii) one side (corresponding) and two angles

are the same for both.

If the **three angles** of one triangle are respectively equal to the three angles of the other, the two triangles are not necessarily congruent, but are said to be **similar**. They are of the same *shape*, but may be unequal in *size*, as in Fig. 62. The corresponding sides

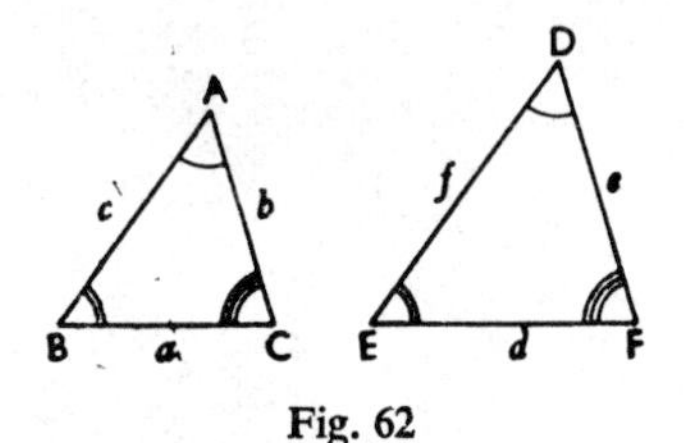

Fig. 62

are not equal, but are proportional. For example, if equiangular triangles are drawn as in Fig. 62 with AB equal to $\frac{2}{3}$ of DE, then BC will be found to be $\frac{2}{3}$ of EF, and CA will be $\frac{2}{3}$ of FD. Hence AB and DE, BC and EF, CA and FD are all in the ratio 2:3,

$$\text{i.e.}\quad \frac{AB}{DE}=\frac{BC}{EF}=\frac{CA}{FD}=\frac{2}{3},$$

or using small letters for the lengths of the sides,

$$\frac{c}{f}=\frac{a}{d}=\frac{b}{e}=\frac{2}{3}.$$

Also, since $\frac{c}{f} = \frac{a}{d}$,

then multiplying both sides by *fd*,

$$\frac{c}{f} \times fd = \frac{a}{d} \times fd$$

$$\therefore cd = af.$$

∴ dividing both sides by *ad*,

$$\frac{cd}{ad} = \frac{af}{ad}$$

$$\therefore \frac{c}{a} = \frac{f}{d}$$

$$\therefore \frac{\text{AB}}{\text{BC}} = \frac{\text{DE}}{\text{EF}}.$$

Similarly $\frac{\text{BC}}{\text{CA}} = \frac{\text{EF}}{\text{FD}}$ and $\frac{\text{CA}}{\text{AB}} = \frac{\text{FD}}{\text{DE}}$.

These results may perhaps be more easily seen by taking an example with numbers as in Fig. 63. If AB, BC, CA are 12, 10, 8

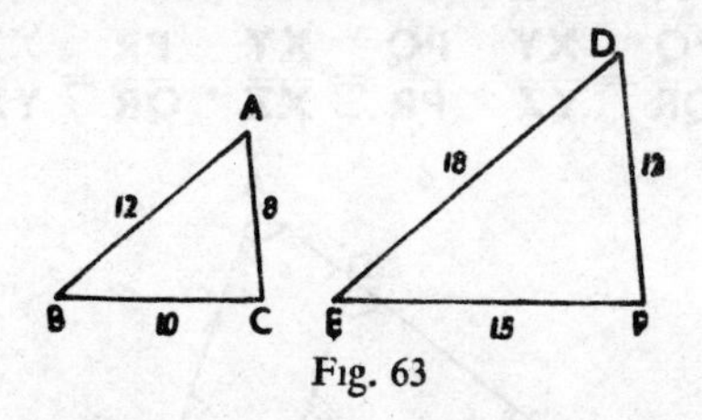

Fig. 63

centimetres respectively, then DE, EF, FD are 18, 15, 12 centimetres respectively. (AB is $\frac{2}{3}$ of DE, etc.)

Hence $\frac{\text{AB}}{\text{BC}} = \frac{12}{10} = \frac{6}{5}$ and $\frac{\text{DE}}{\text{EF}} = \frac{18}{15} = \frac{6}{5}$

$$\therefore \frac{\text{AB}}{\text{BC}} = \frac{\text{DE}}{\text{EF}}$$

and similarly $\frac{\text{BC}}{\text{CA}} = \frac{\text{EF}}{\text{FD}}$ and $\frac{\text{CA}}{\text{AB}} = \frac{\text{FD}}{\text{DE}}$.

Care should be taken to name similar triangles with the letters in the right (corresponding) order. For example if $\triangle GHK$ is similar to $\triangle XYZ$, then without the necessity of referring to a figure it should be clear that the side $\overline{GK}$ of the first triangle corresponds to the side $\overline{XZ}$ of the second, $\overline{GH}$ to $\overline{XY}$, and $\overline{HK}$ to $\overline{YZ}$.

Notice that it is unnecessary for all three angles of a triangle to be given equal respectively to the three angles of another. If two angles of a triangle are respectively equal to two angles of another, the third angles must be equal, since the three angles of any triangle add up to 180°.

The results of this chapter so far may be summarised as follows:

Equiangular triangles are similar.

Equiangular triangles have their corresponding sides proportional.

If two triangles have the three sides of one proportional to the corresponding sides of the other, then the triangles are equiangular and similar.

If $\triangle PQR$ is similar to $\triangle XYZ$

then $$\frac{PQ}{XY} = \frac{QR}{YZ} = \frac{PR}{XZ}$$

or $$\frac{PQ}{QR} = \frac{XY}{YZ}, \quad \frac{PQ}{PR} = \frac{XY}{XZ}, \quad \frac{PR}{QR} = \frac{XZ}{YZ}$$

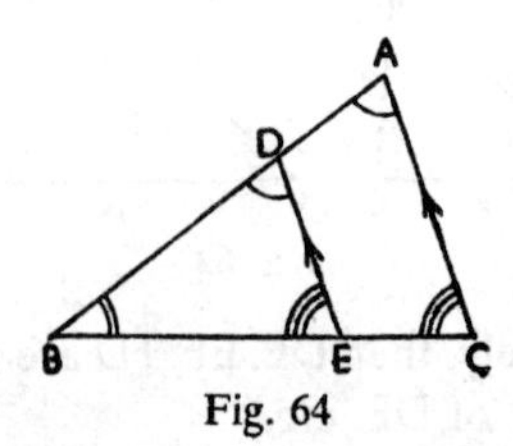

Fig. 64

If a line is drawn parallel to the side $\overline{AC}$ of $\triangle ABC$ to meet $\overline{AB}$ in D and $\overline{BC}$ in E,

then in $\triangle$s ABC, DBE

$B\hat{A}C = B\hat{D}E$ *corr. ∠s*

$\hat{B}$ is common

∴ $\triangle$s ABC, DBE are equiangular and similar.

$$\therefore \frac{BA}{BD} = \frac{BC}{BE} = \frac{AC}{DE}$$

and
$$\frac{AB}{BC} = \frac{DB}{BE}, \frac{AC}{BC} = \frac{DE}{BE}, \frac{AB}{AC} = \frac{DB}{DE}.$$

In Fig. 64, $\triangle ABC$ can be considered as an **enlargement** of $\triangle DBE$. $\triangle DBE$ is said to be mapped into $\triangle ABC$ by an enlargement of ratio BA: BD with centre B.

Example 1 *In Fig.* 65, *calculate* MN *and* MY.

Since $\overline{YZ} \parallel \overline{MN}$,

$$X\hat{Y}Z = X\hat{M}N \quad \text{and} \quad X\hat{Z}Y = X\hat{N}M \text{ (corr.)}$$

$\therefore$ $\triangle$s XYZ, XMN are equiangular and similar.

$\triangle XMN$ is the enlargement of $\triangle XYZ$ in the ratio XM: XY with centre X.

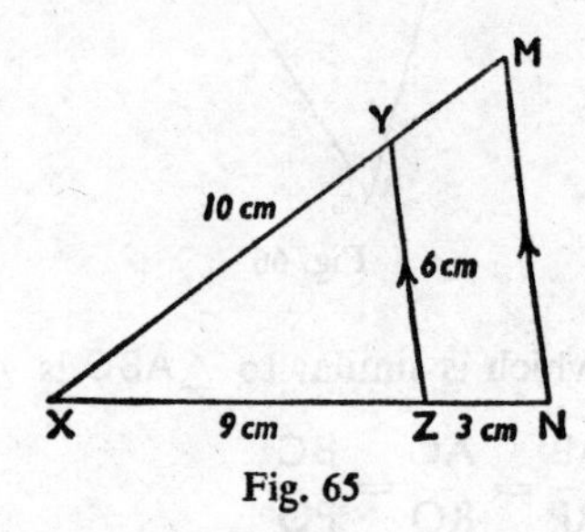

Fig. 65

$$\therefore \frac{XY}{XM} = \frac{XZ}{XN} = \frac{YZ}{MN}$$

$$\therefore \frac{10}{XM} = \frac{9}{12} = \frac{6}{MN}$$

$$\therefore \frac{10}{XM} = \frac{3}{4} \quad \text{and} \quad \frac{6}{MN} = \frac{3}{4}$$

$\therefore$ 3XM = 40 and 3MN = 24

$\therefore$ XM = $13\frac{1}{3}$ cm and MN = 8 cm

$\therefore$ YM = $3\frac{1}{3}$ cm and MN = 8 cm.

Example 2 *In Fig.* 66, *name the triangle which is similar to* $\triangle$ABC, *and calculate* BC *and* RQ.

$$\hat{B} = 180° - 49° - 109° = 22°$$
$$\hat{R} = 180° - 22° - 109° = 49°$$

$\therefore$ the $\triangle$s are equiangular, and A corresponds to R, B to P, and C to Q.

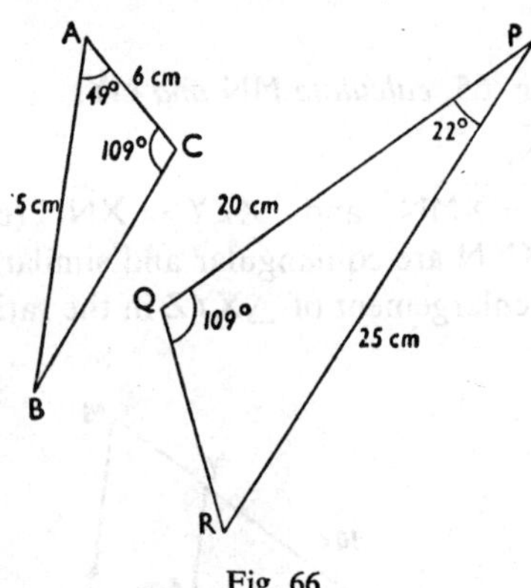

Fig. 66

$\therefore$ the triangle which is similar to $\triangle$ABC is $\triangle$RPQ.

$$\therefore \quad \frac{AB}{RP} = \frac{AC}{RQ} = \frac{BC}{PQ}$$

$$\therefore \quad \frac{15}{25} = \frac{6}{RQ} = \frac{BC}{20}$$

$$\therefore \quad \frac{3}{5} = \frac{6}{RQ} \quad \text{and} \quad \frac{3}{5} = \frac{BC}{20}$$

$$\therefore \; 3RQ = 30 \quad \text{and} \quad 5BC = 60$$

$$\therefore \quad RQ = 10 \text{ cm} \quad \text{and} \quad BC = 12 \text{ cm.}$$

To map $\triangle$ABC into $\triangle$RPQ, $\triangle$ABC would be displaced through $\overrightarrow{CQ}$, rotated about Q, and enlarged in the ratio 5:3, centre Q.

Exercise 16

1 Draw $\triangle$s ABC, PQR as in Fig. 67, so that $\hat{B} = \hat{Q} = 35°$, $\hat{C} = \hat{R} = 80°$, BC = 8 cm, QR = 10 cm. Measure AB, AC, PQ, PR and complete the following:

$$\frac{BC}{QR} = \frac{8}{10} = 0{\cdot}8, \quad \frac{AB}{PQ} = \frac{\quad}{\quad} = 0{\cdot}\ldots, \quad \frac{AC}{PR} = \frac{\quad}{\quad} = 0{\cdot}\ldots$$

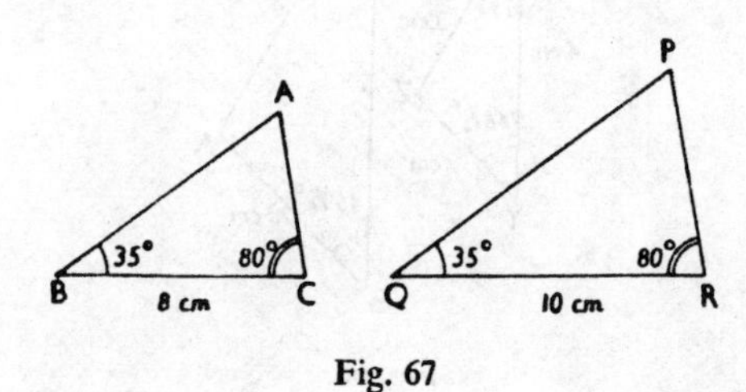

Fig. 67

2 Draw triangles with angles as in Fig. 67 but with BC = 6 cm, QR = 9 cm. Measure AB, AC, PQ, PR and complete the following in decimal form:

(i) $\frac{AB}{BC} = \frac{\quad}{6} = \quad , \quad \frac{PQ}{QR} = \frac{\quad}{9} =$

(ii) $\frac{AC}{BC} = \frac{\quad}{6} = \quad , \quad \frac{PR}{QR} = \frac{\quad}{9} =$

(iii) $\frac{AB}{AC} = \frac{\quad}{\quad} = \quad , \quad \frac{PQ}{PR} = \frac{\quad}{\quad} =$

3 Draw triangles with sides of 6 cm, 8 cm, 10 cm and 9 cm, 12 cm, 15 cm. Measure all the angles.

In nos. 4–13 name the triangle which is similar to $\triangle XYZ$, arranging the letters in the right order, and calculate those of its sides and angles which are not given. Describe the appropriate mappings as in Example 2.

4

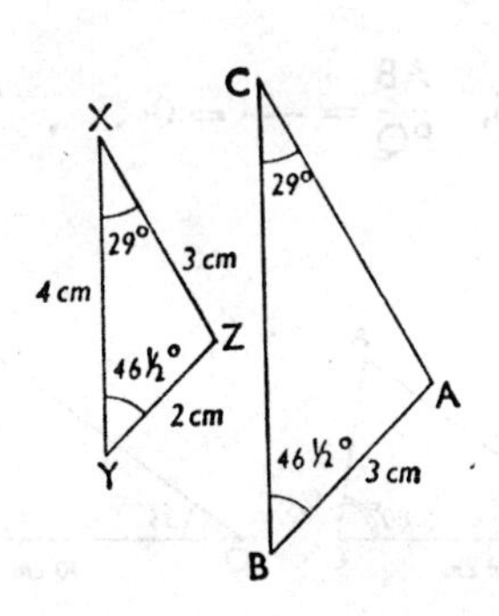

Fig. 68

5

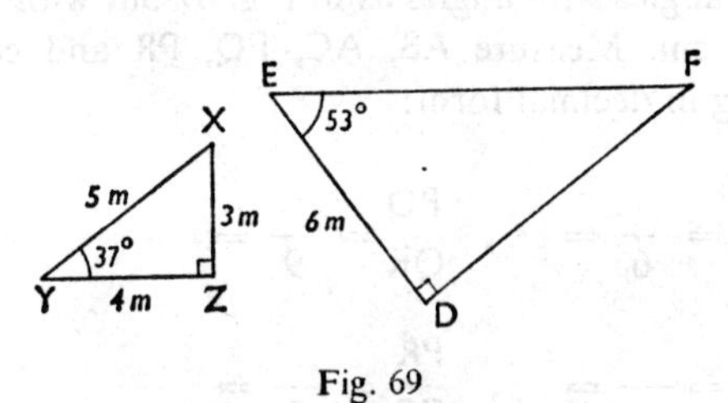

Fig. 69

6

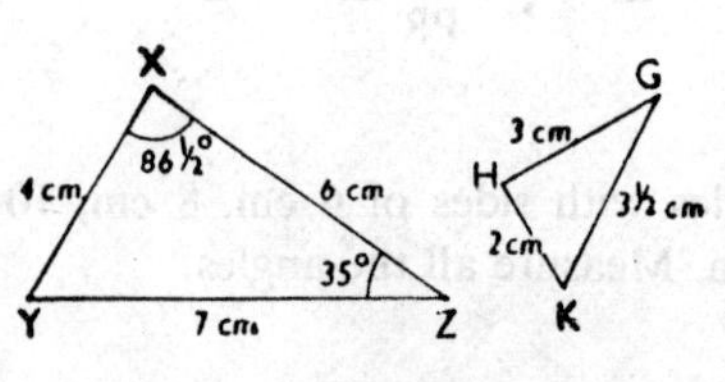

Fig. 70

7

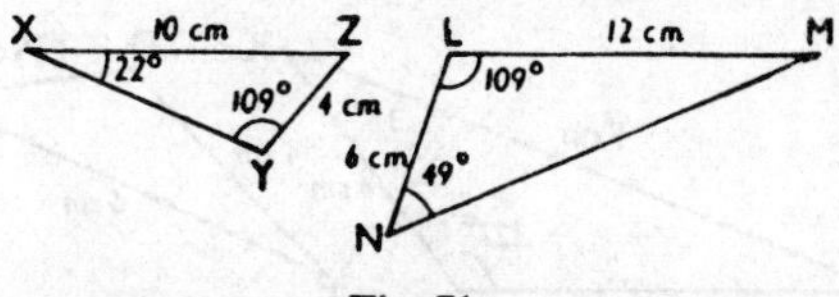

Fig. 71

8

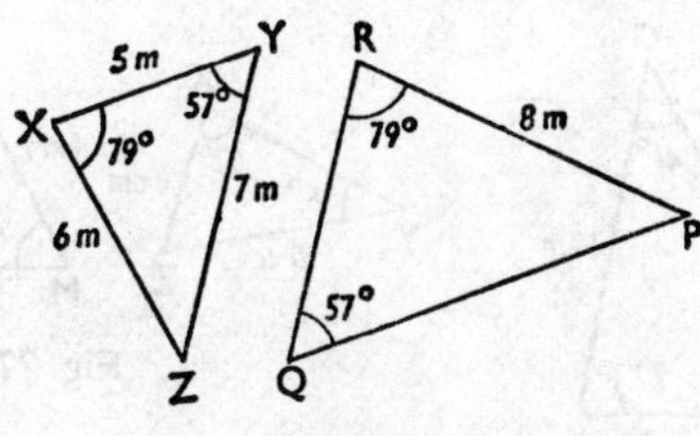

Fig. 72

9

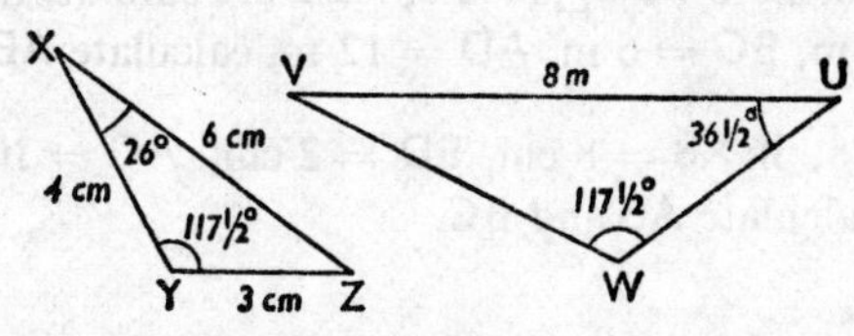

Fig. 73

10

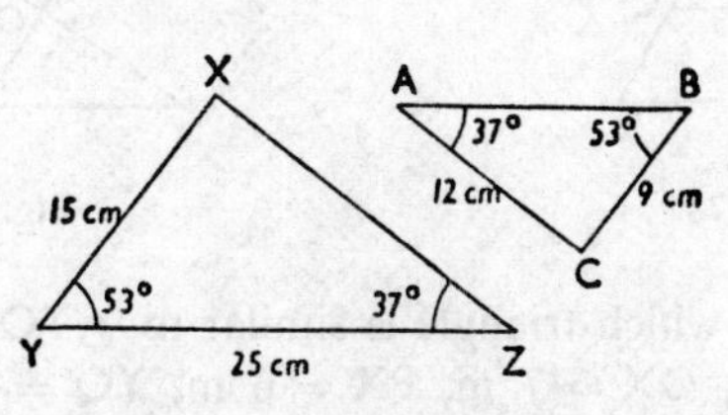

Fig. 74

11

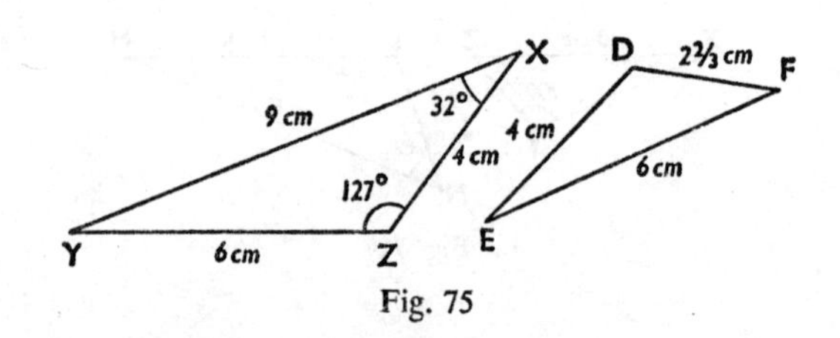

Fig. 75

12

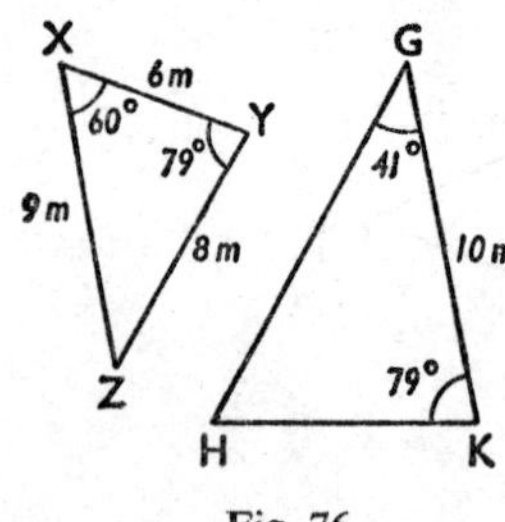

Fig. 76

13

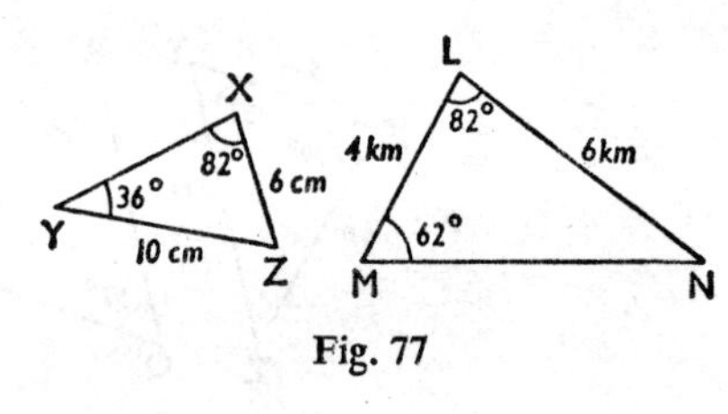

Fig. 77

14 In Fig. 78, state why $\triangle$s ABC, ADE are similar. If AB = 8 m, AC = 9 m, BC = 6 m, AD = 12 m, calculate AE and DE.

15 In Fig. 78, if AB = 8 cm, BD = 2 cm, AC = 10 cm, DE = $6\frac{1}{4}$ cm, calculate AE and BC.

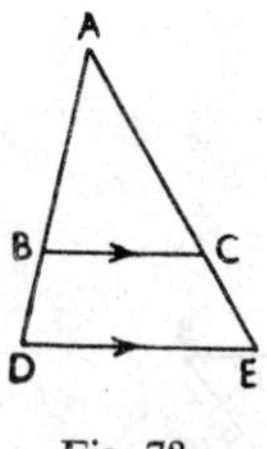

Fig. 78

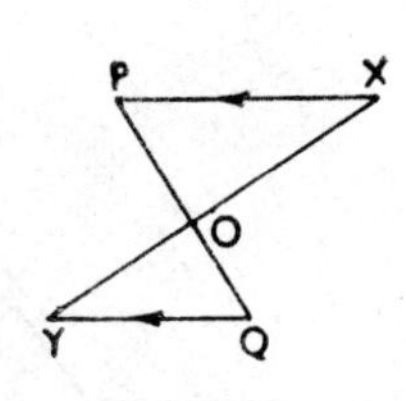

Fig. 79

16 In Fig. 79, which triangle is similar to $\triangle$YOQ, and why? If OP = 4 m, OX = 7 m, PX = 6 m, YQ = $4\frac{1}{2}$ m, calculate OY and OQ. Describe the mapping.

17 In Fig. 79, if OP = 6 cm, PX = 9 cm, OY = 6 cm, YQ = $5\frac{2}{5}$ cm, calculate OX and OQ.

18 Fig. 80 represents a fence $\overline{\text{FN}}$, 2 m high, which is 3 m from the wall of a building $\overline{\text{LW}}$. A ladder $\overline{\text{LR}}$ leans against the wall and just touches the top of the fence. If the foot of the ladder is $\frac{1}{2}$ m from the fence, find how far up the wall the ladder reaches.

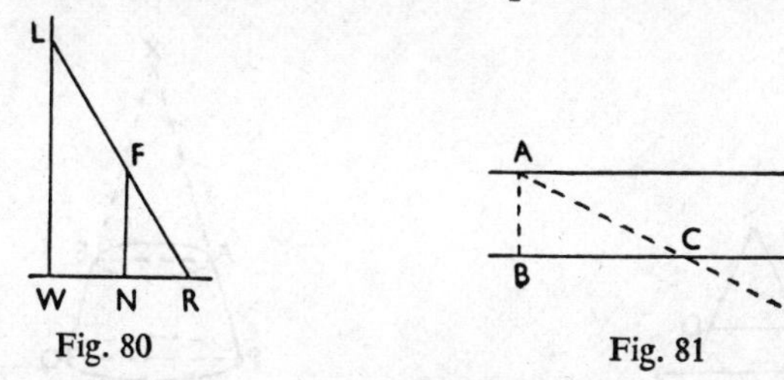

Fig. 80 Fig. 81

19 A man wishes to find the width of a river (see Fig. 81). There is a post at A on the far bank, and at C and D. He puts a post at B, directly opposite to A, and another at E, so that A, C, E are in line with each other, $\overline{\text{ED}}$ being at right angles to the bank. He measures BC, CD, DE and finds them to be 117 m, 26 m, 16 m respectively. Find the width of the river.

20 Find the height of a spectators' stand which throws a shadow 40 m long when a rugger post 9 m high throws a shadow 16 m long.

21 In Fig. 82, name the triangle which is similar to $\triangle$OAB, and

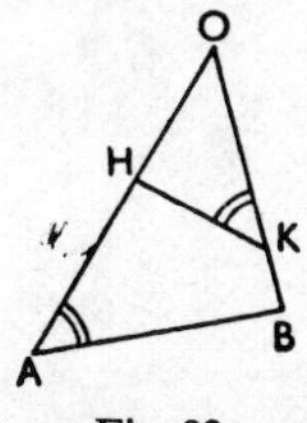

Fig. 82

give reasons. If OA = 10 cm, OB = 8 cm, OK = 6 cm, AB = 7 cm, calculate OH and HK.

22 In Fig. 82, if OH = 9 m, HA = 5 m, HK = 6 m, AB = 8 m, calculate OK and KB.

23 Find the height of a flagpole 45 metres away from an observer, if a 30-cm rule held 75 cm from the observer's eye just hides the flagpole from view.

24 Fig. 83 represents a pair of steps. The vertical height is 1·92 m when the feet are 1·14 m apart as shown. Find the length of the cord CD if it is 64 cm from the ground.

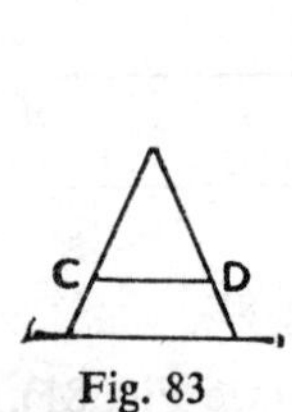

Fig. 83

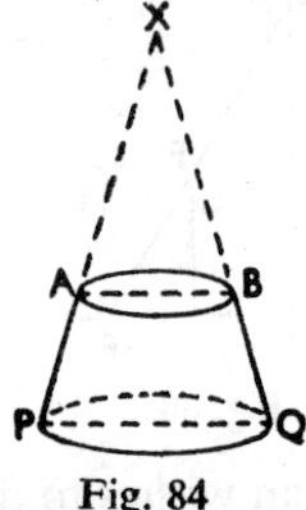

Fig. 84

25 A lampshade is in the form of part of the curved surface of a cone, as in Fig. 84. If AP = 22 cm, AB = 30 cm, PQ = 36 cm, find the distance AX.

26 In Fig. 85, $\overline{VN}$ and $\overline{WM}$ are altitudes of $\triangle$UVW. Which triangle is similar to $\triangle$UMW, and why? If UM = 3 m, MV = 4 m = MW, UW = 5 m, calculate UN and VN.

27 In Fig. 85, which triangle is similar to $\triangle$OMV? Give reasons. If OM = 15 cm, OV = 25 cm = MW, NW = 8 cm, calculate MV and ON.

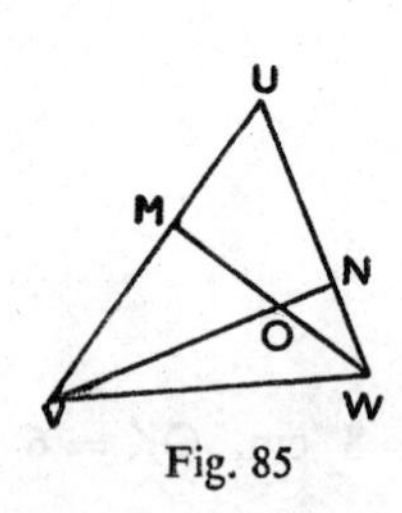

Fig. 85

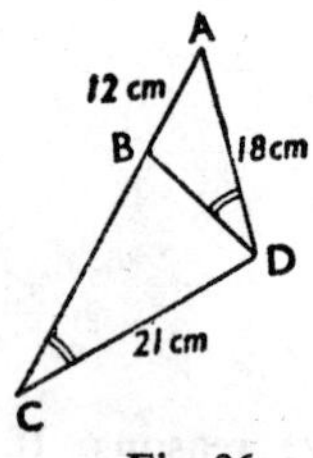

Fig. 86

28 In Fig. 86, name the triangle which is similar to $\triangle$ABD. Give reasons. Calculate BD and BC.

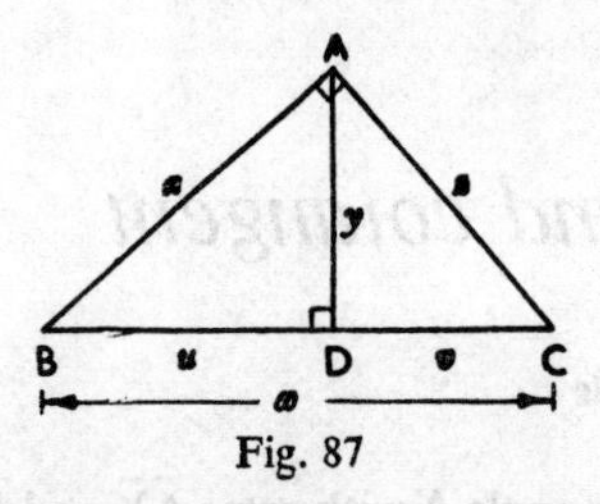

Fig. 87

29 In Fig. 87, $\triangle$ABC is right-angled at A, and $\overline{AD}$ is an altitude. Name two triangles that are similar to $\triangle$ABD, and give reasons. Hence prove that

$$y^2 = uv, \quad x^2 = uw, \quad xz = yw.$$

30 In Fig. 87, if AB = 40 cm, AC = 30 cm, BC = 50 cm, calculate AD, BD, CD.

Chapter 17

Tangent and cotangent

Tangent of an angle

Fig. 88 shows an angle A with arms $\overline{AX}$ and $\overline{AY}$. Any two points H and P are taken on $\overline{AX}$, and from them perpendiculars are drawn to $\overline{AY}$ meeting $\overline{AY}$ in K and M. Since $\overline{HK}$ and $\overline{PM}$ are

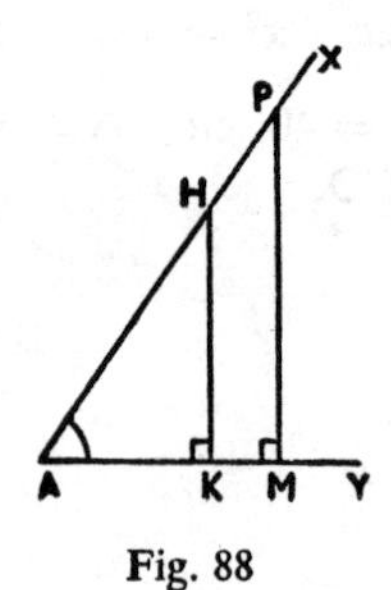

Fig. 88

parallel, the triangles AHK, APM are equiangular and therefore similar.

$$\therefore \frac{HK}{KA} = \frac{PM}{MA}.$$

Hence if any number of points were taken on $\overline{AX}$ and the perpendiculars drawn, the ratio of the length of the perpendicular to the length of the base-line would be the same for each.

Hence the value of the ratio $\frac{HK}{KA}$ is independent of the position of H on $\overline{AX}$, and depends only on the size of the angle A.

The ratio $\frac{HK}{KA}$ is called the **tangent** of the angle A, and this is usually abbreviated to tan A.

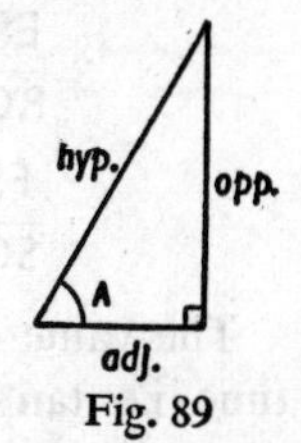

Fig. 89

The sides of the $\triangle AHK$ are:

$\overline{AH}$, the hypotenuse,
$\overline{HK}$, the side opposite to the angle A,
$\overline{KA}$, the side adjacent to the angle A.

These are abbreviated to **hyp., opp., adj.** respectively, so that

$$\tan A = \frac{\text{opp.}}{\text{adj.}}$$

In Fig. 90 angle AOB is 41°, and perpendiculars $\overline{CP}$, $\overline{DQ}$, $\overline{ER}$, $\overline{FS}$ are drawn so that OP = 4 cm, OQ = 7 cm, OR = 10 cm, OS = 11·5 cm.

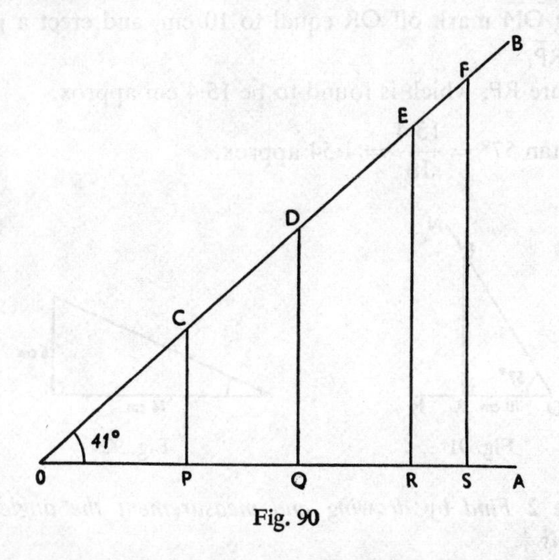

Fig. 90

By measurement CP, DQ, ER, FS are found to be approximately 3·5 cm, 6·1 cm, 8·7 cm, 10 cm respectively.

Hence $\frac{CP}{PO} = \frac{3{\cdot}5}{4} = 0{\cdot}875$

$\frac{DQ}{QO} = \frac{6{\cdot}1}{7} = 0{\cdot}87\ldots$

$$\frac{\text{ER}}{\text{RO}} = \frac{8{\cdot}7}{10} = 0{\cdot}87$$

$$\frac{\text{FS}}{\text{SO}} = \frac{10}{11{\cdot}5} = 0{\cdot}869\ldots$$

The value of the ratio is seen to be practically the same each time, i.e. tan 41° = 0·87 approximately.

It is clear that the working is simplified if the base-line (adj.) is of some convenient length such as 10 cm.

Example 1 *Find by drawing and measurement the value of tan 57°.*

Draw the angle MON of 57°.

Along $\overline{\text{OM}}$ mark off OR equal to 10 cm, and erect a perpendicular $\overline{\text{RP}}$.

Measure RP, which is found to be 15·4 cm approx.

Then $\tan 57° = \frac{15{\cdot}4}{10} = 1{\cdot}54$ approx.

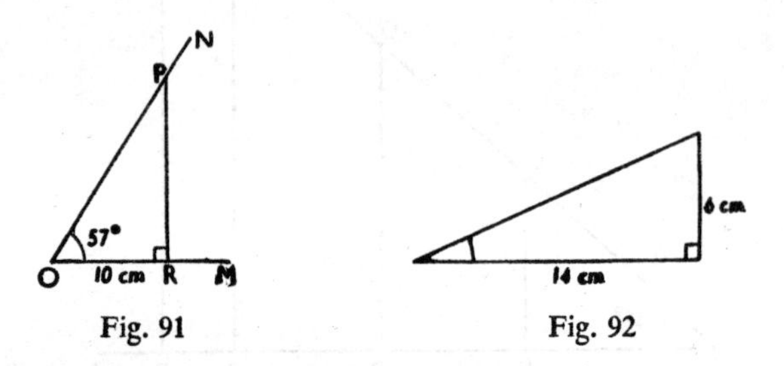

Fig. 91

Fig. 92

Example 2 *Find by drawing and measurement the angle whose tangent is* $\frac{3}{7}$.

The lengths of the opp. and adj. sides are to be in the ratio 3:7.

∴ the lengths could be 3 cm and 7 cm, or 6 cm and 14 cm, and so on.

The bigger the drawing, the better will be the chance of accurate measurement. Hence using the dimensions as in Fig. 92 the triangle is drawn and the angle is found to be 23° approx.

Exercise 17a

1 Copy Fig. 90 making $A\hat{O}B = 51°$, PQ = QR = RS = 1 cm, OP = 7 cm. Measure CP, DQ, ER, FS and calculate the values of tan 51° so obtained.

Find by drawing and measurement the tangents of the following angles:

2 42° **3** 62° **4** 38° **5** 71° **6** 45°
7 27° **8** 77°

Find by drawing and measurement the angles whose tangents are

9 $\frac{5}{9}$ **10** $\frac{2}{7}$ **11** $\frac{4}{3}$ **12** $\frac{8}{5}$ **13** $\frac{5}{7}$
14 $\frac{11}{4}$ **15** $\frac{5}{8}$

Use of tangent of an angle

The use of four-figure tables for finding the tangent of an angle will be explained later in this chapter, but for present use some extracts are given here:

Angle A	Tan A	Angle A	Tan A
25°	0·466 3	50°	1·191 8
30°	0·577 4	55°	1·428 1
35°	0·700 2	60°	1·732 1
40°	0·839 1	65°	2·144 5
45°	1·000 0	70°	2·747 5

Example 3 *The angle of elevation of the top of a building is 25° from a point 70 m away on the level ground. Find the height of the building.*

A is the point of observation and $\overline{HK}$ is the edge of the building.

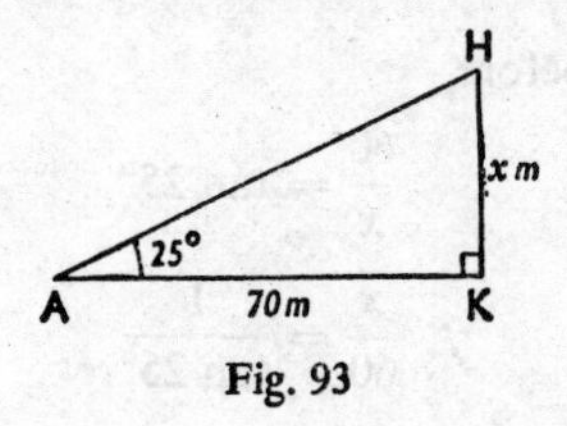

Fig. 93

Let HK be x m

Then $\dfrac{\text{HK}}{\text{KA}} = \tan 25°$

$$\therefore \frac{x}{70} = 0{\cdot}466\,3$$

$$\therefore x = 0{\cdot}466\,3 \times 70$$

$$= 32{\cdot}641$$

However, the answer cannot be given to this **degree of accuracy,** which involves 5 significant figures, because the working depends on a reading taken from four-figure tables. Even the **fourth significant figure as given in the tables is only approximate,** so that when 0·466 3 has been multiplied by 7 the best that can be hoped for is accuracy to 3 significant figures.

Hence the height of the building is 32·6 m to 3 sig. fig.

Cotangent of an angle

In Example 3, the length given was AK, the side *adjacent* to angle A, and the side to be found was HK, the side *opposite* to angle A.

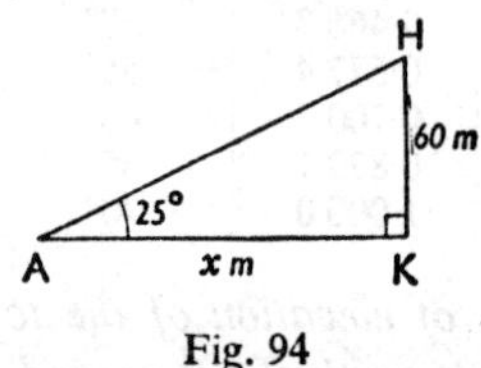

Fig. 94

Suppose HK is given as 60 m, and AK is to be found.
Let AK be x m.
Then, working as before,

$$\frac{60}{x} = \tan 25°$$

$$\therefore \frac{x}{60} = \frac{1}{\tan 25°}$$

$$\therefore\ x = \frac{60}{\tan 25^\circ}$$

$$= \frac{60}{0{\cdot}466\ 3}$$

This clearly involves some troublesome working, and a different method becomes desirable.

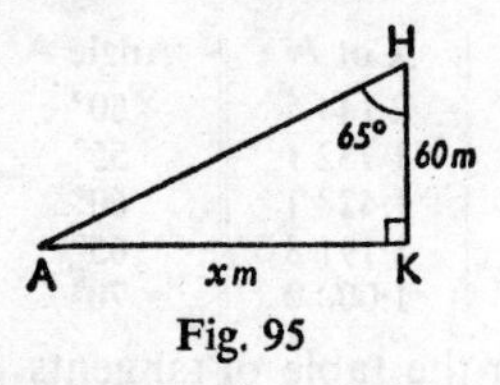

Fig. 95

In the right-angled $\triangle$AHK,

$$\hat{H} = 90^\circ - 25^\circ = 65^\circ$$

$$\therefore\ \frac{x}{60} = \tan 65^\circ$$

$$\therefore\ x = 60 \tan 65^\circ$$
$$= 60 \times 2{\cdot}144\ 5$$
$$= 128{\cdot}67$$
$$= 129 \text{ to 3 sig. fig.}$$
$$\therefore\ \text{AK} = 129 \text{ m}$$

The angle of 65° is the complement of 25°. To avoid finding the complement of the given angle and looking up its tangent, a name is given to the ratio which in this example is $\frac{\text{AK}}{\text{KH}}$. $\frac{\text{AK}}{\text{KH}}$ is said to be the **cotangent** of 25°, usually abbreviated to cot 25°.

The cotangent of an angle is the tangent of its complement.

In Fig. 96, $\quad \cot\theta = \frac{\text{adj.}}{\text{opp.}}$

Fig. 96

Notice also that

$$\cot\theta = \frac{\text{adj.}}{\text{opp.}} = \frac{1}{\frac{\text{opp.}}{\text{adj.}}} = \frac{1}{\tan\theta}$$

The following is an extract from the four-figure tables of cotangents.

Angle A	Cot A	Angle A	Cot A
25°	2·144 5	50°	0·839 1
30°	1·732 1	55°	0·700 2
35°	1·428 1	60°	0·577 4
40°	1·191 8	65°	0·466 3
45°	1·000 0	70°	0·364 0

Compare this with the table of tangents of angles on page 175, and notice for example that tan 25° = cot 65°.

Example 4 *From a peg in the horizontal ground the angle of elevation of the top of a pole 20 m high is 40°. Find the distance of the peg from the foot of the pole.*

P is the peg and $\overline{UV}$ is the pole.

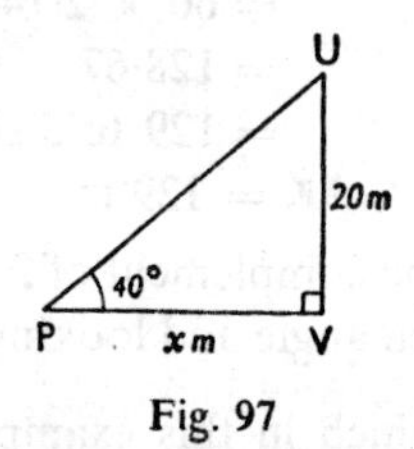

Fig. 97

Let PV be x m

$$\text{Then } \frac{PV}{VU} = \cot 40°$$

$$\therefore \frac{x}{20} = 1{\cdot}191\ 8$$

$$\therefore x = 1{\cdot}191\ 8 \times 20$$

$$= 23{\cdot}836$$

∴ the required distance is 23·8 m to 3 sig. fig.

Exercise 17b

Find the value of x in each of the triangles shown in Fig. 98. (Give answers correct to 3 sig. fig.)

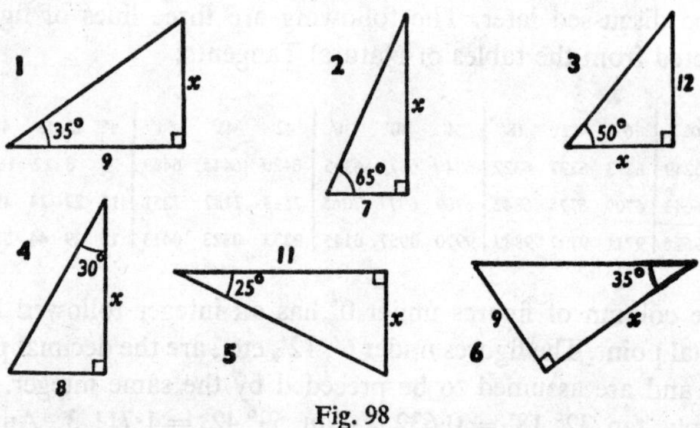

Fig. 98

7 An aerial mast throws a shadow 40 m long on the level ground when the altitude of the sun is 70°. Find the height of the mast.

8 Find the length of the shadow thrown on the level ground by an aerial mast 90 m high when the altitude of the sun is 40°.

9 The angle of elevation of the top of a cliff from a boat 80 m away from its foot is 25°. Find the height of the cliff.

10 From a window 15 metres up, the angle of depression of an object on the ground is 20°. Find the distance of the object from the base of the building.

Find the value of x in each of the triangles shown in Fig. 99. (Give answers correct to 3 sig. fig.)

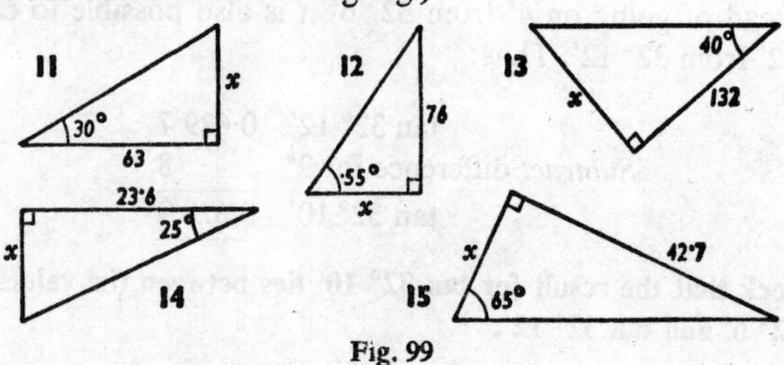

Fig. 99

Use of tables

The tables to be considered now are those of Natural Tangents, so called to distinguish them from Logarithmic Tangents which will be discussed later. The following are three lines of figures extracted from the tables of Natural Tangents:

	0′	6′	12′	18′	24′	30′	36′	42′	48′	54′	1′	2′	3′	4′	5′
32°	0·6249	6273	6297	6322	6346	6371	6395	6420	6445	6469	4	8	12	16	20
59°	1·6643	6709	6775	6842	6909	6977	7045	7113	7182	7251	11	23	34	45	56
63°	1·9626	9711	9797	9883	9970	0057	0145	0233	0323	0413	15	29	44	58	73

The column of figures under 0′ has an integer followed by a decimal point. The figures under 6′, 12′, etc., are the decimal parts only, and are assumed to be preceded by the same integer. For example tan 32° 18′ = 0·632 2, tan 59° 42′ = 1·711 3. An exception occurs when the integer changes in the course of a line. For example tan 63° 24′ = 1·997 0, but tan 63° 30′ = 2·005 7. This is fairly obvious as 1·997 0 would hardly be followed by 1·005 7, but most books of tables draw attention to the change of integer by the use of italics or heavier type.

The tables give the tangents of angles at intervals of 6′, and the difference columns on the right are used for intermediate values.

For example, to find tan 32° 10′:

tan 32° 6′	0·627 3
Add difference for 4′	1 6
tan 32° 10′	0·628 9

Instead of going on 4′ from 32° 6′ it is also possible to come back 2′ from 32° 12′. Thus:

tan 32° 12′	0·629 7
Subtract difference for 2′	8
tan 32° 10′	0·628 9

Check that the result for tan 32° 10′ lies between the values for tan 32° 6′ and tan 32° 12′.

The results by the two methods are the same in this case, but not always.

For example, to find tan 59° 47′:

tan 59° 42′	1·711 3	tan 59° 48′	1·718 2
Add diff. for 5′	5 6	Subtr. diff. for 1′	1 1
tan 59° 47′	1·716 9	tan 59° 47′	1·717 1

The second result, 1·717 1, is preferable because it uses a smaller difference. The figures in the difference columns are not exact, but are rather in the nature of a compromise; the larger the difference, the greater is the chance of error. It may be argued that in all work with four-figure tables the fourth figure must in any case be regarded as unreliable, so that there is no need to 'get out at the nearest milestone', but it is just as well to be as accurate as the tables will allow.

When the angle concerned is approaching 90° (say between 80° and 90°) its tangent increases rapidly, and the ordinary difference columns would be completely unreliable. For example the difference for 1′ at 83° 6′ would not be the same as the difference for 1′ at 83° 48′.

To find tan 83° 8′,

tan 83° 12′ = 8·386
tan 83° 6′ = 8·264
Difference for 6′ = 0·122
∴ average difference for 1′ = 0·020 3 . . .
∴ difference for 2′ = 0·041
∴ tan 83° 8′ = 8·305.

To find the angle whose tan is 0·458 4, look in the tables for the nearest number to this. It is 0·457 8, which is tan 24° 36′, and the difference is that 458 4 is 6 *more* than 457 8. The nearest to 6 in the difference columns is 7, which makes a difference of 2′. Therefore the required angle is 2′ *more* than 24° 36′, i.e. 24° 38′.

Check that 24° 38′ lies between 24° 36′ and 24° 42′, since 458 4 lies between 457 8 and 459 9.

The explanation just given for the tables of Natural Tangents may be adapted to apply to the tables of Natural Cotangents. The important difference is that the **larger** the angle, the **smaller** is the cotangent. Hence the numbers obtained from the difference columns must be **subtracted** where, in the tables for tangents, they would be added, and vice versa.

Exercise 17c

From the tables write down the tangents of

1 32° 48′	**2** 32° 49′	**3** 32° 47′	**4** 56° 14′
5 63° 49′	**6** 18° 3′	**7** 27° 43′	**8** 48° 19′
9 67° 11′	**10** 36° 32′	**11** 49° 28′	**12** 78° 54′
13 68° 13′	**14** 39° 16′	**15** 11° 59′	**16** 71° 56′
17 80° 21′	**18** 55° 46′	**19** 85° 37′	**20** 81° 44′

From the tables write down the angles whose tangents are

21 0·881 6	**22** 0·882 6	**23** 0·880 6	**24** 0·809 3
25 1·175 0	**26** 1·547 0	**27** 0·052 8	**28** 2·197 3
29 2·026 5	**30** 1·600 0	**31** 0·264 0	**32** 0·958 0
33 13	**34** 3·220 8	**35** 3·065 0	**36** 1·949 6
37 7·332	**38** 0·032 5	**39** 3·343 4	**40** 10·42

Find by drawing and measurement the tangents of the following angles. Check by writing down the values as found from the tables.

41 13° **42** 64° **43** 35° **44** 55° **45** 74°

Find by drawing and measurement the angles whose tangents are the following fractions. Check by expressing each fraction as a decimal and finding the angle from the tables.

46 $\frac{5}{3}$ **47** $\frac{5}{8}$ **48** $\frac{10}{7}$ **49** $\frac{7}{9}$ **50** $\frac{17}{9}$

From the tables write down the cotangents of

51 65° 12′	**52** 65° 14′	**53** 65° 10′	**54** 78° 27′
55 33° 49′	**56** 26° 26′	**57** 26° 46′	**58** 47° 3′
59 84° 19′	**60** 30° 56′	**61** 11° 32′	**62** 5° 45′
63 88° 35′	**64** 18° 44′	**65** 6° 14′	

From the tables write down the angles whose cotangents are

66 1·204 5	**67** 1·206 7	**68** 1·202 3	**69** 0·621 6
70 0·310 5	**71** 1·762 7	**72** 3·035 7	**73** 0·501 8
74 0·159 5	**75** 1·246 9	**76** 7·879	**77** 0·585 2
78 0·027 5	**79** 3·986 0	**80** 13·43	

Capital letters have usually been used for points, and small letters for lengths of lines. When a single letter is required to name an angle, Greek letters are often used. Among the commonest for this purpose are θ (theta) and ϕ (phi); also α (alpha), β (beta), γ (gamma) and δ (delta).

Example 5 *A spire is* $83\frac{1}{2}$ *metres high. Find the angle of elevation of its top from a point* 120 *metres away on the level ground.*

Let the angle of elevation be θ.

$$\text{Then } \tan\theta = \frac{83\cdot5}{120}$$

$$= \frac{8\cdot35}{12}$$

$$= 0\cdot695\,8 \text{ to 4 dec. pl.}$$

$$\therefore \theta = 34° \ 50'$$

$\therefore$ the angle of elevation is **34° 50′**

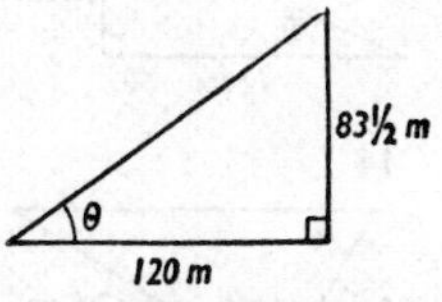

Fig. 100

It is recommended that the examples in Exercise 17*d should be supplemented by others based on the pupils' own practical measurements taken in the class-room, the school buildings, grounds and playing-fields.*

Exercise 17d

Find the lengths marked x in the triangles shown in Fig. 101, all lengths being in metres.

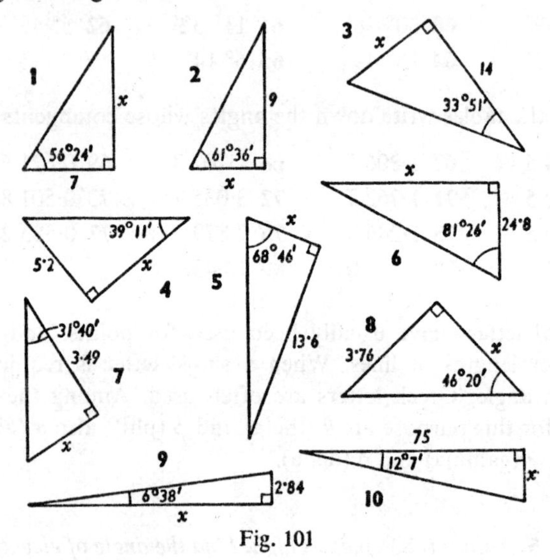

Fig. 101

Find the angles marked θ in the following triangles:

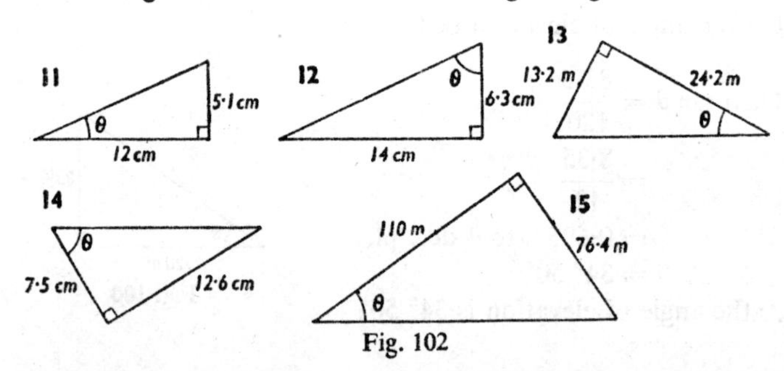

Fig. 102

16 A cone is $8\frac{1}{2}$ cm high and its vertical angle is 62°. Find the diameter of its base.

17 An isosceles triangle has a vertical angle of 116°, and its base is 8 cm long. Find its altitude.

18 A boy is flying a kite which is 59·5 m vertically above a point which is 42 m away from the boy horizontally. Assuming that the string is straight, find the angle which it makes with the ground.

19 Find the angle of elevation of the top of a flagstaff 31·9 m high, from a point 55 m away on the level ground.

20 A man wishes to find the width of a river. He places a peg at a point P on one bank directly opposite a post Q on the opposite bank. From P he walks 200 metres along the bank to a point R, and finds that $P\hat{R}Q = 23\frac{1}{2}°$. Find the width of the river.

21 The roof of a garage 3·6 metres wide rises symmetrically to a ridge. If each face slopes at 48° to the horizontal, find the height of the ridge above the tops of the walls.

22 An aerial mast is supported by four cables attached to its top and to points on the ground which are each 54 metres from the foot of the mast. If each cable (assumed to be straight) makes an angle of 20° with the mast, find the height of the mast.

23 A trestle has legs of equal length, and their feet are 1·2 metres apart. If the height of the trestle is 1·65 metres find the angle between the legs.

24 The gradient of a road is 1 in $4\frac{1}{2}$ (horizontally). Find the angle which the road makes with the horizontal.

25 From a point on the level ground 40 m away, the angle of elevation of the top of a tree is $32\frac{1}{2}°$. Calculate the height of the tree in metres, correct to 3 sig. fig.

26 In no. 25, if the tree had been 21·7 m high, what would have been the angle of elevation?

27 A rectangle has sides of lengths 14·3 m and 3·9 m. Find the angle between a diagonal and a longer side.

28 From a certain point at the same level as the foot of a tower 40 metres high the angle of elevation of its top is 51° 25′. Find the distance of the point of observation from the foot of the tower.

29 From a point 100 metres from the foot of a cliff the angle of elevation of the top is 38° 42′. Find the height of the cliff.

30 A man travels 12 km north and then 5 km east. What is then his bearing from his starting point?

31 A man travels 4 km south-east and then 13 km north-east. What is then his bearing from his starting point?

32 Two points A and B lie on a line running due east and west. A point C lies 1 600 metres south of the line $\overline{AB}$. The bearing of C from A is S 21° E, and from B it is S 34° W. Find the distance AB.

33 A point P lies due north of Q, and X lies west of the line $\overline{PQ}$. The bearing of X from P is S 56° W, and from Q it is N 34° W. If PX = 1 650 metres, calculate QX.

34 The plan in Fig. 103 represents a rugger player at P kicking at the goal $\overline{AB}$. If AB = 5·64 m, BM = 6·36 m, PM = 12 m, find to the nearest degree the angle θ which the goal subtends at P.

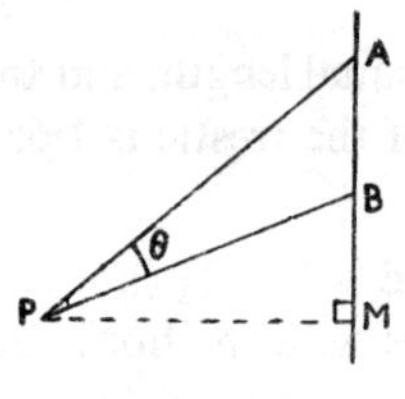

Fig. 103

35 Find the altitude of the sun when a church spire 91 metres high casts a shadow 65 metres long.

36 A lighthouse is 57 metres high and from its top the angles of depression of two buoys due south of it are 29° and 25°. Find the distance between the buoys.

37 From a boat 200 metres from a vertical cliff the angle of elevation of the top of the cliff is $18\frac{1}{2}°$. At the edge of the cliff is a flagpole, and the angle of elevation of its top from the boat is 21°. Find the height of the flagpole.

38 From an observation point A the bearings of two points B and C are N 33° W and N 57° E respectively. If AB = 1 800 metres, and C is due east of B, find the distance AC.

39 A flagpole is 31 metres high, and the angle of elevation of the top of it from a point A on the ground is 37°. From another point B, in line with A and the foot of the pole, the angle of elevation is 52°. Find the distance AB.

40 From a point P the bearings of two points X and Y are N 62° W and N 28° E respectively, and the bearing of Y from X is N 66° E. If PX = 130 metres, calculate PY (nearest metre).

41 A spire is 56 m high. P is a point on the ground due east of the spire, and Q is due west of the spire. The angles of elevation of the top of the spire from P and Q are 58° and 35°. Find the distance PQ.

42 A ship is 310 m from a cliff. From the deck of the ship the angle of elevation of the top of the cliff is 23°, and from the top of a mast it is 18°. Find the height of the mast.

43 From the top and bottom of a cliff the angles of depression and elevation of the top of a ship's mast are 31° and 20° respectively. If the height of the mast is 20 metres, find the height of the cliff.

44 From the top of a lighthouse two buoys can be seen, in line with the lighthouse, and their angles of depression are 29° 30′ and 36° 15′. If the nearer buoy is 80 metres from the lighthouse, find the height of the lighthouse and the distance between the buoys.

45 A, B, C are three points in a straight line on the level ground. A helicopter is hovering immediately above C, and its angles of elevation from A and B are 37° and 73°. If BC = 170 metres, find the distance AB.

Chapter 18

Square root and cube root

6^2 means 6 multiplied by 6, which is 36. In words, the square of 6 is 36, and conversely the square root of 36 is 6, which is written $\sqrt{36} = 6$.

Square root by factors

Example 1 *Evaluate* $\sqrt{11\,025}$.

$$
\begin{array}{r}
3\overline{)11\,025} \\
3\overline{)3\,675} \\
5\overline{)1\,225} \\
5\overline{)245} \\
7\overline{)49} \\
7
\end{array}
$$

$\therefore \quad 11\,025 = 3^2 \times 5^2 \times 7^2$

$\therefore \quad \sqrt{11\,025} = 3 \times 5 \times 7 = 105.$

Example 2 *Evaluate* $\sqrt{5\,184}$.

$$
\begin{array}{r}
4\overline{)5\,184} \\
4\overline{)1\,296} \\
2\overline{)324} \\
2\overline{)162} \\
9\overline{)81} \\
9
\end{array}
$$

$\therefore \quad 5\,184 = 4^2 \times 2^2 \times 9^2$

$\therefore \quad \sqrt{5\,184} = 4 \times 2 \times 9 = 72.$

In Example 2, 5 184 has not been expressed strictly in prime factors, as we know that 81 is 9^2, and there is nothing to be gained by writing it as 3^4. Similarly, in Example 3, the factors can be written down immediately.

Example 3 *Evaluate* $\sqrt{6\,400}$.

$$6\,400 = 64 \times 100$$
$$= 8^2 \times 10^2$$
$$\therefore \sqrt{6\,400} = 8 \times 10 = 80.$$

Exercise 18a

Find by factors the square root of

1 225	**2** 196	**3** 324	**4** 441	**5** 484
6 576	**7** 784	**8** 1 600	**9** 1 936	**10** 1 764
11 2 025	**12** 2 304	**13** 2 916	**14** 3 600	**15** 3 025
16 3 969	**17** 3 136	**18** 4 356	**19** 5 625	**20** 6 561
21 5 184	**22** 7 056	**23** 8 100	**24** 9 216	**25** 7 744
26 11 025	**27** 14 400	**28** 11 664	**29** 122 500	**30** 12 544

If a number is a perfect square it is possible to express it in factors with even indices. If it is required to find the smallest number which will make a given number into a perfect square, all that is necessary is to satisfy this requirement.

Example 4 *Find the smallest number by which* 540 *must be multiplied in order to make the product a perfect square.*

```
2)540
 2)270
 3)135
  3)45
  3)15
     5
```

$\therefore 540 = 2^2 \times 3^3 \times 5.$

(Here the index of 2 is even, but of 5 and of 3 it is odd; therefore one more 5 and one more 3 are needed in order to make all the indices even, and hence the number into a perfect square.)

$\therefore$ the number required is $5 \times 3 = 15$.

Exercise 18b

Find the smallest numbers by which the following must be multiplied in order to form exact squares.

1 162	**2** 147	**3** 54	**4** 405	**5** 99
6 240	**7** 252	**8** 432	**9** 1 536	**10** 504
11 490	**12** 832	**13** 1 377	**14** 1 029	**15** 4 464

Square root of a fraction

Example 5 $\sqrt{\frac{4}{25}} = \sqrt{\frac{2^2}{5^2}} = \frac{2}{5}.$

Example 6 $\sqrt{5\frac{4}{9}} = \sqrt{\frac{49}{9}} = \sqrt{\frac{7^2}{3^2}} = \frac{7}{3} = 2\frac{1}{3}.$

Exercise 18c

1 Explain why $\sqrt{1\frac{9}{16}}$ is not $1\frac{3}{4}$. What is it?
Does $(a + b)^2 = a^2 + b^2$?

Find the square root of

2 $\frac{9}{25}$	**3** $\frac{16}{49}$	**4** $2\frac{1}{4}$	**5** $1\frac{7}{9}$	**6** $\frac{48}{75}$
7 $3\frac{1}{16}$	**8** $1\frac{25}{144}$	**9** $4\frac{21}{25}$	**10** $\frac{72}{98}$	**11** $4\frac{25}{36}$
12 $7\frac{21}{25}$	**13** $14\frac{1}{16}$	**14** $28\frac{4}{9}$	**15** $17\frac{39}{108}$	**16** $14\frac{70}{121}$

General method

Since $\sqrt{1} = 1$ and $\sqrt{100} = 10$, the square root of any number lying between 1 and 100 must lie between 1 and 10, i.e. the square root of a number of one or two digits is a number of one digit.

Similarly, since $\sqrt{100} = 10$ and $\sqrt{10\,000} = 100$, the square root of any number lying between 100 and 10 000 must lie between 10 and 100, i.e. the square root of a number with 3 or 4 digits is a number with 2 digits.

Similarly, the square root of a number with 5 or 6 digits is a number with 3 digits, and so on.

Hence, if the digits of a given number are marked off in groups of two, starting from the right, the number of groups will show the number of digits that there will be in the square root. (The last group, on the left, may consist of only one digit.)

e.g. $\sqrt{86|49}$ has 2 digits,

$\sqrt{7|39|84}$ „ 3 „ ,

$\sqrt{86|67|61}$ „ 3 „ , etc.

The general method for finding square roots is as follows:

Example 7 *Evaluate* $\sqrt{405\,769}$.

```
            6  3  7
       6 | 40|57|69
         | 36
         |
     123 |  4 57
         |  3 69
         |
    1267 |    88 69
         |    88 69
         |    .....
```

$\therefore \sqrt{405\,769} = 637.$

The successive steps are:

1 Mark off the digits from the right in groups of two.
2 Find the largest number whose square is not greater than 40, i.e. 6.
3 Put 6 in the working above the 40, and also as divisor.
4 Multiply 6 by 6, subtract the resulting 36 from 40, leaving 4, and bring down the next group, i.e. 57.
5 Double the 6 on the top line and put down 12 as the first part of the next divisor, which will be one hundred and twenty-something. $124 \times 4 = 496$, which is greater than 457, but $123 \times 3 = 369$.

6 Put 3 in the top line above the 57 and also after the 12 in the divisor, to complete the 123. Multiply 123 by 3, subtract, and bring down the next group, i.e. 69.
7 Double the 63 on the top line and put down 126 as the first part of the next divisor, which will be 126*. The * is found by division to be 7.
8 Put 7 on the top line and also to complete 1267 as divisor. Multiply 1267 by 7 and subtract. There is no remainder.

Therefore 637 is the required square root of 405 769.

This result can be checked by squaring 637, when the result will be found to be 405 769, which justifies the method.

In Example 8 notice that 0 is obtained in the divisor and in the answer when 61×1 would be too great.

Example 8 *Evaluate* $\sqrt{95\,481}$.

```
       3  0  9
    3 |9|54|81
      |9
  609 |  54 81
      |  54 81
      |  ....
```

$\therefore \sqrt{95\,481} = 609.$

Notice also the final 0 in Example 9 below.

Example 9 *Evaluate* $\sqrt{280\,900}$.

```
        5  3  0
     5 |28|09|00
       |25
   103 | 3 09
       | 3 09
  1060 |     00
```

$\therefore \sqrt{280\,900} = 530.$

Exercise 18d

Find the square root of

1 529	**2** 1 369	**3** 7 569	**4** 5 625
5 8 464	**6** 15 129	**7** 17 161	**8** 53 361
9 20 736	**10** 43 681	**11** 139 876	**12** 49 284
13 165 649	**14** 1 440 000	**15** 156 816	**16** 1 742 400
17 519 841	**18** 956 484	**19** 1 234 321	**20** 7 306 209
21 996 004	**22** 54 272 689	**23** 17 640 000	**24** 4 036 081
25 146 894 400	**26** 54 007 801	**27** 36 663 025	**28** 75 724 804
29 489 427 129	**30** 100 440 484		

If decimals occur, the digits should be marked off in groups of two, to the left and to the right, starting from the decimal point: e.g. $5_{|}76_{|}92\cdot36_{|}47$, $86_{|}47\cdot92_{|}56_{|}30$, etc.

If the number of which the square root is being found is not an exact square, the root may be found to any number of decimal places by bringing down groups of 00, once the actual figures given have come to an end, as in Example 11 below.

Example 10 *Evaluate* $\sqrt{2\,746\cdot808\,1}$.

	5 2·4 1
5	$27_{|}46\cdot80_{|}81$
	25
102	2 46
	2 04
1044	42 80
	41 76
10481	1 04 81
	1 04 81
	. . . . .

$\therefore \sqrt{2\,746\cdot808\,1} = 52\cdot41.$

Example 11 *Evaluate* $\sqrt{0{\cdot}005\ 898}$, *correct to* 3 *decimal places.*

```
             0· 0  7  6  7
        7 | 0·00|58|98|00
          |       49
      146 |        9 98
          |        8 76
     1527 |        1 22 00
          |        1 06 89
```

$\therefore \sqrt{0{\cdot}005\ 898} = 0{\cdot}077$, correct to 3 dec. pl.

Exercise 18e

Find the square root of

1 14·44	**2** 50·41	**3** 0·016 9
4 0·000 081	**5** 334·89	**6** 3·348 9
7 0·000 324	**8** 90·630 4	**9** 0·324 9
10 151·782 4	**11** 0·001 156	**12** 626·500 9
13 39·866 596	**14** 1 429·066 809	**15** 62 520·001 6

Find, correct to 2 decimal places, the square root of

16 24·094 2	**17** 327·65	**18** 0·000 8
19 0·009	**20** 80·986	**21** 15·78
22 0·097 63	**23** 25·217	**24** 0·003 642
25 12·315 7	**26** 458·246	**27** 0·000 047
28 30·008 1	**29** 19·9	**30** 8 512·807 6
31 15	**32** 0·466 3	**33** 723·518 61
34 0·635 776	**35** 9·020 101	

Find, correct to 3 decimal places, the square root of

36 0·003 596	**37** 1·4	**38** 0·14
39 0·000 659 2	**40** 6·342	**41** 0·634 2
42 0·000 058	**43** 81·105 3	**44** 141·72
45 914·322 5		

Find, correct to 4 significant figures, the square root of

46 8 649·5 **47** 70·307 8 **48** 9 379 080 456
49 0·004 956 3 **50** 0·000 156

Cube root by factors

$5^3 = 5 \times 5 \times 5 = 125$; i.e. the cube of 5 is 125, and the cube root of 125 is 5, written $\sqrt[3]{125} = 5$.
Similarly $\sqrt[3]{8} = 2$, $\sqrt[3]{216} = 6$, etc.

Example 12 *Evaluate* $\sqrt[3]{21\,952}$.

$$21\,952 = 2^6 \times 7^3$$
$$\therefore \sqrt[3]{21\,952} = 2^2 \times 7 = 28.$$

Example 13 *Find the smallest number by which* 40 500 *must be multiplied in order to make a perfect cube.*

$40\,500 = 2^2 \times 3^4 \times 5^3$.
2^2 must be brought up to 2^3, by multiplying by 2
3^4 „ „ „ „ „ 3^6, „ „ „ $3^2 = 9$
5^3 is a perfect cube already.
$\therefore$ the required multiplier is $2 \times 9 = 18$.

Example 14 $\sqrt[3]{2\frac{93}{125}} = \sqrt[3]{\frac{343}{125}} = \sqrt[3]{\frac{7^3}{5^3}} = \frac{7}{5} = 1\frac{2}{5}$.

Cube root by inspection

If a number is known to be a perfect cube, its cube root can often be written down without having to work it out fully.

Example 15 *Evaluate* $\sqrt[3]{314\,432}$, *given that the root is a whole number.*

The last digit is 2, therefore the last digit of the cube root must be 8 (since 8 is the only number of which the cube ends in 2).

There are 6 digits in 314 432, therefore there are 2 digits in its cube root (since $1^3 = 1$, $10^3 = 1\,000$, $100^3 = 1\,000\,000$, etc.: 314 432 lies between 1 000 and 1 000 000, so that its cube root must lie between 10 and 100).

Therefore the required root must be one of the numbers 18, 28, 38, . . . 98.

But $60^3 = 216\,000$, which is smaller than 314 432,
and $70^3 = 343\,000$, which is larger than 314 432.

Therefore the required root is 68.

Exercise 18f

Find, by factors or by inspection, the cube root of

1 729	**2** 1 728	**3** 2 197	**4** 4 096
5 9 261	**6** 42 875	**7** 74 088	**8** 15 625
9 24 389	**10** 50 653	**11** 1 601 613	**12** $\frac{8}{125}$
13 $42\frac{7}{8}$	**14** $11\frac{25}{64}$	**15** $151\frac{19}{27}$	**16** 91 125
17 148 877	**18** 250 047	**19** 85 184	**20** $421\frac{7}{8}$
21 830 584	**22** $791\frac{29}{64}$	**23** 421 875	**24** $1\,213\frac{17}{27}$
25 592 704	**26** 19·683	**27** 5·832	**28** 46·656
29 110·592	**30** 132·651		

Find the smallest numbers by which the following must be multiplied in order to make exact cubes:

31 72	**32** 200	**33** 108	**34** 189	**35** 432
36 297	**37** 3 000	**38** 225	**39** 1 125	**40** 1 764

Chapter 19

Factors

Exercise 19a Revision

Factorise

1 $2x + 6y - 4z$

2 $15a - 10b + 25c$

3 $2mu - mv - 3m$

4 $a^2 + 5a + 6$

5 $b^2 - 7b + 12$

6 $3 - 6x - 9y + 3z$

7 $c^2 + 6c + 5$

8 $d^2 + 10d + 21$

9 $12a + 20b - 8c - 28d$

10 $3ax - bx + 2cx - dx$

11 $3ac - 2bc + c^2 - 5cd$

12 $e^2 + 7e + 10$

13 $f^2 - 7f + 10$

14 $g^2 + 3g - 10$

15 $h^2 - 3h - 10$

16 $6m^3 + 4m^2 - 4m$

17 $3a^2b - 4ab^2 + 2abc$

18 $m^5 - m^4 + m^3 + m^2$

19 $h^2 + h - 6$

20 $k^2 - k - 6$

21 $3u^2v - u^2v^2 - 4uv^2$

22 $3p^2r - 3pr^2 + 6p^2r^2$

23 $3x^5 - x^4 + 4x^3 - 3x^2$

24 $x^2 - 8x + 7$

25 $y^2 - 6y - 7$

26 $3l^2mn + lm^2n - 2lmn^2 + 3lmn$

27 $u^2 - u - 12$

28 $v^2 + 11v - 12$

29 $w^2 + 8w + 12$

30 $3d^4 + 3d^3 - 3d^2n - 6d^2$

31 $x^2 + 2x - 15$

32 $y^2 - 3y - 18$

33 $z^2 - 2z - 63$

34 $h^2 + 2h - 48$

35 $k^2 + 13k - 48$

36 $l^2 + 14l + 48$

37 $5u^2v^2 - 15uv^3 + 10uv^2$

38 $a^2 + 15a + 36$

39 $b^2 + 13b + 36$

40 $c^2 + 16c - 36$

41 $d^2 - 35d - 36$

42 $e^2 + 37e + 36$

43 $3a^2x^2y - 6ax^2y^2 + 3axy^3$

44 $m^2 + m - 90$

45 $n^2 - 17n + 72$

46 $p^2 - 17p + 70$

47 $q^2 + 7q - 60$

48 $12c^2u^3v^3 - 15cu^5v^2$

49 $b^2 - 8b - 33$

50 $a^2 + a - 132$

Example 1 *Factorise* $2x(5a + 2) - 3y(5a + 2)$.

This expression is of the same kind as $2xm - 3ym$, in which m is common to both terms, so that

$$2xm - 3ym = m(2x - 3y).$$

In the given expression,

$$2x(5a + 2) = 2x \text{ times } (5a + 2)$$

$$\text{and} \quad 3y(5a + 2) = 3y \text{ times } (5a + 2).$$

Hence the products $2x(5a + 2)$ and $3y(5a + 2)$ have the factor $(5a + 2)$ in common.

$$\therefore 2x(5a + 2) - 3y(5a + 2) = (5a + 2)(2x - 3y).$$

Example 2 *Factorise* $2d^3 + d^2(3d - 1)$.

$2d^3$ and $d^2(3d - 1)$ have the factor d^2 in common.

$$\begin{aligned} \therefore 2d^3 + d^2(3d - 1) &= d^2[2d + (3d - 1)] \\ &= d^2[2d + 3d - 1] \\ &= d^2(5d - 1). \end{aligned}$$

Example 3 *Factorise* $(a + m)(2a - 5m) - (a + m)^2$.

The two parts of the expression have the factor $(a + m)$ in common.

$$\begin{aligned} \therefore (a + m)(2a - 5m) - (a + m)^2 & \\ &= (a + m)\{(2a - 5m) - (a + m)\} \\ &= (a + m)\{2a - 5m - a - m\} \\ &= (a + m)(a - 6m). \end{aligned}$$

Example 4 *By factorising, simplify* $79 \times 37 + 21 \times 37$.

$$\begin{aligned} 79 \times 37 + 21 \times 37 &= 37(79 + 21) \\ &= 37 \times 100 \\ &= 3\,700. \end{aligned}$$

Exercise 19b

Factorise

1 $3m + m(u - v)$

2 $2a - a(3x + y)$

3 $x(3 - a) + bx$

4 $(4m - 3n)p - 5p$

5 $a(m + 1) + b(m + 1)$

6 $a(n + 2) - b(n + 2)$

7 $ax - x(b - 4c)$

8 $5x(a - b) - 2y(a - b)$

9 $3h(5u - v) + 2k(5u - v)$

10 $m(u - v) + m^2$

11 $d(3h + k) - 4d^2$

12 $5a^2 + a(b - c)$

13 $4x^2 - x(3y + 2z)$

14 $3d^3 - d^2(e - 4f)$

15 $a(3u - v) + a(u + 2v)$

16 $(5x - y)a - (3x + 5y)a$

17 $3(3u + 2v) - a(3u + 2v)$

18 $(4a - b)3x + (4a - b)2y$

19 $h(2a - 7b) - 3k(2a - 7b)$

20 $m(3m - 2) + 2m^2$

21 $a^2(5a - 3b) - 3a^3$

22 $5x^2 - x(x + 4)$

23 $2d(3m - 4n) - 3e(3m - 4n)$

24 $(a + 2b)(x - y) - 3(x - y)$

25 $p(2m + n) + (q - r)(2m + n)$

26 $(h + k)(r + s) + (h + k)(r - 2s)$

27 $(3x - y)(u + v) + (x + 2y)(u + v)$

28 $(b - c)(3d + e) - (b - c)(d - 2e)$

29 $(a + 2b)^2 - 3(a + 2b)$

30 $(3m - 2n)^2 + 5p(3m - 2n)$

31 $(2u - 3v)(3m - 4n) - (2u - 3v)(m + 2n)$

32 $a(x + 2y) + (x + 2y)^2$

33 $3u(2x + y) - (2x + y)^2$

34 $(f - g)4e - (f - g)^2$

35 $(a - 3b)(2u - v) + (a - 3b)(u + 7v)$

36 $(5m + 2n)(6a + b) - (5m + 2n)(a - 4b)$

37 $(x + 3y)(m - n) + x + 3y$

38 $(2a - 3b)(c + d) - 2a + 3b$

39 $7u - 2v + (7u - 2v)^2$

40 $(2u - 7v)^2 + 7v - 2u$

By factorising, simplify

41 $34 \times 48 + 34 \times 52$

42 $61 \times 87 - 61 \times 85$

43 $128 \times 27 - 28 \times 27$

44 $693 \times 7 + 693 \times 3$

45 $\frac{8}{13} \times 125 + \frac{5}{13} \times 125$

46 $\frac{22}{7} \times 10 + \frac{22}{7} \times 4$

47 $121 \times 67 + 79 \times 67$

48 $67 \times 23 - 67 \times 13$

49 $\frac{22}{7} \times 3\frac{1}{4} - \frac{22}{7} \times 2\frac{1}{4}$

50 $53 \times 49 - 53 \times 39$

51 $\frac{3}{4} \times 133 - \frac{3}{4} \times 93$

52 $35 \times 29 + 35 \times 11$

53 $27 \times 354 + 27 \times 646$

54 $\frac{22}{7} \times 1\frac{1}{4} + \frac{22}{7} \times 2\frac{3}{4}$

55 $762 \times 87 - 562 \times 87$

The preceding method can be extended for factorising certain expressions after the terms have been suitably grouped together.

Example 5 *Factorise* $cx - 2dy + cy - 2dx$.

The terms cx and cy have c in common
" " $2dx$ " $2dy$ " $2d$ " "

Grouping in pairs in this way,

$$\begin{aligned} cx - 2dy + cy - 2dx &= cx + cy - 2dx - 2dy \\ &= c(x + y) - 2d(x + y) \\ &= (x + y)(c - 2d). \end{aligned}$$

Notice that it would not have been possible to factorise in this way if $(x + y)$ had not occurred twice in the second line of the working. Since there must be such a repeated bracket if there are to be any factors of the given expression, it is usually simplest to write this bracket down again *immediately*, as soon as it has occurred once. This is illustrated in Example 6.

Example 6 $2am^2 - 2amn - 3bmy + 3bny$

$$= 2am(m - n) \ldots (m - n).$$

The terms $-3bmy + 3bny$ are obtained by multiplying $(m - n)$ by $-3by$.

$$\begin{aligned} \therefore 2am^2 - 2amn - 3bmy + 3bny &= 2am(m - n) - 3by(m - n) \\ &= (m - n)(2am - 3by). \end{aligned}$$

If the first attempt at 'pairing off' the terms does not produce a satisfactory result, they should be regrouped,

e.g. $cd - de + d^2 - ce = d(c - e) \ldots (\quad)$

d^2 and ce have nothing in common.

$$\begin{aligned} \text{Regrouping,} \quad cd + d^2 - ce - de &= d(c + d) - e(c + d) \\ &= (c + d)(d - e) \\ \text{or} \quad cd - ce + d^2 - de &= c(d - e) + d(d - e) \\ &= (d - e)(c + d). \end{aligned}$$

It will be seen that the four terms can be grouped in pairs in three ways. If there are factors, two of these ways will give the required result and one will not.

If all the terms contain a common factor, it should be taken out *first* as in Example 7. *This should always be the rule, in factorising any type of expression.*

Example 7 $2sru + 6tru - 4srv - 12trv$

$$\begin{aligned} &= 2r[su + 3tu - 2sv - 6tv] \\ &= 2r[u(s + 3t) - 2v(s + 3t)] \\ &= 2r(s + 3t)(u - 2v). \end{aligned}$$

Exercise 19c

Factorise the following where possible. If there are no factors, say so.

1 $mx + nx + my + ny$ **2** $ax - ay + bx - by$

3 $hu + hv - ku - kv$ **4** $au - bu - av + bv$

5 $am + 2bm + 2bn + an$ **6** $cx - dx + 2cy - 2dy$

7 $2ce + 4df - de - 2cf$ **8** $ab + 4xy - 2bx - 2ay$

9 $am - an + m - n$ **10** $u + v - dv + du$

11 $a^3 + a^2 + a + 1$ **12** $2mh - 3nh - 3nk + 2mk$

13 $3sx - 5ty + 5tx - 3sy$ **14** $abx^2 + bxy + axy + y^2$

15 $hk - 2km + 3hn - 6mn$ **16** $mn - 6xy - 3nx + 3my$

17 $2gk - 3gl + 2hk - 3hl$ **18** $2fh + 4gh - fk - 2gk$

19 $3eg - 4eh - 6fg + 2fh$ **20** $hl + 2kl - 3hm - 6km$

21 $3ce + 4df - 2de - 6cf$ **22** $xy - 2ny - 6n^2 + 3nx$

23 $ab + 2b^2 - 2ac - 4bc$ **24** $cd - ce + d^2 + de$

25 $8uv - 2v^2 + 12uw - 3vw$ **26** $mn - 6pn + 3pm - 2n^2$

27 $3xy - 2ay - 3ax + 2y^2$ **28** $3ab - 3bu + 3av - 3uv$

29 $ab + 6mn - 2bm - 3bn$ **30** $8ce + 12de - 2cf - 3df$

31 $nuv - muv + mnu^2 - v^2$ **32** $5mx - 5nx - 5my + 5ny$

33 $3ab + 3cd - bc - 9ad$ **34** $6ab - 15bc - 10cd + 4ad$

35 $2amu + 2anu - 2amv - 2anv$

36 $abm^2 + 2bm - 3am - 6$

37 $4ax + 2bx + 8ay + 4by$ **38** $21mn - xy - 3nx + 7my$

39 $3ax - 2a - 6bx + 2b$ **40** $2am - 3m^2 + 4an - 6mn$

41 $10uv + 5u - 2v - 1$ **42** $a^2m + am^2 - mn - an$

43 $2x^2y - xy^2 + 2ax - ay$ **44** $1 + 3x - 5a - 15ax$

45 $2d^2x + 4dxy^2 - 3dy - 6xy^2$

Harder trinomials

Simple factors of the type $a^2 - 2a - 15 = (a - 5)(a + 3)$ have already been discussed in Chapter 8. There are, however, more difficult cases of this kind of expression, e.g. when the coefficient of a^2 is not unity, or when more than one letter is involved. The following examples illustrate some of these variations. In practice these factors should always be found by inspection, and the results checked by multiplication.

Example 8 *Factorise* $2a^2 + 7a - 15$.

The first term is $2a^2$, which is the product of $2a$ and a.

Hence $\quad 2a^2 + 7a - 15 = (2a\ldots)(a\ldots)$.

The last term is -15, which is the product of 15 and 1, or 5 and 3, with *unlike* signs.

This produces as possible factors:

$$(2a - 15)(a + 1) \qquad (2a - 5)(a + 3)$$
$$(2a + 15)(a - 1) \qquad (2a + 5)(a - 3)$$
$$(2a - 1)(a + 15) \qquad (2a - 3)(a + 5)$$
$$(2a + 1)(a - 15) \qquad (2a + 3)(a - 5)$$

These all give $2a^2$ as the first term, and -15 as the last term. The only one which gives $+7a$ as the middle term is

$$(2a - 3)(a + 5).$$

Hence $\qquad 2a^2 + 7a - 15 = (2a - 3)(a + 5).$

With practice it will be found unnecessary to write down all the possibilities.

Example 9 *Factorise* $2a^2 + 7ab - 15b^2$.

This example is closely related to Example 8 as the coefficients are the same, and it is easily seen that

$$2a^2 + 7ab - 15b^2 = (2a - 3b)(a + 5b).$$

Example 10 *Factorise* $2a^2b^2 + 7ab - 15$.

This example has the same coefficients as those in Example 8.

$$2a^2b^2 + 7ab - 15 = (2ab - 3)(ab + 5).$$

Example 11 *Factorise* $7 - 22x + 3x^2$.

The first term is the product of 7 and 1.

The last term is the product of $3x$ and x, with *like* signs. This gives the possibilities:

$$(7 + 3x)(1 + x) \qquad (7 - 3x)(1 - x)$$
$$(7 + x)(1 + 3x) \qquad (7 - x)(1 - 3x)$$

Two of these need not have been written down and may be discarded at once, as they could not possibly produce a minus sign for the middle term of the given expression.

Considering the other two,

$$(7 - 3x)(1 - x) = 7 - 10x + 3x^2$$
$$\text{and} \quad (7 - x)(1 - 3x) = 7 - 22x + 3x^2.$$

Hence the required factors are $(7 - x)(1 - 3x)$.

Example 12 *Factorise* $7 - 20x - 3x^2$.

For producing the 7 and the $-3x^2$ the possibilities are

$$(7 - 3x)(1 + x) \qquad (7 + 3x)(1 - x)$$
$$(7 - x)(1 + 3x) \qquad (7 + x)(1 - 3x)$$

and of these, the last one gives $-20x$ for the middle term.

Hence $\quad 7 - 20x - 3x^2 = (7 + x)(1 - 3x)$.

Example 13 *Factorise* $6a^2 - 15a + 9$.

$$\begin{aligned} 6a^2 - 15a + 9 &= 3(2a^2 - 5a + 3) \\ &= 3(2a - 3)(a - 1). \end{aligned}$$

Notice that the factor 3, which is common to all the terms, is taken out first.

Exercise 19d

Factorise

1 $a^2 + 8a + 15$
2 $b^2 - 7b + 10$
3 $c^2 + 4c - 21$
4 $d^2 - 5d - 14$
5 $e^2 + 2e - 8$
6 $w^2 + 5w + 6$
7 $x^2 + 5x - 6$
8 $y^2 - 5y + 6$
9 $z^2 - 5z - 6$
10 $2d^2 + 3d + 1$
11 $2e^2 - 3e + 1$
12 $2f^2 - f - 1$
13 $a^2 + 7a + 10$
14 $a^2 + 7ab + 10b^2$
15 $a^2b^2 + 7ab + 10$
16 $x^2 - 2xy - 15y^2$
17 $m^2 + 10m - 24$
18 $n^2 - 10n - 24$
19 $u^2 - 10u + 24$
20 $v^2 - 11v + 24$
21 $m^2 + 4m - 21$
22 $m^2 + 4mn - 21n^2$
23 $m^2n^2 + 4mn - 21$
24 $3a^2 - 4a + 1$
25 $3b^2 + b - 2$
26 $2x^2 + 5x - 3$
27 $2y^2 - 5y - 3$
28 $2z^2 - 5z + 3$
29 $1 + 3m + 2m^2$
30 $15 - 2n - n^2$
31 $1 - 2u - 8u^2$
32 $u^2 + 2uv - 8v^2$

33 $a^2 + 5ab - 36b^2$

34 $a^2 + 9ab - 36b^2$

35 $a^2 + 16ab - 36b^2$

36 $2b^2 - 10b + 12$

37 $c^2 - 4c - 77$

38 $77 - 4d - d^2$

39 $3e^2 + 3e - 18$

40 $3f^2 + 2f - 1$

41 $a^2 + 4ab + 3b^2$

42 $1 + 4x + 3x^2$

43 $2g^2 - 5g + 2$

44 $2h^2 + 5h + 3$

45 $3h^2 + 7hk + 2k^2$

46 $12x^2 - 13x - 14$

47 $a^2 + 25a - 150$

48 $b^2 + 25b + 150$

49 $3c^2 - 11c + 6$

50 $3d^2 + 7d - 6$

51 $5e^2 - 9e - 2$

52 $7f^2 + 10f + 3$

53 $35 - 12a + a^2$

54 $35 - 2b - b^2$

55 $35 + 36c + c^2$

56 $35 + 30d - 5d^2$

57 $3a^2 + 5ab + 2b^2$

58 $3m^2 + 5mn - 2n^2$

59 $3u^2 + 7uv + 2v^2$

60 $6n^2 - 7n - 3$

61 $7v^2 + 22v + 3$

62 $4y^2 - 12y + 5$

63 $2h^2 - 15h - 27$

64 $2k^2 - 15k + 27$

65 $x^2y^2 - xy - 30$

66 $2u^2v^2 + uv - 6$

67 $5 - 7a - 6a^2$

68 $10p^2 - 41p - 45$

69 $10q^2 - 43q + 45$

70 $8a^2 - 17a + 9$

71 $8b^2 - 18b + 9$

72 $8c^2 - 21c - 9$

73 $8d^2 - 22d + 9$

74 $8e^2 - 49e + 75$

75 $8f^2 - 50f + 75$

76 $12a^2b^2 + 11ab - 5$

77 $12m^2 - 4mn - 5n^2$

78 $12t^2 - 11t + 2$

79 $12x^2y^2 - 11xy - 1$

80 $24p^2 + pq - 23q^2$

Squares

$$(a + b)^2 = (a + b)(a + b) = a^2 + ab + ab + b^2$$

$$\therefore (a + b)^2 = a^2 + 2ab + b^2.$$

$$(a - b)^2 = (a - b)(a - b) = a^2 - ab - ab + b^2$$

$$\therefore (a - b)^2 = a^2 - 2ab + b^2.$$

These two results, which should be memorised, may be expressed in words, as follows:

The square of the *sum* of two quantities is equal to the sum of their squares *plus* twice their product.

The square of the *difference* of two quantities is equal to the sum of their squares *minus* twice their product.

Thus the expansion of $(3m + 7n)^2$ is equal to the square of $3m$ + twice the product of $3m$ and $7n$ + the square of $7n$.

$$\text{i.e.} \quad (3m + 7n)^2 = (3m)^2 + 2 \times 3m \times 7n + (7n)^2$$
$$= 9m^2 + 42mn + 49n^2.$$

Similarly

$$(4u - 5v)^2 = (4u)^2 - 2 \times 4u \times 5v + (5v)^2$$
$$= 16u^2 - 40uv + 25v^2.$$

Notice that the squared terms are *always positive.*

These results may sometimes conveniently be used to shorten the work of squaring numbers,

$$\text{e.g.} \quad 104^2 = (100 + 4)^2 = 100^2 + 2 \times 100 \times 4 + 4^2$$
$$= 10\,000 + 800 + 16 = 10\,816$$
$$\text{and} \quad 97^2 = (100 - 3)^2 = 100^2 - 2 \times 100 \times 3 + 3^2$$
$$= 10\,000 - 600 + 9 = 9\,409.$$

Fig. 104 shows a geometrical representation of the statement that $(a + b)^2 = a^2 + 2ab + b^2$.

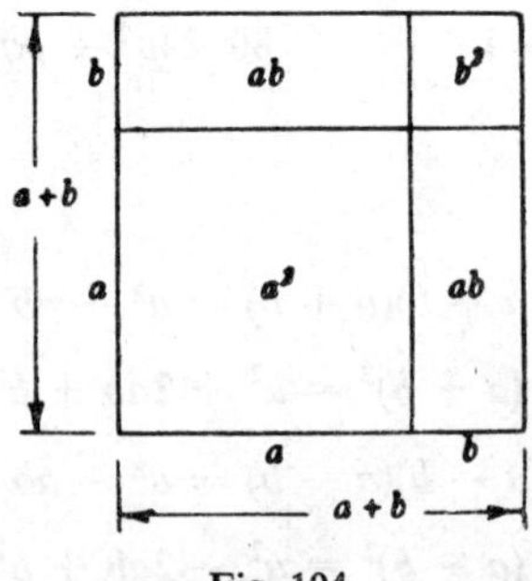

Fig. 104

Further explanation should be unnecessary, and as an exercise the corresponding figure should be drawn to show that

$$(a - b)^2 = a^2 - 2ab + b^2.$$

Example 14 *Factorise* $h^2 + 12h + 36$.

$$h^2 + 12h + 36 = (h + 6)(h + 6)$$
$$= (h + 6)^2.$$

This result might have been written down at once, without the intermediate step, by noticing that h^2 is the square of h, 36 is the square of 6, and $12h$ is twice the product of h and 6.

Example 15 *Factorise* $25h^2 - 30hk + 9k^2$.

$25h^2$ is the square of $5h$
$9k^2$ is the square of $3k$
$30hk$ is twice the product of $5h$ and $3k$

$$\therefore 25h^2 - 30hk + 9k^2 = (5h - 3k)^2.$$

Exercise 19e

Write down the expansions of

1 $(a + 4)^2$ **2** $(b - 3)^2$ **3** $(5 + c)^2$
4 $(2 - d)^2$ **5** $(1 + m)^2$ **6** $(2n + 1)^2$
7 $(3x + y)^2$ **8** $(u - 2v)^2$ **9** $(5h - k)^2$
10 $(p + 4q)^2$ **11** $(2a + 3d)^2$ **12** $(3b - 5c)^2$
13 $(7e - 2f)^2$ **14** $(10x - 1)^2$ **15** $(1 + 12y)^2$
16 $(3a + 7b)^2$ **17** $(c - 8d)^2$ **18** $(9u + v)^2$
19 $(5m - 7n)^2$ **20** $(6x - 5y)^2$ **21** $(ab + 2)^2$
22 $(cd - 3)^2$ **23** $(4 + ef)^2$ **24** $(5 - gh)^2$
25 $(2a - mn)^2$ **26** $(ab + 3m)^2$ **27** $(a + \frac{1}{3})^2$
28 $(b - \frac{1}{2})^2$ **29** $(c - \frac{2}{3})^2$ **30** $(d + 1\frac{1}{2})^2$
31 $\left(\frac{m}{3} + \frac{n}{2}\right)^2$ **32** $(2ab - 3m)^2$ **33** $(5n + 2xy)^2$
34 $(a^2 + 1)^2$ **35** $(b^2 - 3)^2$ **36** $(4 - c^2)^2$

37 $(7 + d^2)^2$ **38** $(\frac{1}{2}a + 2b)^2$ **39** $(4u - \frac{1}{2}v)^2$
40 $(3x^2 - 2y^2)^2$

Find the squares of the following numbers:

41 101 **42** 99 **43** 103 **44** 98 **45** 72
46 83 **47** 79 **48** 1 005 **49** 996 **50** 995

Write the following as the square of a bracket:

51 $a^2 + 10a + 25$ **52** $b^2 - 8b + 16$ **53** $c^2 + 6c + 9$
54 $m^2 - 6m + 9$ **55** $n^2 - 12n + 36$ **56** $x^2 + 4x + 4$
57 $y^2 + 2y + 1$ **58** $4u^2 - 12u + 9$ **59** $1 - 2a + a^2$
60 $4 - 4b + b^2$

Factorise

61 $x^2 + 6xy + 9y^2$ **62** $d^2 + 10d + 9$
63 $m^2 - 4mn + 4n^2$ **64** $a^2 + a + \frac{1}{4}$
65 $4v^2 - 13v + 9$ **66** $9a^2 - 24ab + 16b^2$
67 $9a^2 - 25ab + 16b^2$ **68** $b^2 - \frac{2}{3}b + \frac{1}{9}$
69 $x^2 + 20x + 100$ **70** $121 - 22y + y^2$
71 $9m^2 - 12mn + 4n^2$ **72** $4x^2 + 37x + 9$
73 $4y^2 + 20y + 9$ **74** $4z^2 + 15z + 9$
75 $16m^2 - 41mn + 25n^2$ **76** $16u^2 - 40uv + 25v^2$
77 $4a^2 + 28am + 49m^2$ **78** $25n^2 - 30nv + 9v^2$
79 $16h^2 - 56hk + 49k^2$ **80** $9x^2 - 145xy + 16y^2$

Difference of two squares

$$(a + b)(a - b) = a^2 + ab - ab - b^2 = a^2 - b^2$$

Hence $\boldsymbol{a^2 - b^2 = (a + b)(a - b)}$,

or in words, **the difference of the squares of two quantities is equal to the product of their sum and their difference.**

Example 16 *Factorise* $25m^2 - 9n^2$.

$$\begin{aligned} 25m^2 - 9n^2 &= (5m)^2 - (3n)^2 \\ &= (5m + 3n)(5m - 3n). \end{aligned}$$

Example 17 *Factorise* $\frac{16}{49}x^6y^2 - 1$.

$$\begin{aligned}\tfrac{16}{49}x^6y^2 - 1 &= (\tfrac{4}{7}x^3y)^2 - 1^2 \\ &= (\tfrac{4}{7}x^3y + 1)(\tfrac{4}{7}x^3y - 1).\end{aligned}$$

Example 18 *Find the value of* $173^2 - 127^2$.

$$\begin{aligned}173^2 - 127^2 &= (173 + 127)(173 - 127) \\ &= 300 \times 46 \\ &= 13\,800.\end{aligned}$$

Example 19 *Factorise* $5a^2 - 45$.

The two terms have the factor 5 in common, and this must be taken out first.

$$\begin{aligned}5a^2 - 45 &= 5(a^2 - 9) \\ &= 5(a^2 - 3^2) \\ &= 5(a + 3)(a - 3).\end{aligned}$$

Example 20 *Factorise* $a^4 - b^4$.

$$\begin{aligned}a^4 - b^4 &= (a^2)^2 - (b^2)^2 \\ &= (a^2 + b^2)(a^2 - b^2) \\ &= (a^2 + b^2)(a + b)(a - b)\end{aligned}$$

Notice that $a^2 + b^2$ has no factors.

Fig. 105 illustrates geometrically that

$$(a + b)(a - b) = a^2 - b^2.$$

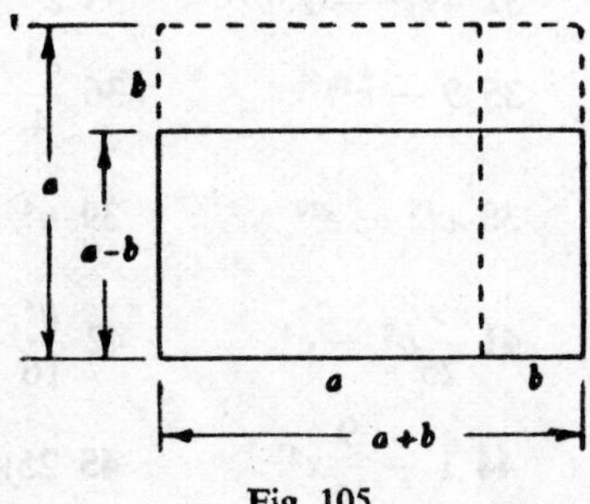

Fig. 105

The proof may be supplied as an exercise.

Fig. 106 suggests a model that could be cut out of cardboard to show that $a^2 - b^2 = (a + b)(a - b)$.

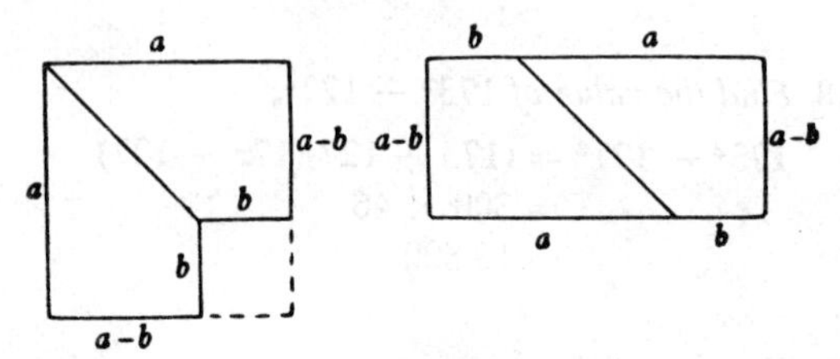

Fig. 106

Exercise 19f

Factorise

1 $x^2 - 1$	**2** $1 - y^2$	**3** $4m^2 - n^2$
4 $u^2 - 16v^2$	**5** $1 - a^2b^2$	**6** $9 - 4c^2$
7 $4d^2 - 9e^2$	**8** $3 - 3f^2$	**9** $4g^2 - 4$
10 $4h^2 - 25$	**11** $25k^2 - 16$	**12** $49m^2 - n^2$
13 $p^2q^2 - 9$	**14** $25 - u^2v^2$	**15** $81 - w^2$
16 $100x^2 - 1$	**17** $16y^2 - 4z^2$	**18** $16h^2 - k^2$
19 $4c^2 - 49d^2$	**20** $e^2 - 4f^2$	**21** $36a^2 - 49b^2$
22 $5c^2 - 45d^2$	**23** $x^2y^2 - z^2$	**24** $100 - w^2$
25 $49a^2 - b^2c^2$	**26** $9 - d^2e^2f^2$	**27** $a^2b^2 - 121$
28 $x^4 - 16$	**29** $81m^2 - 100u^2v^2$	**30** $m^6 - u^2$
31 $9x^2 - 25a^2$	**32** $49y^2 - 25b^2$	**33** $z^{10} - 100$
34 $25a^2 - 49b^4$	**35** $9 - c^{10}$	**36** $\frac{a^2}{4} - \frac{d^2}{9}$
37 $1 - \frac{4}{9}b^2$	**38** $c^{14} - e^{10}$	**39** $u^4 - 81v^4$
40 $9a^{16} - 1$	**41** $\frac{9}{25}b^2 - c^4$	**42** $\frac{u^2}{16} - \frac{v^2}{25}$
43 $x^{10} - y^8$	**44** $1 - \frac{9}{16}x^4$	**45** $25y^6 - 81$

46 $16c^2e^2 - 2\frac{1}{4}$ **47** $81 - 16a^4$ **48** $36x^2y^2 - 9z^2$

49 $121h^2 - 144k^4$ **50** $100a^2d^4 - 121e^6$

Find the value of

51 $96^2 - 4^2$ **52** $118^2 - 18^2$ **53** $73^2 - 71^2$

54 $98^2 - 4$ **55** $103^2 - 9$ **56** $52^2 - 48^2$

57 $63^2 - 37^2$ **58** $57^2 - 55^2$ **59** $1\,004^2 - 16$

60 $997^2 - 9$

Example 21 *Factorise* $25m^2 - 4(u - v)^2$.

$25m^2$ is the square of $5m$

$4(u - v)^2$ is the square of $2(u - v)$

$$\therefore 25m^2 - 4(u - v)^2 = [5m + 2(u - v)][5m - 2(u - v)]$$
$$= (5m + 2u - 2v)(5m - 2u + 2v).$$

Example 22 *Factorise* $16(2a + b)^2 - 9(a - 3b)^2$.

$16(2a + b)^2$ is the square of $4(2a + b)$

$9(a - 3b)^2$ is the square of $3(a - 3b)$

$$\therefore 16(2a + b)^2 - 9(a - 3b)^2$$
$$= [4(2a + b) + 3(a - 3b)][4(2a + b) - 3(a - 3b)]$$
$$= (8a + 4b + 3a - 9b)(8a + 4b - 3a + 9b)$$
$$= (11a - 5b)(5a + 13b).$$

Example 23 *Factorise* $(6x - 5y)^2 - 16x^2$.

$$(6x - 5y)^2 - 16x^2 = [(6x - 5y) + 4x][(6x - 5y) - 4x]$$
$$= (6x - 5y + 4x)(6x - 5y - 4x)$$
$$= (10x - 5y)(2x - 5y)$$
$$= 5(2x - y)(2x - 5y).$$

Notice the last step, in which the bracket $(10x - 5y)$ is factorised into $5(2x - y)$.

Exercise 19g

Factorise

1 $(u+v)^2-w^2$
2 $(x-y)^2-z^2$
3 $(a-3b)^2-c^2$
4 $(2d+e)^2-f^2$
5 $a^2-(m+n)^2$
6 $b^2-(u-v)^2$
7 $c^2-(3x-y)^2$
8 $d^2-(h+2k)^2$
9 $(3m+n)^2-4x^2$
10 $9d^2-(x-4y)^2$
11 $(m+n)^2-(u+v)^2$
12 $(a-b)^2-(c-d)^2$
13 $16(x+y)^2-9m^2$
14 $4u^2-25(h+k)^2$
15 $9a^2-(b-c)^2$
16 $16(a+3b)^2-25c^2$
17 $(3p+2q)^2-(r-3s)^2$
18 $(2a-b)^2-(c+3d)^2$
19 $9(x-2y)^2-25z^2$
20 $49a^2-9(3m-2n)^2$
21 $(x+y+z)^2-4$
22 $(3a-b)^2-a^2$
23 $16x^2-(2x+y)^2$
24 $25m^2-(3m-5n)^2$
25 $(4a-5d)^2-9a^2$
26 $(3u-v)^2-4v^2$
27 $(5a+3d)^2-16a^2$
28 $36m^2-(5m+2n)^2$
29 $64h^2-(3h-4k)^2$
30 $(7p+2q)^2-49p^2$
31 $(5d-2e)^2-9e^2$
32 $49m^2-(4m-3n)^2$
33 $25u^2-(5u+3v)^2$
34 $(7a+b)^2-9(2a+b)^2$
35 $9(p+q)^2-4(p-q)^2$
36 $49(m-n)^2-16(m+n)^2$
37 $20(2x-3y)^2-5(2x+y)^2$
38 $4(2a-d)^2-25(a+3d)^2$
39 $36(h+3k)^2-25(2h-3k)^2$
40 $9(c+3e)^2-4(3c-2e)^2$
41 $4(2a+b)^2-25(3a+2b)^2$
42 $81(m+2n)^2-49(m-2n)^2$
43 $(3a+5c-e)^2-(a-2c+3e)^2$
44 $4(3x-2y-z)^2-(4x+y-3z)^2$
45 $(5p-q+2r)^2-9(p+q-2r)^2$

Exercise 19h

Miscellaneous factors

Factorise

1 $(p-x)^2-4y^2$
2 $k^2-4(m+n)^2$
3 $2uv-3xy+3uy-2vx$
4 $2xy-6ab-3ay+4bx$
5 $44a^2-a-24$
6 $48u^2+2uv-63v^2$
7 $(2a-3)^2-81$
8 $3(5b-2)^2-12$
9 $45-4m-m^2$
10 $4+n-3n^2$
11 a^4-2a^2-15
12 $14-9d^2+d^4$
13 u^4-13u^2+36
14 $\frac{m^4}{81}-\frac{n^4}{16}$
15 $3m^2-48$
16 $3n^4-48$
17 $4a(2u+3v)-6b(2u+3v)$
18 $(3a+u)^2-2u(3a+u)$
19 $h^2+15h+54$
20 $k^2+15k-54$
21 $x^2+(a+b)x+ab$
22 $y^2+(m-n)y-mn$
23 $x^2+x-\frac{3}{4}$
24 u^3v-uv^3
25 $x^2-(c+d)x+cd$
26 $y^2-(p-q)y-pq$
27 $\frac{m^2}{u^2}-\frac{n^2}{v^2}$
28 $y^2+y+\frac{1}{4}$
29 d^4+8d^2+15
30 e^4-7e^2+12
31 $16x^2y^2-24xy-16$
32 $3(d-e)^2-3$
33 a^3-a^2+a-1
34 $b^4-b^3-b^2+b$
35 $8ab-6bc+15cd-20ad$
36 $a+9x^2-3x-3ax$
37 $u^2+u-240$
38 $-v^2-3v+28$
39 $5a^2-20$
40 $27d^3-48d$
41 $-x^2+9x-20$
42 $24-2y-y^2$
43 $m^4-2m^2n^2-24n^4$
44 $u^4+2u^2v^2-24v^4$
45 $5(x-1)^2-5$
46 $2a(m-2n)-b(2n-m)$
47 $(2u-v)(2a+b)+(v-2u)(a+2b)$
48 $(2u-3v)^2-(u-6v)^2$
49 $(m-n)^2-3m+3n$
50 $u^2-2u-2v-v^2$

Chapter 20

Sine and cosine

In Fig. 107 the $\triangle$s HAK, PAM, XAY are similar.

$$\therefore \frac{KH}{AH} = \frac{MP}{AP} = \frac{YX}{AX}.$$

The value of this ratio depends only upon the size of the angle A, and it is called the **sine of** $\hat{A}$ (abbreviated to sin A).

Also $\frac{AK}{AH} = \frac{AM}{AP} = \frac{AY}{AX}$ = the **cosine of** $\hat{A}$ (abbreviated to cos A).

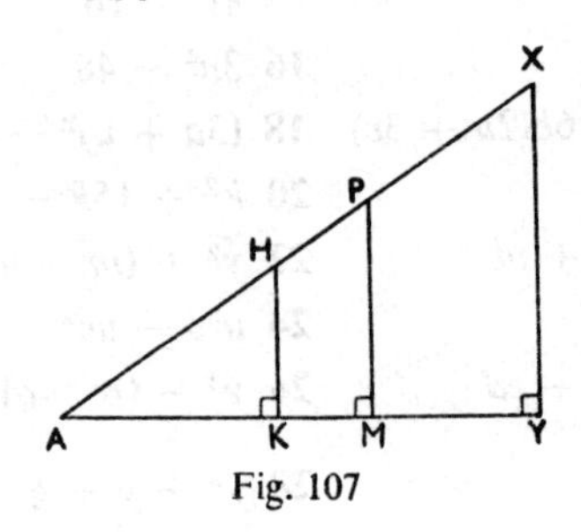

Fig. 107

In general, in any right-angled triangle, in which the sides are the hypotenuse, that opposite θ and that adjacent to θ, as shown in Fig. 108,

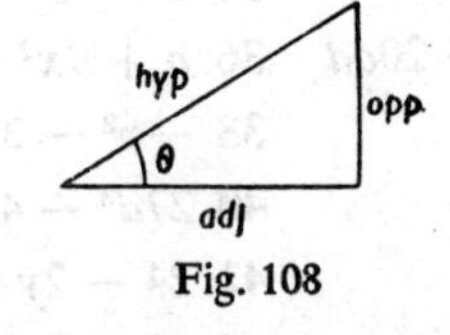

Fig. 108

$$\sin \theta = \frac{\text{opp.}}{\text{hyp.}} \qquad \cos \theta = \frac{\text{adj.}}{\text{hyp.}}$$

Example 1 *Find, by drawing, approximate values for sin* 25°, *cos* 25°, *sin* 48°, *cos* 48°, *sin* 70°, *cos* 70°.

Using graph-paper ruled in 2-cm squares, draw a quadrant of a circle of radius 10 cm.

Draw $\hat{AOB} = 25°$

Then $\sin 25° = \frac{BA}{OA} = \frac{4{\cdot}23}{10} = 0{\cdot}423$

$$\cos 25° = \frac{OB}{OA} = \frac{9{\cdot}06}{10} = 0{\cdot}906$$

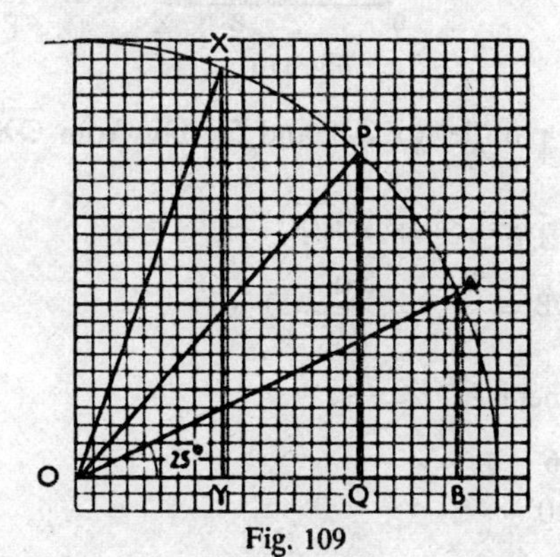

Fig. 109

Similarly $\sin 48° = \frac{QP}{OP} = \frac{7{\cdot}43}{10} = 0{\cdot}743$

$$\cos 48° = \frac{OQ}{OP} = \frac{6{\cdot}70}{10} = 0{\cdot}670$$

$$\sin 70° = \frac{YX}{OX} = \frac{9{\cdot}40}{10} = 0{\cdot}940$$

$$\cos 70° = \frac{OY}{OX} = \frac{3{\cdot}42}{10} = 0{\cdot}342$$

Example 2 *Find by drawing* (i) *the angle whose sine is* 0·56, (ii) *the angle whose cosine is* 0·60.

(i) $0{\cdot}56 = \frac{5{\cdot}6}{10}$.

Draw an arc of a circle centre O and radius 10 cm.

Mark perpendicular radii $\overline{OX}$ and $\overline{OY}$.

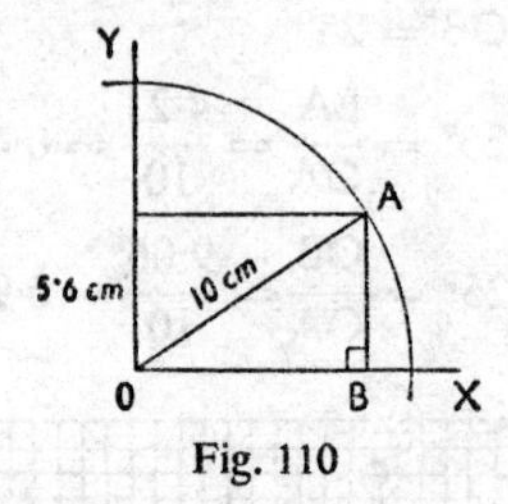

Fig. 110

Draw a line parallel to $\overline{OX}$ and 5·6 cm from $\overline{OX}$ to cut the arc at A.

Draw $\overline{AB}$ perpendicular to $\overline{OX}$.

Then $\sin A\hat{O}B = \frac{BA}{OA} = \frac{5{\cdot}6}{10} = 0{\cdot}56$.

By measurement $A\hat{O}B \simeq 34°$.

(ii) $0{\cdot}60 = \frac{6}{10}$.

Taking $\overline{OX}$ and $\overline{OY}$ as before, draw an arc of radius 10 cm.

Mark off OB = 6 cm along $\overline{OX}$.

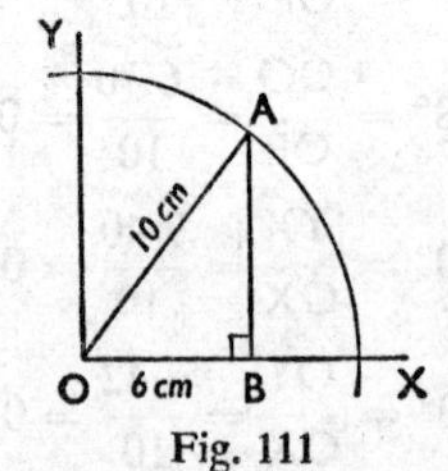

Fig. 111

Construct $\overline{BA}$ perpendicular to $\overline{OX}$, to cut the arc at A.

Then $\cos A\hat{O}B = \frac{6}{10} = 0{\cdot}60$.

By measurement $A\hat{O}B \simeq 53°$.

Exercise 20a

1 Find by drawing and measurement, as in Example 1, approximate values for sin 20°, cos 20; sin 40°, cos 40°; sin 65°, cos 65°.

2 Find by drawing and measurement, as in Example 2, approximate values for the angles A, B, C, D, E, F where

$\sin A = \frac{1}{2}$, $\cos B = \frac{3}{8}$, $\sin C = \frac{3}{5}$, $\cos D = 0{\cdot}95$,
$\sin E = 0{\cdot}26$, $\cos F = 0{\cdot}34$.

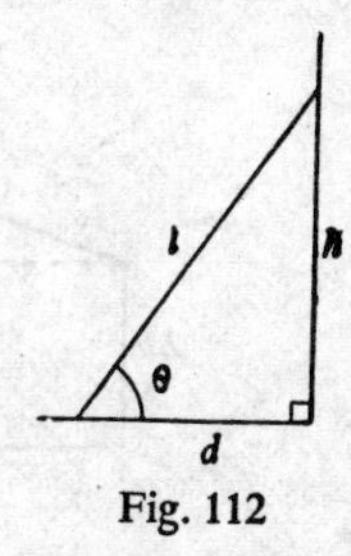

Fig. 112

If a ladder is leaning against a wall so that it makes an angle θ with the ground, $\sin\theta = \frac{h}{l}$, so that $\sin\theta$ increases with h; but $\cos\theta = \frac{d}{l}$, so that $\cos\theta$ decreases as θ increases.

This means that, when tables of sine and cosine are used, the figure in the 'difference' column is added for sines, just as it was for tangents, but subtracted for cosines, as it was for cotangents.

e.g. $\sin 26^\circ 36' = 0{\cdot}447\,8$
difference for $2' = \quad 5$ $\quad \sin 26^\circ 38' = 0{\cdot}448\,3$
$\cos 26^\circ 36' = 0{\cdot}894\,2$
difference for $2' = \quad 3$ $\quad \cos 26^\circ 38' = 0{\cdot}893\,9$

Conversely, $\sin\theta = 0{\cdot}859\,4$
$= 0{\cdot}859\,0$
$+ \quad 4$ $\quad \theta = 59^\circ 12' + 3' = 59^\circ 15'$

$\cos\phi = 0{\cdot}552\,4$
$= 0{\cdot}553\,4$
$- \quad 1\,0$ $\quad \phi = 56^\circ 24' + 4' = 56^\circ 28'$.

Notice particularly that, when $\sin\theta = 0{\cdot}859\,4$, this numerical value comes somewhere between 0·859 0 and 0·859 9, i.e. θ must be between 59° 12′ and 59° 18′.

Similarly, when $\cos\phi = 0{\cdot}552\,4$, this numerical value lies between 0·553 4 and 0·551 9 (the numbers decreasing as the angle increases), so that ϕ lies between 56° 24′ and 56° 30′.

Example 3 *A ladder 7 metres long just reaches the sill of a window when it makes an angle of 57° with the ground. How high is the window above the ground, and how far is the foot of the ladder from the bottom of the wall?*

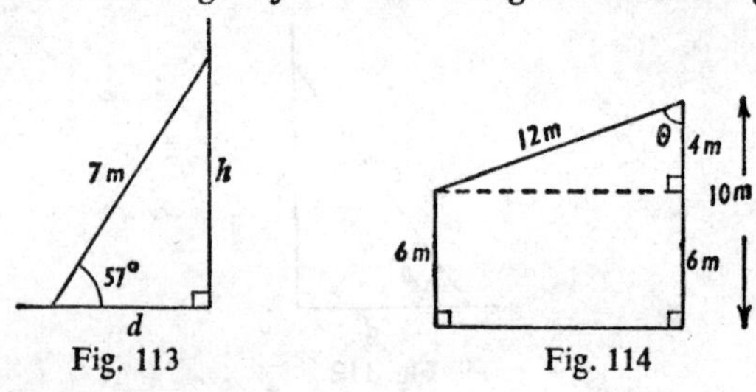

Fig. 113　　Fig. 114

$$\frac{h}{7} = \sin 57°$$

$$\therefore h = 7 \times \sin 57° = 7 \times 0{\cdot}838\,7 = 5{\cdot}870\,9 \simeq 5{\cdot}87$$

$$\frac{d}{7} = \cos 57°$$

$$\therefore d = 7 \times \cos 57° = 7 \times 0{\cdot}544\,6 = 3{\cdot}812\,2 \simeq 3{\cdot}81$$

$\therefore$ height of sill = 5·87 m

and distance of foot of ladder from wall = 3·81 m.

Example 4 *A wire 12 m long reaches from the top of a 6-metre pole to the sill of a window 10 m above the ground. What is the angle between the aerial and the wall?*

Adding the construction line shown dotted in Fig. 114

$$\cos\theta = \frac{4}{12} = 0{\cdot}333\,3$$

$$\therefore \theta = 70°\ 32'.$$

Exercise 20b

A Write down, using tables, the sines of the following angles:

1 21° 24′	**2** 21° 26′	**3** 21° 22′	**4** 47° 42′
5 47° 40′	**6** 47° 45′	**7** 64° 58′	**8** 65° 2′
9 28° 17′	**10** 13° 29′	**11** 82° 26′	**12** 53° 44′
13 36° 34′	**14** 3° 13′	**15** 74° 20′	

B Write down the cosines of the angles in **A** 1 to 15.

C Write down the angles whose sines are

16 0·710 8	**17** 0·711 2	**18** 0·710 0	**19** 0·438 4
20 0·438 9	**21** 0·437 9	**22** 0·045 7	**23** 0·893 0
24 0·383 8	**25** 0·556 8	**26** 0·777 8	**27** 0·964 9
28 0·308 0	**29** 0·029 1	**30** 0·677 8	

D Write down the angles whose cosines are given by **C** 16 to 30.

31 Find the lengths a, b, c, d, e, f, g, h, in Fig. 115.

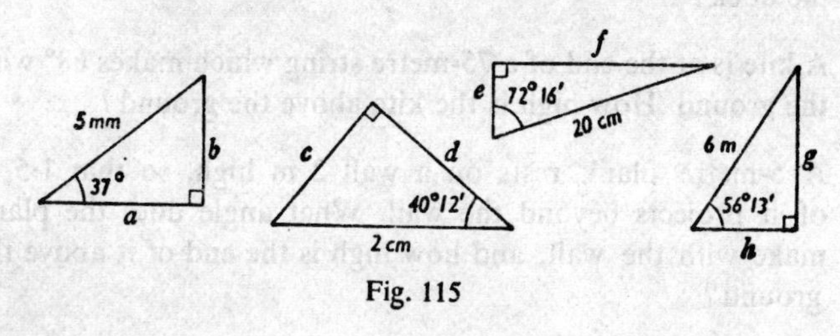

Fig. 115

32 Find the angles $\alpha, \beta, \gamma, \delta$ in Fig. 116.

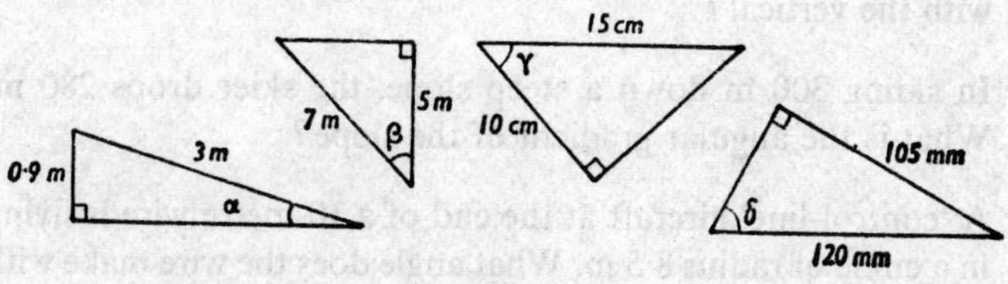

Fig. 116

33 Find α, β, γ, δ and AB in Fig. 117.

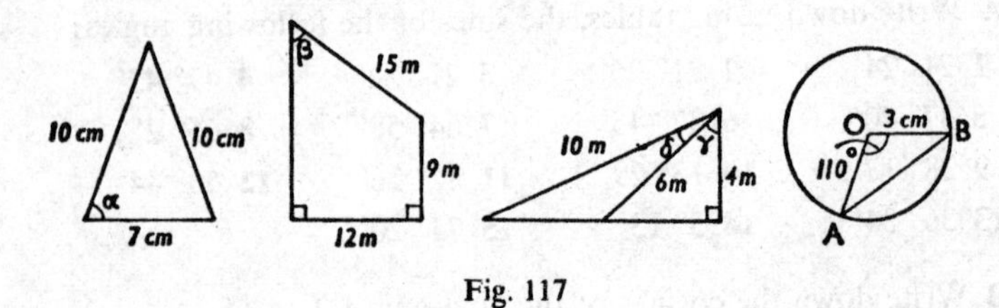

Fig. 117

34 A boat is moored to a ring 4 m above the water by a rope 15 m long. If the rope is tightly stretched, what angle does it make with the water?

35 A rhombus of side 5 cm has acute angles 84°. How long are the diagonals of the rhombus?

36 The gangplank from the dock to a ship's side is inclined at 25° to the horizontal and is 8 m long. How high is the deck above the dock?

37 A kite is at the end of a 75-metre string which makes 68° with the ground. How high is the kite above the ground?

38 A 5-metre plank rests on a wall 2 m high, so that 1·5 m of it projects beyond the wall. What angle does the plank make with the wall, and how high is the end of it above the ground?

39 A buoy is secured to a harbour bottom by a 10-metre chain. If the tide is running 7 m deep, what angle does the chain make with the vertical?

40 In skiing 300 m down a steep slope, the skier drops 280 m. What is the angular gradient of the slope?

41 A 'control-line' aircraft at the end of a 10-metre wire is flying in a circle of radius 8·5 m. What angle does the wire make with the ground?

42 A piece of corrugated iron forming the roof of a penthouse is 2·3 m long and is inclined at 18° to the horizontal. How far from the wall does the corrugated iron stick out?

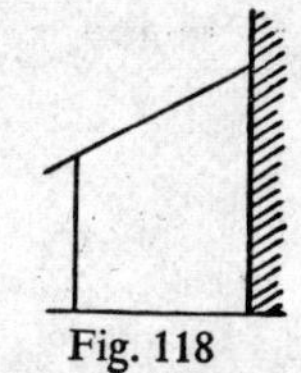
Fig. 118

43 In sliding heavy packing-cases out of a warehouse it is found that a sloping ramp must be used, with an angle of not less than 12°. If the ramp is 5 m long, how high must the delivery platform be above the ground?

44 A tripod made of rods 1·45 m long is put up so that its feet are on a circle of radius 58 cm. What angle do the rods make with the vertical?

45 How far apart are the points of a pair of dividers with arms 13·5 cm long if the angle between the arms is 35°?

In Fig. 119, $\frac{b}{a}$ is equal to sin B and also to cos C.

$$\therefore \sin\theta = \cos(90° - \theta).$$

Similarly $$\cos\theta = \sin(90° - \theta).$$

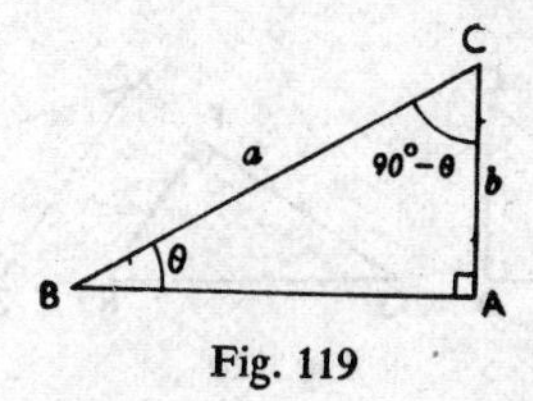

Fig. 119

In general, the sine of any angle is equal to the cosine of the complementary angle, and conversely (just as $\tan\theta = \cot(90°-\theta)$, $\cot\theta = \tan(90° - \theta)$; see page 177):

e.g. $\sin 20° = \cos 70°$, $\cos 20° = \sin 70°$, $\sin 35° = \cos 55°$, $\cos 28° = \sin 62°$, etc.

Example 5 *Solve the equations* (*a*) $\cos\theta = \sin 40°$,
(*b*) $\sin\phi = \cos 2\phi$.

$$(a)\ \cos\theta = \sin 40^\circ$$
$$= \cos 50^\circ$$
$$\therefore \theta = 50^\circ.$$
$$(b)\ \sin\phi = \cos 2\phi$$
$$= \sin(90^\circ - 2\phi)$$
$$\therefore \phi = 90^\circ - 2\phi$$
$$\therefore 3\phi = 90^\circ$$
$$\therefore \phi = 30^\circ.$$

Exercise 20c

Sine, cosine, tangent and cotangent

1 From Fig. 120 write down two trigonometrical equivalents for each of the following ratios (e.g. $\frac{PQ}{QR} = \sin R$ or $\cos Q$):

(i) $\frac{BC}{AC}$ (ii) $\frac{PR}{PQ}$ (iii) $\frac{XZ}{XY}$ (iv) $\frac{AB}{BC}$

(v) $\frac{PR}{QR}$ (vi) $\frac{YZ}{XY}$ (vii) $\frac{PQ}{PR}$ (viii) $\frac{AB}{AC}$

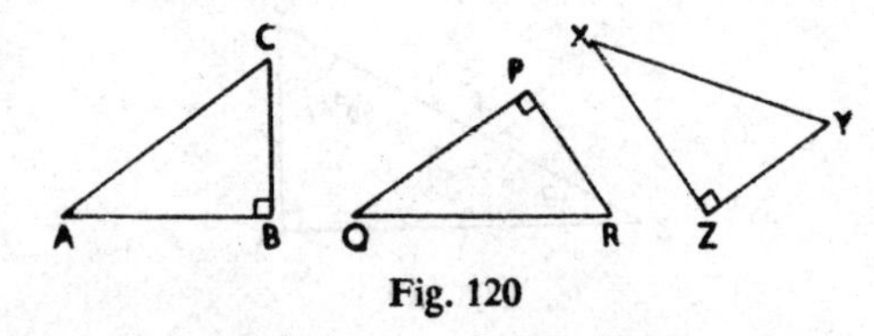

Fig. 120

2 From Fig. 121 write down the values of (i) $\sin\theta$ (ii) $\cos\theta$ (iii) $\tan\theta$ in as many ways as possible in terms of a, b, c, d, e.

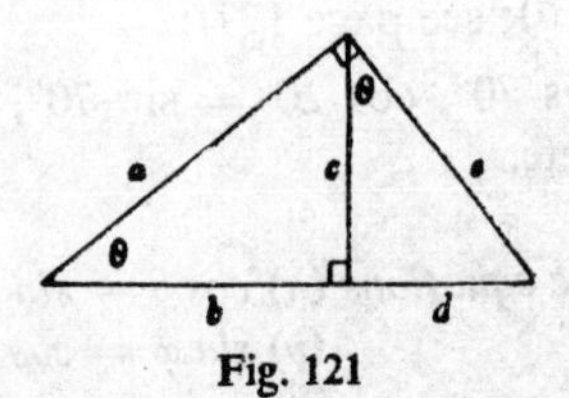

Fig. 121

3 If $\sin \theta = \cos 30°$, what is θ?

4 Solve the equations

(i) $\cos \alpha = \sin 40°$ (ii) $\sin \beta = \cos 80°$

(iii) $\sin \gamma = \cos (\gamma + 20°)$ (iv) $\tan \delta = \cot (\delta - 10°)$

(v) $\sin \theta - \cos \theta = 0$ (vi) $\cot \phi = \tan 3\phi$

5 Find to the nearest centimetre the length of the shadow of a 3-metre post when the sun's altitude is 33°.

6 A regular pentagon is inscribed in a circle of radius 4·5 cm. What is the length of a side of the pentagon?

7 A rectangular table with sides 1·2 m and 2 m is pushed into the corner of a room so that one of the long sides makes 20° with

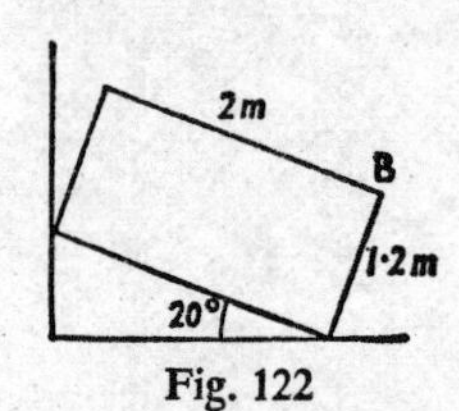

Fig. 122

a wall (Fig. 122). How far is the corner B of the table from each wall?

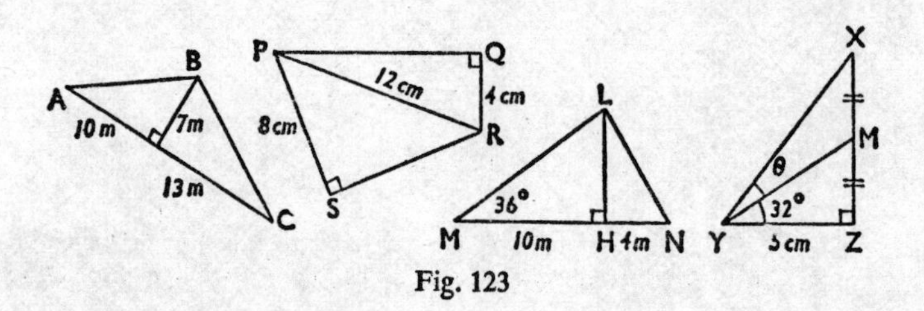

Fig. 123

8 In Fig. 123 find $A\hat{B}C$.

9 „ „ „ „ $Q\hat{R}S$.

10 „ „ „ „ $L\hat{N}M$.

11 „ „ „ „ $X\hat{Y}M$ (M is the mid-point of $\overline{XZ}$).

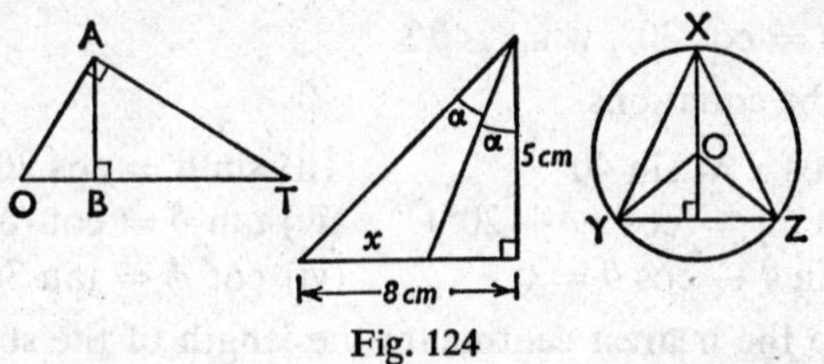

Fig. 124

12 In Fig. 124 find TA and AB (OA = 3 cm, OT = 18 cm).

13 „ „ „ „ α and x.

14 „ „ „ „ YZ and XY (O is the centre of the circle, which has radius 5 cm; $Y\hat{O}Z = 100°$).

Revision examples

XXI

1 What principal will earn £298·80 in 15 years at 3% per annum simple interest?

2 An isosceles triangle stands on a base 8 cm long, and the angle opposite this side is 103°. Find the height of the triangle.

3 A boy scout trying to find the height of a tree notices that a post 3 metres high throws a 5-metre shadow. If the shadow of the tree is 35 metres long, how tall is the tree?

4 Factorise
(i) $2a^2 - 18$ (ii) $2a^2 - 5a - 18$
(iii) $2a^2 - 5a + 5b - 2ab$.

5 A rectangular tin 15 cm by 20 cm is rolled end-over-end until the corner A is back again on the floor. Draw a scale diagram (1 cm to 5 cm) to show A's path.

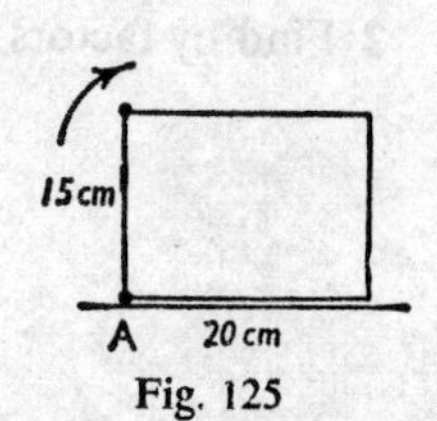

Fig. 125

6 D, E and F are the mid-points of the sides $\overline{BC}$, $\overline{CA}$ and $\overline{AB}$ of a triangle ABC. Prove that $\overline{BE}$ and $\overline{FD}$ bisect one another.

7 Find by factors the square root of 3 969.

8 Solve the equations $\frac{x}{2} + \frac{y}{9} = 6$, $\frac{3x}{5} - \frac{2y}{3} = 0$.

9 A ladder 5 m long rests against a vertical wall with one end 4·25 m above the ground. What angle does the ladder make with the wall?

10 The height above the ground of a shell from a trench-mortar at various distances from the firing-point are given in the table below, all distances being in metres:

Distance	0	50	100	150	200	250	300	350	400
Height	0	67	115	150	175	185	177	131	0

Draw a graph of the track of the shell, taking a scale of 1 cm to 20 m on both axes. Read off (i) the distance by which a spire 60 m high, 70 m from the firing-point, would be cleared by the shell (ii) the horizontal distance for which the shell is over 150 m above the ground (iii) the height of the shell when it is 10 m (horizontally) from the target.

XXII

1 Convert the following denary numbers to binary: 99, 111. Convert the following binary numbers to denary: 1 000 111, 1 110 001.
Base 3—add together 1 022 122 and 212 101.

2 Find by factors the cube root of 2 744.

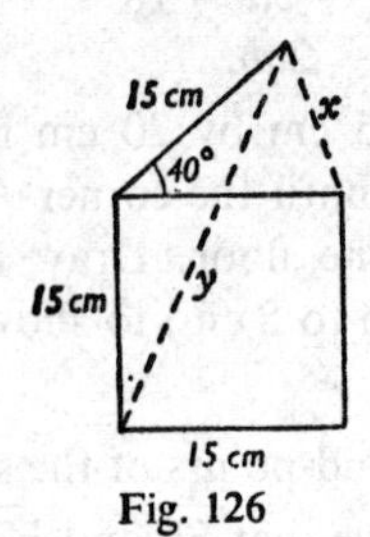

Fig. 126

3 The lid of a cubical box made of thin material is propped open at an angle of 40°. Find the distances x and y (Fig. 126).

4 Find the amount of £152 after 2 yr 3 m at $2\frac{1}{2}$% per annum simple interest.

5 Solve the equation $\frac{1}{2}\left(\frac{x}{2}+2\right)-\frac{1}{4}\left(\frac{x}{4}-\frac{1}{2}\right)=\frac{1}{4}(x+1)$.

Check the answer.

6 The sides of a triangle are 9, 10 and 15 m. The longest side of a similar triangle is 6 cm long. Calculate the other sides of this triangle.

7 ABCD is a square: M and N are the mid-points of $\overline{AB}$ and $\overline{AD}$ respectively: the square AMXN is completed. Prove that the line joining A to the mid-point of $\overline{MX}$, when produced, bisects $\overline{BC}$.

8 Factorise (i) $3x^2 - 7x - 6$ (ii) $m^2 + mq - mn - nq$ (iii) $\pi x^2 - \pi y^2$.

9 On a '1 cm to 1 km' map two peaks are marked as being 1 318 m and 2 182 m high, and the distance between them is exactly 1·5 cm. What is the angle of depression of the lower peak from the higher one?

10 A man is four times as old as his son. Five years ago he was nine times as old. When will he be only twice as old?

XXIII

1 Factorise (i) $ab - 2xy - bx + 2ay$ (ii) $6 + p - 2p^2$ (iii) $6y^3 - 15y^2z$.

2 ABCD is a trapezium, and X and Y are any points on the parallel sides $\overline{AB}$ and $\overline{DC}$ respectively. Prove that the line joining the mid-points of $\overline{AD}$ and $\overline{BC}$ bisects $\overline{XY}$.

3 Find to the nearest penny the simple interest on £1 000 for 14 days at $4\frac{1}{2}\%$.

4 Find by factors the square root of 15 876.

5 A triangle ABC is right-angled at B; AB = 5 cm, BC = 8 cm. The bisector of $B\hat{A}C$ cuts $\overline{BC}$ at X. Calculate CX and XB.

6 In the triangle ABC shown (Fig. 127) find BC.

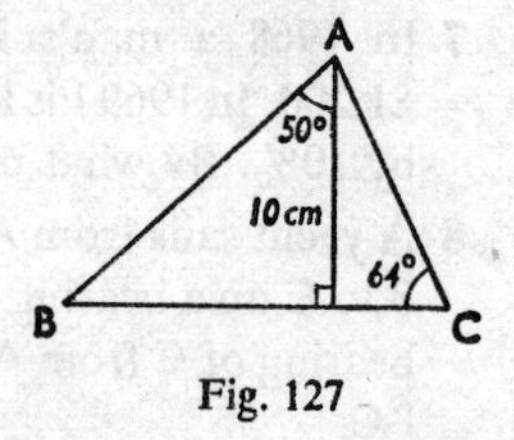

Fig. 127

7 In a triangle ABC, AB = 9 cm, BC = 12 cm, and X is a point on $\overline{AB}$ such that AX = 6 cm. If $\overline{XY}$, drawn parallel to $\overline{BC}$, cuts $\overline{AC}$ in Y, calculate XY.

8 In one house there are human beings, cats and dogs, all of them having the proper number of limbs. Altogether there are 10 heads and 30 legs in the house. How many people are there?

9 Construct a regular nonagon inside a circle of radius 6 cm. Measure its sides.

10 Find graphically the point of intersection of the lines $2x + 3y = 6$ and $2y - 3x = 12$.

XXIV

1 It is known that a triangle with sides 8, 15 and 17 metres is right-angled. Which of the triangles whose sides are given is also right-angled? (i) 4, 7·5, 8·5 cm (ii) 35, 29, 16 cm (iii) 75, 85, 40 m.

2 Evaluate $\sqrt{39\frac{1}{16}}$, $\sqrt[3]{12\frac{19}{27}}$.

3 (i) A man buys goods for £x and sells them for £y. If his profit is 20%, find the equation connecting x and y.
(ii) A man buys goods for £x and sells them at a profit of y%. Find the selling price in terms of x and y.

4 In going half a kilometre along a road a traveller rises 65 m. What angle does the road make with the horizontal?

5 Draw a rectangle with sides 11 cm and 7 cm. Use a geometrical method to divide one of the diagonals into three equal parts. Measure one of these parts as accurately as possible.

6 (i) Simplify $\dfrac{b}{a^2 - ab} + \dfrac{a + b}{ab}$.
(ii) Find the L.C.M. of $6x^2y$, $9xy^3z$, x^3z^2.

7 In 1968 a man's income was £1 600 and his expenditure £1 200. In 1969 his income went up by 5%, and his expenditure by 10%. By what percentage did his savings go up or down?

8 A yacht sails from A to B on a bearing N 68° E, and then from B to C on a bearing S 22° E. The distance AC is 20 km, and the bearing of C from A is S 65° E. Calculate the distances AB and BC.

9 Evaluate, using factors, (i) $7{\cdot}62^2 - 2{\cdot}38^2$
(ii) $567 \times 314 - 314 \times 295 + 728 \times 314$
(iii) $\pi[(5\frac{1}{4})^2 - (1\frac{3}{4})^2]$. Take $\pi = \frac{22}{7}$.

10 In what time will £17·78 amount to £35·56 at $6\frac{1}{4}$% per annum simple interest?

XXV

1 Factorise (i) $12 - 27p^2$ (ii) $2x - x^3 + 2x^2 - 4$ (iii) $12y^2 - y - 6$.

2 'Rosedale Chimney' in Yorkshire has a gradient of 1 in $2\frac{1}{2}$, which means that the traveller rises 1 metre for every $2\frac{1}{2}$ metres he goes on the road. What angle does the road make with the horizontal?

3 Find the square root of 69 169.

4 Solve the equations $a + 400b = 26$, $a + 900b = 51$.

5 ABCD is a parallelogram with M the mid-point of $\overline{AD}$ and X a point on $\overline{AC}$ such that $AX = \frac{1}{3}XC$. Prove $\overline{MX} \parallel \overline{BD}$ and $MX = \frac{1}{4}BD$.

6 At what rate per cent simple interest will £60·42 earn £8·46 in $3\frac{1}{2}$ years?

7 What is the ratio $x : y$ in Fig. 128?

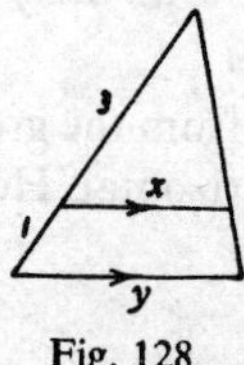

Fig. 128

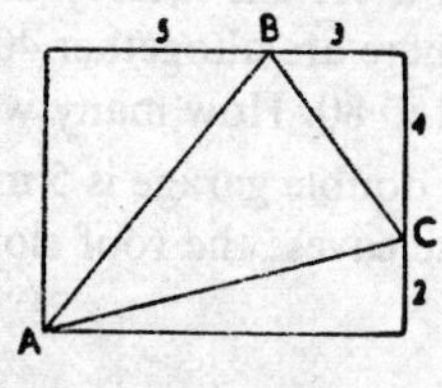

Fig. 129

8 Calculate the angles of the triangle ABC shown, the surrounding figure being a rectangle (Fig. 129).

9 A boy cycled to a town at 12 km/h and returned at 16 km/h. If the double journey took $3\frac{1}{2}$ hours, how far away was the town?

10 Without using a protractor construct a parallelogram with sides 7·5 cm and 9 cm, and one angle 60°. Measure the diagonals of the parallelogram.

XXVI

1 In any trapezium prove that the length of the line joining the mid-points of the oblique sides is half the sum of the parallel sides.

2 Factorise
(i) $5f^2 + 7fg - 6g^2$ (ii) $5f^2 + 29fg - 6g^2$
(iii) $ab - 2ac - 2b^2 + 4bc$.

3 Calculate the largest angle of a triangle with sides 4 cm, 4 cm and 5 cm.

4 A car travelled 195 km in $3\frac{3}{4}$ hours. What was its average speed? The motorist had in fact 153 km further to go, and had planned to average 58 km/h for the whole journey. How fast did he have to go for this last 153 km?

5 ABC is a triangle, and X, Y are points on the sides $\overline{AB}$, $\overline{AC}$ respectively such that $A\hat{X}Y = \hat{C}$. AX = 7 cm, XY = 6 cm, YA = 5 cm and BX = 8 cm. Calculate BC and CY.

6 In what time does the simple interest on £257·17 at $6\frac{1}{4}$% amount to £6·43?

7 In a certain factory men get £5·20 a day and women £3·60. There are altogether 40 employees, and the total daily wage is £180·80. How many women are employed?

8 A double garage is 5 m wide and 3 m high from the ground to the eaves: the roof slopes at 32° to the horizontal. How high

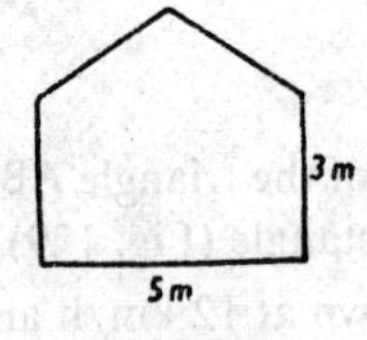

Fig. 130

is the ridge of the roof above the ground, to the nearest centimetre?

9 Find the square root of 5 026·81.

10 Draw the graph of $y = x^2 + x - 2$ for values of x from -3 to $+2$. (i) For what values of x does $y = 0$? (ii) What is the least value of $x^2 + x - 2$?

XXVII

1 In a laboratory experiment the answers given by a class of boys were respectively 37·1, 36·0, 37·0, 36·5, 59·2, 36·7, 36·3, 36·9, 36·4, 17·1, 36·8, 36·3. What was probably the correct answer?

2 Find a and b in the given figure.

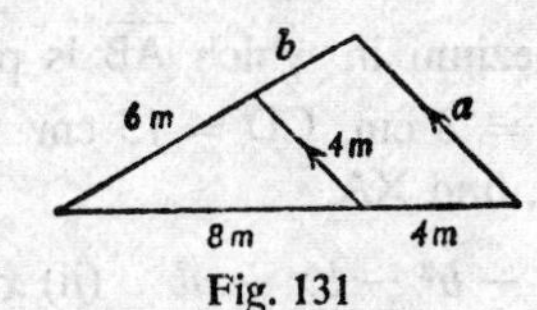

Fig. 131

3 Solve $\frac{x+2}{3} - \frac{3-x}{5} = \frac{5x+2}{10}$. Check the answer.

4 Find to the nearest penny the amount of £438 in 190 days at $2\frac{1}{3}$% simple interest.

5 Draw $\overline{AB}$ 3 cm long. Find by construction a point X in $\overline{AB}$ produced such that $BX = \frac{3}{5}AX$. Measure AX.

6 In an athletics team 15 are runners, 10 are hurdlers and 12 take part in field events. Seven of the runners are also hurdlers, 8 runners and 5 hurdlers also take part in field events, and 3 of the athletes take part in all three kinds of event. By means of a Venn diagram find how many athletes there are in the team.

7 Factorise
(i) $6 - 11y - 10y^2$ (ii) $2pr + 4pq - 3qr - 6q^2$
(iii) $20x^2 - 45y^2$.

8 In Fig. 132 O is the centre of the circle, which is 10 cm in diameter, and $\hat{AXO} = \hat{BYO} = 90°$, $\overline{XOY}$ being a straight line. If $\hat{AOB} = 70°$ and AX = 3 cm, calculate BY and XY.

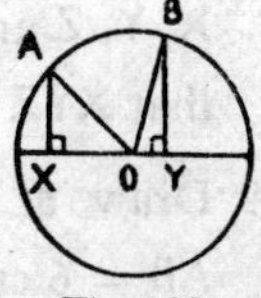

Fig. 132

9 A yacht sails for 5 km on a bearing of 052°, then turns right-handed through 90° and sails a further 6 km to a buoy. What is the bearing of the starting-point from the buoy?

10 Find the square root of 51, correct to 3 decimal places.

XXVIII

1 ABCD is a trapezium in which $\overline{AB}$ is parallel to $\overline{DC}$, and AB = 9 cm, AD = 8 cm, CD = 15 cm. If $\overline{DA}$ and $\overline{CB}$ produced meet in X, find XA.

2 Factorise (i) $ax - b^2 - bx + ab$ (ii) $x^5 - x^3$
(iii) $6a^2 - 17ab - 14b^2$.

3 What principal amounts to £478·80 after 4 yr 8 m at 3% per annum simple interest?

4 A triangle ABC is right-angled at B. AB = 10 cm and BC = 17 cm. M is the mid-point of $\overline{AB}$. Calculate $B\hat{C}M$ and $A\hat{C}M$.

5 A car's average speed over a 384-km journey was 48 km/h. If stops accounted for 96 minutes of the time spent on the road, what was the average speed while running?

6 Solve the equations $2x + 3y = 15$, $3x - y = 4\frac{1}{6}$.

7 Find the square root of 0·007 259 04.

8 $\overline{AD}$ and $\overline{BE}$ are altitudes of a triangle ABC which meet at H, X, Y, Z are the mid-points of $\overline{HB}$, $\overline{BA}$, $\overline{AC}$ respectively. Prove that $X\hat{Y}Z$ is a right angle.

9 Draw a triangle ABC with BC = 12 cm, CA = 9 cm. AB = 6 cm. Construct the bisector of $\hat{B}$ and produce it to cut $\overline{AC}$ in X. Measure AX.

10 A rectangular table 1·8 m by 1·2 m is pushed into the corner of a room so that one of the long sides makes an angle of 36°

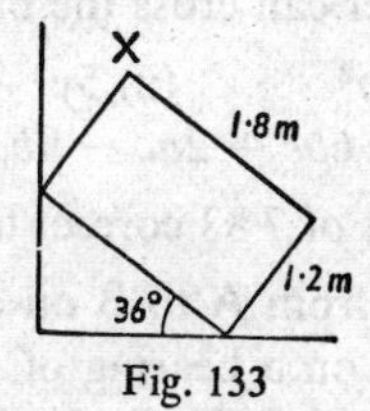

Fig. 133

with a wall. What is the perpendicular distance of the corner X of the table from each wall? (nearest centimetre)

XXIX

1 Find a and b in the figure shown.

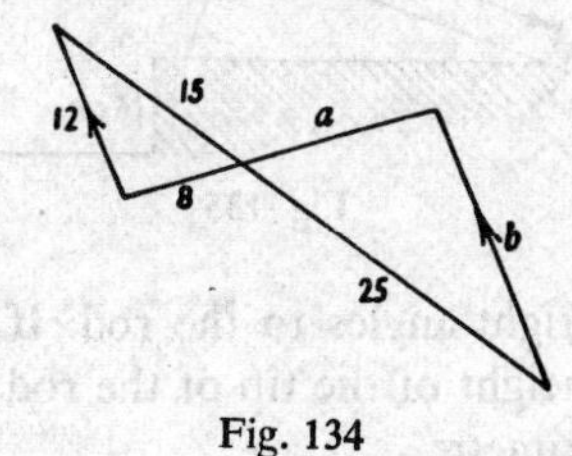

Fig. 134

2 Find to the nearest penny the amount of £217·51 after 292 days at $2\frac{1}{4}$% per annum simple interest.

3 A vertical pole 4·5 m high is erected 7 m away from the wall of a house. A wire is tightly stretched from the top of the pole to a point in the wall opposite the pole and 2·5 m above the ground. What angle does the wire make with the pole?

4 The depth, d metres, of water over a harbour bar at time t hours is given in the following table:

t	06.00	07.00	08.00	09.00	10.00	11.00	12.00	13.00	14.00	15.00
d	9·88	11·37	11·59	10·50	8·38	5·80	3·45	1·97	1·74	2·84

At what times are high tide and low tide, and what is the depth of water at these times? What is the latest time that a vessel drawing 4 m of water can cross the bar?

5 Factorise (i) $l^4 - m^2$ (ii) $5y^2 + yz - 6z^2$ (iii) $3ad - 6bc + 2ac - 9bd$.

6 Find the square root of 7·83 correct to four decimal places.

7 A yacht sails 8 km from A to B on a bearing of 060°; then 10 km from B to C on a bearing of 100°. From an accurate scale drawing find (i) AC (ii) the bearing of A from C.

8 A fishing-rod 3·24 m long rests with its butt on the bank at A, supported by a forked stick 18 cm long as shown, the

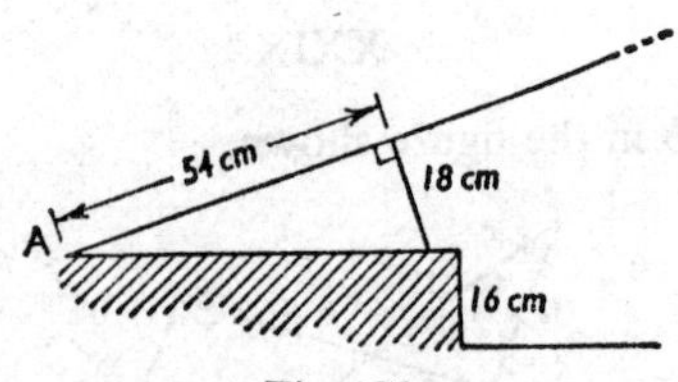

Fig. 135

stick being at right angles to the rod. If the bank is 16 cm high, find the height of the tip of the rod above the water to the nearest centimetre.

9 The average age of 12 boys in a dormitory is 13 years 2 months. If another boy joins them, aged 14 years 3 months, what is the new average age?

10 Draw the graph of $y = 2x^2 + x - 4$ for values of x from -3 to $+3$. Find (i) the values of x when $y = 0$ (ii) the least value of $2x^2 + x - 4$.

XXX

1 Factorise (i) $a^2 - (2b - c)^2$ (ii) $10 - 1\,000p^2$ (iii) $s^3 - (a + b)s^2 + abs$.

2 Find to 4 sig. fig. the square root of 135·798 642.

3 ABCD is a parallelogram: $\overline{AB}$ is trisected at P and Q so that AP = PQ = QB, and $\overline{BC}$ is bisected at M. $\overline{BD}$ cuts $\overline{QM}$ at X. Prove BX = $\frac{1}{5}$BD.

4 An aeroplane flying level at 1 000 m is directly overhead: 20 seconds later it is at an elevation of 15°. How fast is the aeroplane flying in km/h?

5 A man invests £280 in a building society paying 5% p.a., and £700 in a bank paying $3\frac{1}{4}$% p.a. What rate per cent does he receive on both the investments together?

6 Find the ratio $x : y$ in the figure given.

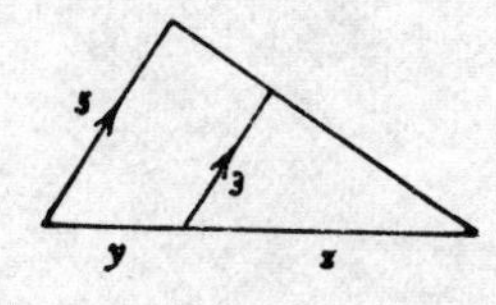

Fig. 136

7 A is (4,1), B is (−2,0), C is (0,3) and D is (3,2). Find the co-ordinates of the vertices of the triangle which is the displacement of △ABC through $\overrightarrow{AD}$.

8 A wall-crane with a jib $\overline{AC}$ 7 m long is hinged to the wall at A and held up by a chain $\overline{BC}$ 3·5 m long, the chain making an angle of 76° with the wall. Find B$\hat{A}$C.
(*First find* CX—Fig. 137.)

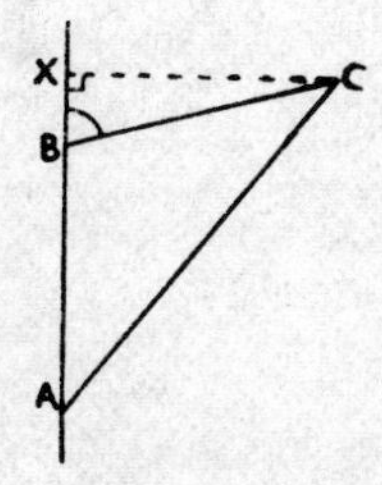

Fig. 137

9 A bag contains 27 coins, which are a mixture of fivepenny pieces and twopenny pieces. The total value of the coins is £1·05. How many of each sort are there?

10 The height of a projectile above the ground is h metres where $h = 4{\cdot}9t(5 - t)$, t being the time in seconds from the start. Plot h against t for values of t from 0 to 5. Read off from the graph the greatest height attained, and also the times when the projectile is 20 m above the ground.

Chapter 21

Matrices (1)

In Chapter 9 a vector was defined as a set or array of numbers. A **matrix** (plural matrices) is a set of numbers in the form of a **rectangular array,** as for example $\begin{pmatrix} 2 & 3 \\ 1 & 4 \end{pmatrix}$ or $\begin{pmatrix} 1 & 12 & 1 \\ 3 & -1 & 2 \end{pmatrix}$. $\begin{pmatrix} 1 & 12 & 1 \\ 3 & -1 & 2 \end{pmatrix}$ has two **rows** and three **columns** and is referred to as a 2 by 3 matrix. A vector is in fact a special case or sub-set of a matrix; for instance (5,7,6) is a 1 by 3 matrix. $\begin{pmatrix} 4 \\ 7 \end{pmatrix}$ which is a 2 by 1 matrix is called a **column vector.** A **square matrix** is one in which there are the same number of rows and columns, for example $\begin{pmatrix} 2 & 4 \\ 5 & 6 \end{pmatrix}$ and $\begin{pmatrix} 2 & 4 & 3 \\ 5 & 6 & 1 \\ 3 & 7 & 5 \end{pmatrix}$.

The information about coins at the beginning of Chapter 9 can be represented by the matrix $\begin{pmatrix} 10 & 6 & 2 \\ 15 & 20 & 4 \end{pmatrix}$.

That is to say 10 twopenny pieces, 6 fivepenny pieces and 2 tenpenny pieces on the first day, and 15 twopenny pieces, 20 fivepenny pieces and 4 tenpenny pieces on the second day.

Addition

If one went to a second bank on each of the two days and obtained a certain amount of money it could also be expressed as a matrix, say $\begin{pmatrix} 20 & 3 & 1 \\ 10 & 12 & 2 \end{pmatrix}$. To find the number of coins obtained on each day the two matrices must be added as follows:

$$\begin{pmatrix} 10 & 6 & 2 \\ 15 & 20 & 4 \end{pmatrix} + \begin{pmatrix} 20 & 3 & 1 \\ 10 & 12 & 2 \end{pmatrix} = \begin{pmatrix} 30 & 9 & 3 \\ 25 & 32 & 6 \end{pmatrix}$$

To add two matrices, each element of one matrix is added to the corresponding element of the other matrix. The result of adding two matrices is another matrix with the same number of rows and columns as the original matrices. The original matrices must both have the same number of rows and of columns and it does not matter in which order they are added.

Example 1 *If* $A = \begin{pmatrix} 2 & 3 & 0 \\ 4 & 2 & 1 \\ 3 & 1 & -2 \end{pmatrix}$ *and* $B = \begin{pmatrix} 3 & -1 & 2 \\ 1 & 3 & 1 \\ 4 & 2 & -1 \end{pmatrix}$ *show that* $A + B = B + A$.

$$\begin{pmatrix} 2 & 3 & 0 \\ 4 & 2 & 1 \\ 3 & 1 & -2 \end{pmatrix} + \begin{pmatrix} 3 & -1 & 2 \\ 1 & 3 & 1 \\ 4 & 2 & -1 \end{pmatrix} = \begin{pmatrix} 5 & 2 & 2 \\ 5 & 5 & 2 \\ 7 & 3 & -3 \end{pmatrix}$$

and $$\begin{pmatrix} 3 & -1 & 2 \\ 1 & 3 & 1 \\ 4 & 2 & -1 \end{pmatrix} + \begin{pmatrix} 2 & 3 & 0 \\ 4 & 2 & 1 \\ 3 & 1 & -2 \end{pmatrix} = \begin{pmatrix} 5 & 2 & 2 \\ 5 & 5 & 2 \\ 7 & 3 & -3 \end{pmatrix}$$

Subtraction

The rules for subtracting matrices are similar to those for addition; namely each element of one matrix is subtracted from the corresponding element of the other matrix: the matrices must have the same number of rows and columns and the resulting matrix will have the same number of rows and of columns.

Example 2 *Using the matrices A and B of Example 1 show that* $A - B$ *does not equal* $B - A$.

$$\begin{pmatrix} 2 & 3 & 0 \\ 4 & 2 & 1 \\ 3 & 1 & -2 \end{pmatrix} - \begin{pmatrix} 3 & -1 & 2 \\ 1 & 3 & 1 \\ 4 & 2 & -1 \end{pmatrix} = \begin{pmatrix} -1 & 4 & -2 \\ 3 & -1 & 0 \\ -1 & -1 & -1 \end{pmatrix}$$

and $$\begin{pmatrix} 3 & -1 & 2 \\ 1 & 3 & 1 \\ 4 & 2 & -1 \end{pmatrix} - \begin{pmatrix} 2 & 3 & 0 \\ 4 & 2 & 1 \\ 3 & 1 & -2 \end{pmatrix} = \begin{pmatrix} 1 & -4 & 2 \\ -3 & 1 & 0 \\ 1 & 1 & 1 \end{pmatrix}$$

$\therefore A - B$ does not equal $B - A$, but it can be seen that

$$A - B = -(B - A).$$

Exercise 21a

Add together the following matrices where possible:

1 $\begin{pmatrix}1 & 2\\3 & 0\end{pmatrix}$ and $\begin{pmatrix}2 & -1\\4 & 5\end{pmatrix}$

2 $\begin{pmatrix}3 & 1\\2 & 0\\4 & 7\end{pmatrix}$ and $\begin{pmatrix}1 & 2\\3 & 1\\2 & -3\end{pmatrix}$

3 $\begin{pmatrix}3 & 1\\2 & 0\end{pmatrix}$ and $\begin{pmatrix}2 & 1\\3 & 0\\4 & 3\end{pmatrix}$

4 $(1 \quad 2 \quad 3)$ and $(4 \quad -3 \quad 5)$

5 $\begin{pmatrix}1{\cdot}3 & 4{\cdot}2\\3{\cdot}1 & 6{\cdot}2\end{pmatrix}$ and $\begin{pmatrix}7{\cdot}1 & -3{\cdot}2\\-2{\cdot}9 & 4{\cdot}3\end{pmatrix}$

6 $\begin{pmatrix}1 & 3 & 2 & -1\\4{\cdot}5 & 2 & 1 & 0\\-3 & 1 & 3 & 2\end{pmatrix}$ and $\begin{pmatrix}4 & 5 & 3 & -1\\-2 & 3{\cdot}5 & 4 & 2\\5{\cdot}6 & 7{\cdot}2 & 2 & -4\end{pmatrix}$

7 $\begin{pmatrix}1 & 3 & 1\\2 & 4 & 1\end{pmatrix}$, $\begin{pmatrix}3 & -3 & 2\\4 & 5 & 7\end{pmatrix}$ and $\begin{pmatrix}3 & -2 & 1 & 5\\4 & 2 & 3 & 2\end{pmatrix}$

8 $\begin{pmatrix}1\\3\\-3\end{pmatrix}$ and $\begin{pmatrix}2\\4\\1\end{pmatrix}$

9 $\begin{pmatrix}3\\1\end{pmatrix}$ and $\begin{pmatrix}-1\\3\\2\end{pmatrix}$

10 $\begin{pmatrix}2 & 1 & 3\\1 & 3 & 2\\4 & 1 & 3\end{pmatrix}$, $\begin{pmatrix}7 & -1 & 0\\2 & 3 & -2\\1 & 4 & 6\end{pmatrix}$ and $\begin{pmatrix}3 & -2 & -1\\4 & -1 & 3\\2 & 3 & 1\end{pmatrix}$

Perform the following subtractions, where possible:

11 $\begin{pmatrix}3 & -1 & -2\\2 & 3 & 1\end{pmatrix} - \begin{pmatrix}2 & -2 & 3\\1 & 3 & 1\end{pmatrix}$

12 $(2 \quad 1 \quad 3) - (3 \quad 4)$

13 $\begin{pmatrix}4\\3\\1\end{pmatrix} - \begin{pmatrix}6\\1\\3\end{pmatrix}$

14 $\begin{pmatrix} 3 & 2 \\ 1 & 0 \\ -1 & 1 \end{pmatrix} - \begin{pmatrix} 2 & 3 \\ -1 & -2 \\ -1 & 3 \end{pmatrix}$

15 $\begin{pmatrix} 2 & 1{\cdot}3 \\ 3 & 2{\cdot}1 \end{pmatrix} - \begin{pmatrix} 4{\cdot}2 & 3 \\ 2{\cdot}1 & 4 \end{pmatrix}$

16 $\begin{pmatrix} 3 & 2{\cdot}2 \\ 2{\cdot}1 & 3 \end{pmatrix} - \begin{pmatrix} 3{\cdot}4 \\ 2{\cdot}1 \end{pmatrix}$

Multiplication by a number

The cutlery used at breakfast consists of 4 knives, 4 spoons and 2 forks, and for lunch it consists of 2 knives, 2 spoons and 4 forks. This can be represented by the matrix $\begin{pmatrix} 4 & 4 & 2 \\ 2 & 2 & 4 \end{pmatrix}$. If the same utensils are used on each of 3 days the total can be represented by the addition:

$$\begin{pmatrix} 4 & 4 & 2 \\ 2 & 2 & 4 \end{pmatrix} + \begin{pmatrix} 4 & 4 & 2 \\ 2 & 2 & 4 \end{pmatrix} + \begin{pmatrix} 4 & 4 & 2 \\ 2 & 2 & 4 \end{pmatrix} = \begin{pmatrix} 12 & 12 & 6 \\ 6 & 6 & 12 \end{pmatrix}$$

This can be represented more simply as

$$3\begin{pmatrix} 4 & 4 & 2 \\ 2 & 2 & 4 \end{pmatrix} = \begin{pmatrix} 12 & 12 & 6 \\ 6 & 6 & 12 \end{pmatrix}$$

From this it can be seen that, to multiply a matrix by a number, each element of the matrix must be multiplied by that number.

Multiplication of two matrices

Consider the first example of Chapter 9 in which 10 twopenny pieces, 6 fivepenny pieces and 2 tenpenny pieces are represented by the vector (10,6,2). The values of the separate coins can be represented by the column vector $\begin{pmatrix} 2 \\ 5 \\ 10 \end{pmatrix}$ and the total value in pence by the product

$$(10 \quad 6 \quad 2)\begin{pmatrix} 2 \\ 5 \\ 10 \end{pmatrix} = 10 \times 2 + 6 \times 5 + 2 \times 10$$

$$= 20 + 30 + 20$$
$$= 70$$
$$\therefore \text{ total value} = 70\text{p.}$$

The total value of each of the two days' sets of coins is given by

$$\begin{pmatrix} 10 & 6 & 2 \\ 15 & 20 & 4 \end{pmatrix} \begin{pmatrix} 2 \\ 5 \\ 10 \end{pmatrix} = \begin{pmatrix} 10 \times 2 + 6 \times 5 + 2 \times 10 \\ 15 \times 2 + 20 \times 5 + 4 \times 10 \end{pmatrix}$$
$$= \begin{pmatrix} 70 \\ 170 \end{pmatrix}.$$

Taking a more general example, multiply

$$\begin{pmatrix} 3 & 2 & 1 \\ 4 & 3 & -1 \\ 6 & 0 & 2 \\ 3 & 1 & 4 \end{pmatrix} \text{ by } \begin{pmatrix} 6 & 0 \\ 1 & -1 \\ 2 & 3 \end{pmatrix}.$$

Each element of the resulting matrix is made up of the multiplication of the appropriate row of the first matrix by the appropriate column of the second matrix. Thus the first element of the first row of the product is given by

$$(3 \quad 2 \quad 1) \begin{pmatrix} 6 \\ 1 \\ 2 \end{pmatrix} = 3 \times 6 + 2 \times 1 + 1 \times 2 = 22$$

The second element of the first row is given by

$$(3 \quad 2 \quad 1) \begin{pmatrix} 0 \\ -1 \\ 3 \end{pmatrix} = 1$$

The first element of the second row is given by

$$(4 \quad 3 \quad -1) \begin{pmatrix} 6 \\ 1 \\ 2 \end{pmatrix} = 25$$

and so on, giving

$$\begin{pmatrix} 3 & 2 & 1 \\ 4 & 3 & -1 \\ 6 & 0 & 2 \\ 3 & 1 & 4 \end{pmatrix} \begin{pmatrix} 6 & 0 \\ 1 & -1 \\ 2 & 3 \end{pmatrix} = \begin{pmatrix} 22 & 1 \\ 25 & -6 \\ 40 & 6 \\ 27 & 11 \end{pmatrix}.$$

In order for it to be possible to multiply two matrices the multiplier must have the same number of rows as the multiplicand has of columns. The product has the same number of rows as the multiplicand and the same number of columns as the multiplier. In particular one can never multiply a vector or a matrix by a row vector.

Example 3 *If* $A = \begin{pmatrix} 3 & 2 \\ 1 & 4 \end{pmatrix}$ *and* $B = \begin{pmatrix} 2 & -1 \\ 0 & 3 \end{pmatrix}$ *show that AB does not equal BA.*

$$AB = \begin{pmatrix} 3 & 2 \\ 1 & 4 \end{pmatrix}\begin{pmatrix} 2 & -1 \\ 0 & 3 \end{pmatrix} = \begin{pmatrix} 6 & 3 \\ 2 & 11 \end{pmatrix}$$

$$BA = \begin{pmatrix} 2 & -1 \\ 0 & 3 \end{pmatrix}\begin{pmatrix} 3 & 2 \\ 1 & 4 \end{pmatrix} = \begin{pmatrix} 5 & 0 \\ 3 & 12 \end{pmatrix}$$

$\therefore$ AB does not equal BA.

Note that AB means that B is **pre-multiplied** by A and BA means that B is **post-multiplied** by A.

Exercise 21b

Perform the following multiplications, where possible:

1 $3\begin{pmatrix} 3 \\ 2 \end{pmatrix}$

2 $2(1 \quad 2 \quad 3)$

3 $4\begin{pmatrix} 2 & 1 \\ 0 & 1 \end{pmatrix}$

4 $6\begin{pmatrix} 3 & -2 & 1 \\ 0{\cdot}5 & 6 & 0{\cdot}3 \\ 2{\cdot}1 & 3 & 4{\cdot}5 \end{pmatrix}$

5 $2{\cdot}5\begin{pmatrix} 6 & 3 & 7 \\ -1 & 0{\cdot}5 & -2 \end{pmatrix}$

6 $\begin{pmatrix} 3 & 2 \\ 1 & 4 \end{pmatrix}\begin{pmatrix} 2 \\ 3 \end{pmatrix}$

7 $\begin{pmatrix} 2 \\ 3 \end{pmatrix}\begin{pmatrix} 3 & 2 \\ 1 & 4 \end{pmatrix}$

8 $\begin{pmatrix} 4 & 1 \\ 3 & 2 \end{pmatrix}\begin{pmatrix} 3 & 1 \\ 2 & 1 \end{pmatrix}$

9 $\begin{pmatrix} 3 & 1 \\ 2 & 1 \end{pmatrix}\begin{pmatrix} 4 & 1 \\ 3 & 2 \end{pmatrix}$

10 $\begin{pmatrix} 11 & 2 \\ 5 & 1 \end{pmatrix}\begin{pmatrix} 1 & -2 \\ -5 & 11 \end{pmatrix}$

11 $\begin{pmatrix} 1 & -2 \\ -5 & 11 \end{pmatrix}\begin{pmatrix} 11 & 2 \\ 5 & 1 \end{pmatrix}$

12 $\begin{pmatrix} 6 & 1 \\ 3 & 2 \end{pmatrix}\begin{pmatrix} 2 & -1 \\ -3 & 6 \end{pmatrix}$

13 $\begin{pmatrix} 2 & -1 \\ -3 & 6 \end{pmatrix}\begin{pmatrix} 6 & 1 \\ 3 & 2 \end{pmatrix}$

14 $\begin{pmatrix} 2 & 3 & 1 \\ 4 & 2 & 1 \\ 3 & 1 & 1 \end{pmatrix}\begin{pmatrix} 2 \\ 1 \\ 3 \end{pmatrix}$

15 $\begin{pmatrix} 2 \\ 1 \\ 3 \end{pmatrix}\begin{pmatrix} 2 & 3 & 1 \\ 4 & 2 & 1 \\ 3 & 1 & 1 \end{pmatrix}$

16 $\begin{pmatrix} 2 & 1 & -1 \\ 3 & -1 & 0 \\ 2 & 1 & 2 \end{pmatrix}\begin{pmatrix} 1 & -1 \\ 3 & 0 \\ 2 & 1 \end{pmatrix}$

17 $\begin{pmatrix} 2 & 1 \\ 3 & 2 \\ 4 & 1 \\ 3 & -1 \end{pmatrix}\begin{pmatrix} 1 & 3 & 1 \\ 2 & 0 & 1 \end{pmatrix}$

18 $\begin{pmatrix} 1 & 2 & -1 \\ 3 & 1 & -2 \end{pmatrix}\begin{pmatrix} 1 & 2 \\ -2 & 1 \\ -3 & 0 \end{pmatrix}$

19 $\begin{pmatrix} 6 & 1 & -1 \\ 3 & 1{\cdot}5 & 2{\cdot}5 \end{pmatrix}\begin{pmatrix} 2 & 4 & 0{\cdot}5 & 1 \\ 6 & 8 & 2 & 4 \\ 3 & 1 & -3 & 0{\cdot}5 \end{pmatrix}$

20 $\begin{pmatrix} 1 & 2 & -1 \end{pmatrix}\begin{pmatrix} 0{\cdot}5 \\ 2 \\ 2{\cdot}5 \end{pmatrix}$

Simultaneous equations—determinants

$$\begin{pmatrix} 9 & 4 \\ 2 & 1 \end{pmatrix}\begin{pmatrix} x \\ y \end{pmatrix} = \begin{pmatrix} 9x + 4y \\ 2x + y \end{pmatrix}$$

Thus the equations $9x + 4y = 17$

and $2x + y = 4$

can be written $\begin{pmatrix} 9 & 4 \\ 2 & 1 \end{pmatrix}\begin{pmatrix} x \\ y \end{pmatrix} = \begin{pmatrix} 17 \\ 4 \end{pmatrix}$

It can be verified that the solution of these equations is $\begin{pmatrix} x \\ y \end{pmatrix} = \begin{pmatrix} 1 \\ 2 \end{pmatrix}$.

The equations $3x + 4y = 7$

and $6x + 8y = 14$

cannot be solved uniquely, as for any value of x there is an appropriate value for y which will satisfy both equations. Similarly the equations

$$3x + 4y = 7$$

and $$9x + 12y = 7$$

have no solutions at all, as it is impossible to find values of x and y which satisfy both simultaneously. In fact whenever the coefficients of x and y in one equation are the same multiple of the coefficients in the other equation there is no solution; the equations are either **consistent** like the first pair above or **inconsistent** like the second.

In general two equations are of the form

$$ax + by = e$$
$$\text{and} \qquad cx + dy = f.$$

If $\frac{a}{c} = \frac{b}{d}$ there are no solutions. This is usually written $ad = bc$, and $ad - bc$ is called the **determinant** of the matrix $\begin{pmatrix} a & b \\ c & d \end{pmatrix}$. If the determinant is zero the equations $\begin{pmatrix} a & b \\ c & d \end{pmatrix}\begin{pmatrix} x \\ y \end{pmatrix} = \begin{pmatrix} e \\ f \end{pmatrix}$ have no unique solution.

The inverse of a matrix

If any two by two matrix is multiplied by $\begin{pmatrix} 1 & 0 \\ 0 & 1 \end{pmatrix}$ it remains the same, because $\begin{pmatrix} 1 & 0 \\ 0 & 1 \end{pmatrix}\begin{pmatrix} a & b \\ c & d \end{pmatrix} = \begin{pmatrix} a & b \\ c & d \end{pmatrix}$.

$\begin{pmatrix} 1 & 0 \\ 0 & 1 \end{pmatrix}$ is called the **identity matrix** and is given the symbol I.

Consider the problem of finding a matrix such that, when multiplied by a given matrix, the product is the identity matrix.

Take $A = \begin{pmatrix} 2 & 5 \\ 3 & 8 \end{pmatrix}$ and $B = \begin{pmatrix} a & b \\ c & d \end{pmatrix}$;

$AB = I$ gives $\qquad \begin{pmatrix} 2 & 5 \\ 3 & 8 \end{pmatrix}\begin{pmatrix} a & b \\ c & d \end{pmatrix} = \begin{pmatrix} 1 & 0 \\ 0 & 1 \end{pmatrix}$

$$\therefore 2a + 5c = 1 \qquad \text{(i)}$$
$$3a + 8c = 0 \qquad \text{(ii)}$$
$$2b + 5d = 0 \qquad \text{(iii)}$$
$$3b + 8d = 1 \qquad \text{(iv)}$$

Solving first (i) and (ii),

$$\text{(i)} \times 3 \qquad 6a + 15c = 3 \qquad \text{(v)}$$
$$\text{(ii)} \times 2 \qquad 6a + 16c = 0 \qquad \text{(vi)}$$
$$\text{(v)} - \text{(vi)} \qquad -c = 3$$
$$\therefore c = -3$$

Substitute in (i) $\quad 2a - 15 = 1$

$$\therefore 2a = 16$$

$$\therefore a = 8$$

Solving (iii) and (iv),

$$\begin{array}{lll} \text{(iii)} \times 3 & 6b + 15d = 0 & \text{(vii)} \\ \text{(iv)} \times 2 & 6b + 16d = 2 & \text{(viii)} \\ \text{(vii)} - \text{(viii)} & -d = -2 & \\ & \therefore d = 2 & \end{array}$$

Substitute in (iii) $\quad 2b + 10 = 0$

$$\therefore b = -5$$

$$\therefore \begin{pmatrix} a & b \\ c & d \end{pmatrix} = \begin{pmatrix} 8 & -5 \\ -3 & 2 \end{pmatrix}$$

Comparing this with $\begin{pmatrix} 2 & 5 \\ 3 & 8 \end{pmatrix}$, it is seen that 2 and 8 are interchanged, and the signs of 3 and 5 are changed.

Note also that $\begin{pmatrix} 8 & -5 \\ -3 & 2 \end{pmatrix}\begin{pmatrix} 2 & 5 \\ 3 & 8 \end{pmatrix} = \begin{pmatrix} 1 & 0 \\ 0 & 1 \end{pmatrix}$.

From this it can be seen that $\begin{pmatrix} 2 & 5 \\ 3 & 8 \end{pmatrix}$ and $\begin{pmatrix} 8 & -5 \\ -3 & 2 \end{pmatrix}$ have a special relationship to each other; one is called the **inverse** of the other. The inverse of a matrix is defined as that matrix which, when either pre-multiplying or post-multiplying the original matrix, has a product equal to the identity matrix I. The inverse of the inverse of a matrix is always the original matrix.

$$\begin{pmatrix} 3 & 2 \\ 4 & 5 \end{pmatrix}\begin{pmatrix} 5 & -2 \\ -4 & 3 \end{pmatrix} = \begin{pmatrix} 7 & 0 \\ 0 & 7 \end{pmatrix}$$

$$= 7\begin{pmatrix} 1 & 0 \\ 0 & 1 \end{pmatrix}$$

$\therefore$ the inverse of $\begin{pmatrix} 3 & 2 \\ 4 & 5 \end{pmatrix}$ is $\frac{1}{7}\begin{pmatrix} 5 & -2 \\ -4 & 3 \end{pmatrix}$ and the inverse of $\begin{pmatrix} 5 & -2 \\ -4 & 3 \end{pmatrix}$ is $\frac{1}{7}\begin{pmatrix} 3 & 2 \\ 4 & 5 \end{pmatrix}$.

7 is the determinant of both $\begin{pmatrix} 3 & 2 \\ 4 & 5 \end{pmatrix}$ and of $\begin{pmatrix} 5 & -2 \\ -4 & 3 \end{pmatrix}$.

In general, the inverse of $\begin{pmatrix} a & b \\ c & d \end{pmatrix}$ is $\dfrac{1}{\mathbf{ad} - \mathbf{bc}}\begin{pmatrix} \mathbf{d} & -\mathbf{b} \\ -\mathbf{c} & \mathbf{a} \end{pmatrix}$.

That is to say; to find the inverse of a two by two matrix the first element of the first row is interchanged with the second element of the second row; the other two elements, namely the second element of the first row and the first element of the second row, are both multiplied by -1, and the resulting matrix is divided by the determinant of the original matrix. It follows that a matrix whose determinant is zero has no inverse.

Example 4 *Find the inverse of* $\begin{pmatrix} 3 & -2 \\ 4 & 1 \end{pmatrix}$.

The determinant of $\begin{pmatrix} 3 & -2 \\ 4 & 1 \end{pmatrix} = 3 \times 1 - 4 \times (-2)$

$$= 3 + 8$$
$$= 11$$

$\therefore$ the inverse of $\begin{pmatrix} 3 & -2 \\ 4 & 1 \end{pmatrix}$ is $\dfrac{1}{11}\begin{pmatrix} 1 & 2 \\ -4 & 3 \end{pmatrix}$.

Check $\begin{pmatrix} 1 & 2 \\ -4 & 3 \end{pmatrix}\begin{pmatrix} 3 & -2 \\ 4 & 1 \end{pmatrix} = \begin{pmatrix} 11 & 0 \\ 0 & 11 \end{pmatrix}$

$$\therefore \frac{1}{11}\begin{pmatrix} 1 & 2 \\ -4 & 3 \end{pmatrix}\begin{pmatrix} 3 & -2 \\ 4 & 1 \end{pmatrix} = \begin{pmatrix} 1 & 0 \\ 0 & 1 \end{pmatrix}$$

Solution of simultaneous linear equations

The technique of multiplying by the inverse can be used to solve simultaneous equations. Considering again the equations on page 243:

$$\begin{pmatrix} 9 & 4 \\ 2 & 1 \end{pmatrix}\begin{pmatrix} x \\ y \end{pmatrix} = \begin{pmatrix} 17 \\ 4 \end{pmatrix},$$

the inverse of $\begin{pmatrix} 9 & 4 \\ 2 & 1 \end{pmatrix}$ is $\begin{pmatrix} 1 & -4 \\ -2 & 9 \end{pmatrix}$ and both sides of the equation are pre-multiplied by this matrix;

$$\begin{pmatrix} 1 & -4 \\ -2 & 9 \end{pmatrix}\begin{pmatrix} 9 & 4 \\ 2 & 1 \end{pmatrix}\begin{pmatrix} x \\ y \end{pmatrix} = \begin{pmatrix} 1 & -4 \\ -2 & 9 \end{pmatrix}\begin{pmatrix} 17 \\ 4 \end{pmatrix}$$

$$\therefore \begin{pmatrix} 1 & 0 \\ 0 & 1 \end{pmatrix}\begin{pmatrix} x \\ y \end{pmatrix} = \begin{pmatrix} 1 \\ 2 \end{pmatrix}$$

$$\therefore x = 1$$
$$\text{and } y = 2.$$

Example 5 *Solve the equations* $3x - 4y = 1$ *and* $7x + y = 23$.

The equations are $\begin{pmatrix} 3 & -4 \\ 7 & 1 \end{pmatrix}\begin{pmatrix} x \\ y \end{pmatrix} = \begin{pmatrix} 1 \\ 23 \end{pmatrix}$.

The determinant of $\begin{pmatrix} 3 & -4 \\ 7 & 1 \end{pmatrix}$ is $3 \times 1 - 7 \times (-4) = 31$,

$\therefore$ the inverse is $\frac{1}{31}\begin{pmatrix} 1 & 4 \\ -7 & 3 \end{pmatrix}$.

Pre-multiplying by the inverse,

$$\frac{1}{31}\begin{pmatrix} 1 & 4 \\ -7 & 3 \end{pmatrix}\begin{pmatrix} 3 & -4 \\ 7 & 1 \end{pmatrix}\begin{pmatrix} x \\ y \end{pmatrix} = \frac{1}{31}\begin{pmatrix} 1 & 4 \\ -7 & 3 \end{pmatrix}\begin{pmatrix} 1 \\ 23 \end{pmatrix}$$

$$\therefore \frac{1}{31}\begin{pmatrix} 31 & 0 \\ 0 & 31 \end{pmatrix}\begin{pmatrix} x \\ y \end{pmatrix} = \frac{1}{31}\begin{pmatrix} 93 \\ 62 \end{pmatrix}$$

$$\therefore \begin{pmatrix} 1 & 0 \\ 0 & 1 \end{pmatrix}\begin{pmatrix} x \\ y \end{pmatrix} = \begin{pmatrix} 3 \\ 2 \end{pmatrix}$$

$$\therefore x = 3, y = 2.$$

Check $3 \times 3 - 4 \times 2 = 1$ and $7 \times 3 + 2 = 23$.

Exercise 21c

Find the determinants of the following matrices:

1 $\begin{pmatrix} 6 & 3 \\ 2 & 1 \end{pmatrix}$ **2** $\begin{pmatrix} 2 & 3 \\ 1 & 2 \end{pmatrix}$

3 $\begin{pmatrix} 120 & 10 \\ 12 & 0{\cdot}5 \end{pmatrix}$ **4** $\begin{pmatrix} 120 & 100 \\ 1{\cdot}2 & 1 \end{pmatrix}$

5 $\begin{pmatrix} 6{\cdot}3 & 2{\cdot}4 \\ 5{\cdot}1 & 3{\cdot}2 \end{pmatrix}$

Find the inverses of the following matrices where possible:

6 $\begin{pmatrix} 3 & -2 \\ -4 & 3 \end{pmatrix}$

7 $\begin{pmatrix} 6 & 3 \\ 2 & 1 \end{pmatrix}$

8 $\begin{pmatrix} 4 & 3 \\ 2 & 1 \end{pmatrix}$

9 $\begin{pmatrix} 4{\cdot}5 & 3{\cdot}2 \\ 5 & 4 \end{pmatrix}$

10 $\frac{1}{2}\begin{pmatrix} 4 & 1 \\ 16 & 3 \end{pmatrix}$ (*Multiply first by the* $\frac{1}{2}$)

Solve the following simultaneous equations where possible, using the matrix method:

11 $6x + 11y = 29$
$x + 2y = 5$

12 $7x + 4y = 29$
$4x + 2y = 16$

13 $2x + y = 3$
$4x + 2y = 6$

14 $21x - 2y = 15$
$13x - y = 10$

15 $4x - 2y = 9$
$x + y = 3$

16 $x - 3y = 2$
$2x + 4y = -1$

17 $2a - 3b = 3$
$a + b = 4$

18 $\frac{u}{2} - \frac{v}{3} = 4$
$\frac{u}{3} + \frac{v}{2} = 7$

19 $5s - 2t = \frac{4}{3}$
$s + 3t = \frac{5}{6}$

20 $\frac{3c}{2} - \frac{d}{4} = -\frac{1}{2}$
$\frac{2c}{3} - \frac{d}{5} = -\frac{2}{3}$

21 What is the inverse of $\begin{pmatrix} 13 & 4 \\ 3 & 1 \end{pmatrix}$?

Hence find the matrix $\begin{pmatrix} a & b \\ c & d \end{pmatrix}$ where

$$\begin{pmatrix} 13 & 4 \\ 3 & 1 \end{pmatrix}\begin{pmatrix} a & b \\ c & d \end{pmatrix} = \begin{pmatrix} 1 & 3 \\ 2 & 0 \end{pmatrix}.$$

22 Use the method of no. 21 to solve,

$$\begin{pmatrix} 5 & 2 \\ 2 & 1 \end{pmatrix}\begin{pmatrix} a & b \\ c & d \end{pmatrix} = \begin{pmatrix} 2 & 5 \\ 6 & 1 \end{pmatrix}.$$

If further examples are required Exercises 14b and 14c can be solved by the matrix method.

Chapter 22

Plans and elevations (1)

Oblique projection

Fig. 138 shows a rectangular box or cuboid: the edges which are not in fact visible are indicated by dotted lines. The front face DCGH is drawn rectangular and to scale, but it will be noticed that all the other faces (except ABFE) are parallelograms, and that the dimension 4 cm is foreshortened in order to give the appearance of solidity.

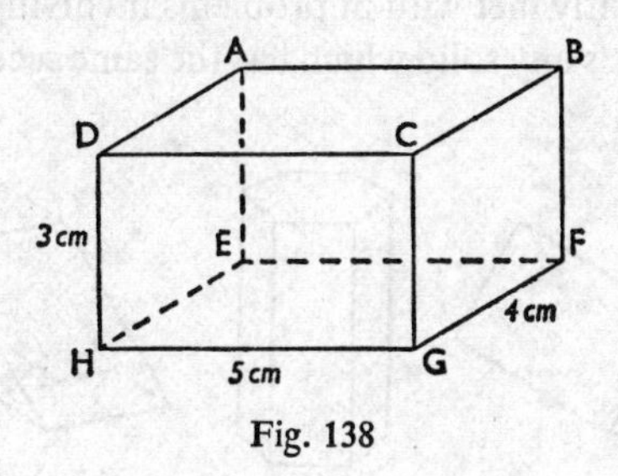

Fig. 138

For convenience in representing solid figures quickly, using ordinary set-squares, the angle at which $\overline{FG}$ is offset is generally 30°, 45° or 60°, and the foreshortening which results in a reasonably lifelike figure is obtained by drawing foreshortened lines about two-thirds or three-quarters of their true scale lengths.

Notice that all lines which are parallel in the solid are also parallel in the drawing, and that vertical lines in the solid are also vertical in the drawing.

In Fig. 139, which shows a pyramid 8 cm high on a base 6 cm square, notice that the height $\overline{OP}$ is drawn vertically so that O comes directly above P, the centre of the base. In this figure only $\overline{OP}$, $\overline{CD}$ and $\overline{AB}$ are drawn their true scale lengths, all the other lines being foreshortened.

This is called a **right pyramid** because the line $\overline{OP}$ is at right angles to the base; i.e. the pyramid stands upright, and is not leaning over at a slant.

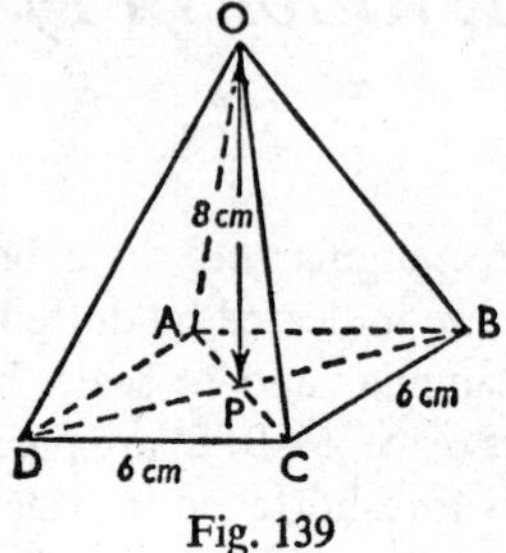

Fig. 139

Solids frequently met with in problems involving projection are **prisms.** A prism is any solid which has the same section throughout its length.

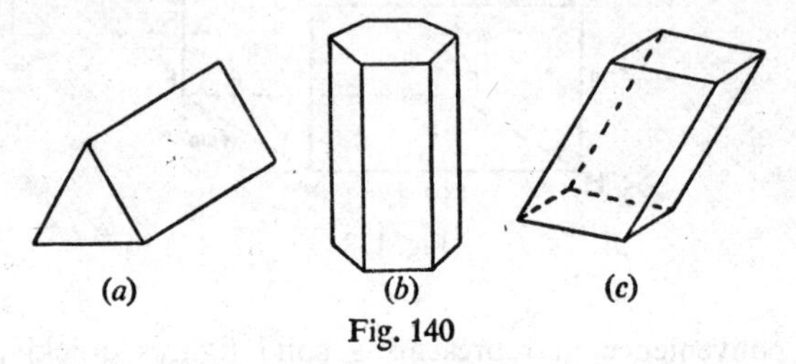

Fig. 140

Fig. 140 (*a*) shows a right triangular prism,
(*b*) „ „ „ hexagonal „ ,
(*c*) „ an oblique quadrilateral prism.

The word 'right', applied to a prism, means that the ends of the prism are at right angles to its length; i.e. that the prism would stand upright if placed on end.

Exercise 22a

Represent the following solids in oblique projection, full size:

1 A cuboid 7 cm long, 5 cm wide and 5 cm high.

2 A cuboid 6 cm long, 4 cm wide and 5 cm high.

3 A right pyramid 8 cm high on a square base of side 5 cm.

4 A right pyramid 9 cm high on a rectangular base 9 cm by 6 cm.

5 A right prism whose section is an equilateral triangle of side 3 cm, 8 cm in length, with one of the rectangular faces as base.

6 A right prism whose section is an isosceles triangle with sides 5 cm, 5 cm, 3 cm, and of length 7 cm, with the rectangular face 3 cm by 7 cm as base.

7 The same prism as that in no. 6, but with a 5 cm by 7 cm face as base.

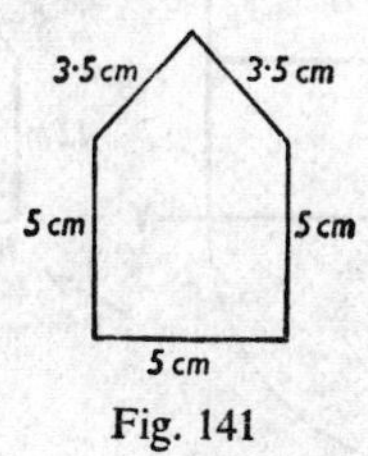

Fig. 141

8 A model of a barn whose section is shown in Fig. 141, the model being 9 cm long.

Plans and elevations

The practical disadvantage of representing a solid by a drawing in oblique projection is that measurements cannot be taken from it. When an architect is designing a building he first draws an oblique projection to give a general impression of the intended appearance of the building, and then breaks this drawing down into a **plan,** which shows the shape of the building when looked at from a point vertically above it, and also **elevations** of both the front of the building and the end of it, as shown in Fig. 142. The end elevation is the true view from P in the oblique projection, and the front elevation the true view from Q.

Notice that the plan and the elevations are connected by fine lines: these lines not only show the connections between the various parts of the figures, but also make it unnecessary to keep on using a ruler to measure lengths. Once lengths have been established in either plan or elevation they are simply transferred to other positions by drawing parallel lines or circular arcs.

In practice, begin by drawing whichever view is the easiest to construct, and then derive the others from it. In Fig 142 for instance, the order of the steps might be

(1) the end elevation, measuring all lines to an appropriate scale;

(2) the plan, drawing fine vertical lines through every point in

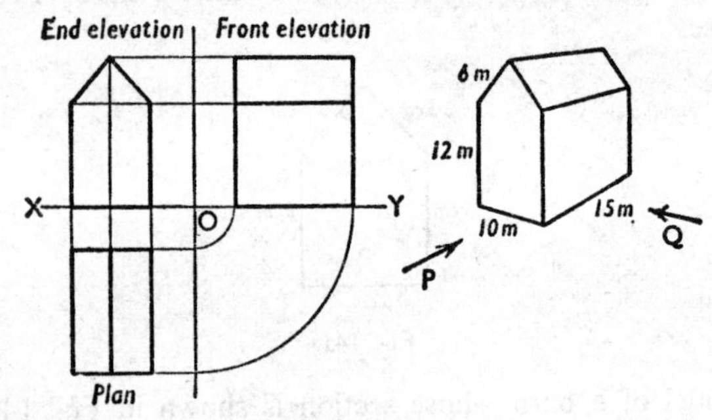

Fig. 142

the end elevation just drawn, and measuring only the length of 15 m to the same scale as before;

(3) the front elevation, constructing it on the same **ground line** XOY as for the end elevation.

Fig. 142 shows what construction lines are necessary, and also

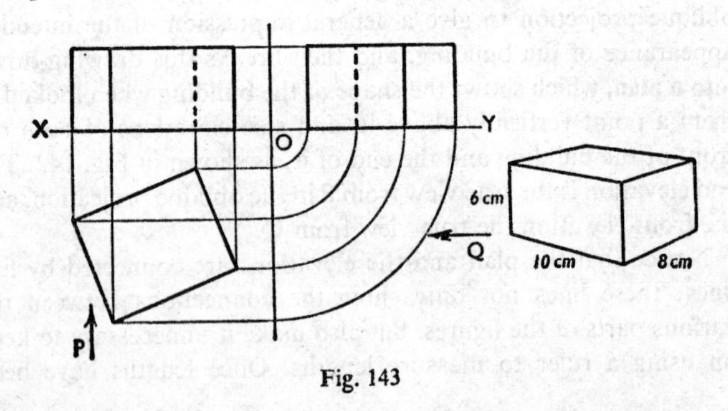

Fig. 143

that no further measurements have to be taken in order to obtain the front elevation, which is fully determined by the intersections of the various construction lines in the figure.

Fig. 143 shows the plan and elevation of a cuboid placed at an angle to the ground line. As the furthest edge of the cuboid is invisible to the viewer from P or from Q, this edge is shown dotted in the respective elevations. Notice particularly that the horizontal lines in these two elevations are foreshortened since the viewer is not looking directly at them.

Exercise 22b

1 Name the solids represented by the plans and elevations given in Fig. 144.

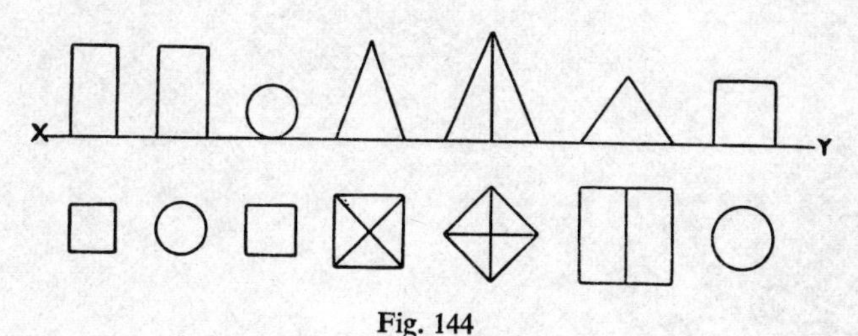

Fig. 144

Draw the plan and the front and end elevations of each of the following solids.

2 A cuboid 7·5 cm long, 5 cm wide and 3·5 cm high, with the long edges parallel to $\overline{XY}$.

3 The same cuboid as in no. 2, but with the long edges making an angle of 30° with $\overline{XY}$ (see Fig. 143).

4 A triangular prism whose section is an isosceles triangle with sides 5 cm, 5 cm, 3 cm, and which is 7 cm long, resting on the 3 cm by 7 cm face and placed parallel to $\overline{XY}$ lengthwise.

5 The same prism as in no. 4, but resting on one of the 5 cm by 7 cm faces.

6 As in no. 4, but with the 7 cm edge at 30° to $\overline{XY}$.

7 A right pyramid 7·5 cm high on a base 5 cm square, two edges of the base being parallel to $\overline{XY}$.

8 As in no. 7, but with the edges of the base at 45° to $\overline{XY}$.

9 As in no. 7, but with two edges of the base at 30° to $\overline{XY}$.

10 A circular disc 8 cm in diameter and 2 cm thick, placed flat on the horizontal plane.

11 A hexagonal prism of side 2 cm and length 6 cm, resting on one of the flat faces.

12 Draw the plan and two elevations of the building in Fig. 142, to a scale of 2 cm to 5 m, one long edge of the building being placed at 30° to $\overline{XY}$.

Chapter 23

Mensuration (2)

When a room is to be carpeted from wall to wall, so that none of the floor itself is left showing, the carpet is bought in rolls, cut into lengths to fit the room, and these lengths sewn together to cover the whole floor. The problem is therefore, knowing the width of the roll, to find out what total length will be needed: this length must be given as a whole number of metres (or yards), since carpeting is not sold in any other way.

Example 1 *French carpeting* 67 *cm wide is bought to cover a floor* 6·7 *m long and* 4·9 *m wide. What length of the carpet will be needed if it is laid* (*i*) *lengthwise?* (*ii*) *crosswise?*

(i) Width of room = 4·9 m = 490 cm

$\therefore$ number of strips $= \dfrac{490}{67} = 7\frac{21}{67}$

$\therefore$ 8 strips, each 6·7 m long, will be needed

$\therefore$ length needed = 8 × 6·7 m = 53·6 m

$\therefore$ 54 m must be bought.

(ii) Length of room = 6·7 m = 670 cm

$\therefore$ number of strips $= \dfrac{670}{67} = 10$

$\therefore$ length needed = 10 × 4·9 m = 49 m

$\therefore$ 49 m must be bought.

N.B. 67 cm is approximately two-thirds of a metre.

Wallpaper is bought by the 'piece', which is 10 m long and 50 cm wide (or 11 yd and 21 in), and enough whole pieces must be bought to cover the wall-space. No allowance is made for doors and windows, as there is bound to be some waste in fitting the pattern properly, and in cutting the paper to make it fit round these and other obstructions.

The process is exactly the same as for carpeting in strips: first find the number of strips required; then the total length needed; finally the number of pieces.

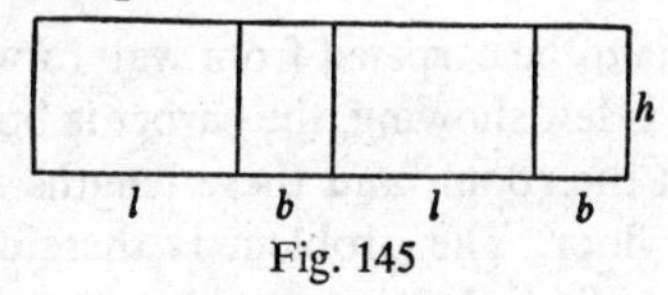

Fig. 145

Imagine the walls laid out flat: the total area to be covered is a rectangle $(2b + 2l)$ units long and h units high, assuming that h units is the height from the top of the skirting-board to the picture rail or to the ceiling, depending on the point at which the paper stops.

Example 2 *How many pieces of wallpaper will be needed for a room* 5·55 *m long,* 3·12 *m wide and* 2·65 *m high to the picture-rail?*

$$\text{Total width to be papered} = (2b + 2l)\text{ m} = (11{\cdot}10 + 6{\cdot}24)\text{ m} = 17{\cdot}34\text{ m}$$

$$\therefore \text{number of strips 50 cm wide} = \frac{1\,734}{50} = 34{\cdot}68$$

$\therefore$ 35 strips are required

$\therefore$ length required $= 35 \times 2{\cdot}65$ m

$$\therefore \text{number of pieces 10 m long required} = \frac{35 \times 2{\cdot}65}{10} = 9{\cdot}275$$

$\therefore$ 10 pieces are required.

Exercise 23a

1 What length of carpeting 2 ft 3 in wide or 70 cm wide, laid lengthwise, will be necessary for floors with the following dimensions?

(i) 20 ft by 15 ft 9 in
(ii) 30 ft by 20 ft 3 in
(iii) 17 ft by 13 ft 6 in
(iv) 15 ft 4 in by 11 ft 3 in
(v) 6 m by 4·2 m
(vi) 9 m by 6·2 m
(vii) 5·2 m by 4·1 m
(viii) 5·83 m by 3·44 m

2 How many pieces of wallpaper will be required for the following rooms?

	l		*b*		*h*			*l*	*b*	*h*
	ft	in	ft	in	ft	in		All lengths in metres		
(i)	7	6	6	6	8	0	(v)	2·8	2·7	2·3
(ii)	9	0	8	6	7	6	(vi)	3·9	3·2	3·1
(iii)	12	3	8	9	7	6	(vii)	2·84	2·27	2·13
(iv)	8	9	7	0	7	0	(viii)	3·15	2·63	2·31

3 What will be the cost of papering a room 3·1 m square and 2·2 m high with paper at 55p per piece?

4 What length of carpet 70 cm wide will be required for a room 4·9 m long and 2·8 m wide? Show that it does not matter which way the carpet is laid.

5 A room 5·5 m long and 4·6 m wide is to be covered with felt strips 105 cm wide, so as to leave a border 50 cm wide all round. How many metres of felt, laid lengthwise, will be needed?

6 How much will it cost to carpet a floor 4·8 m long and 4·3 m wide with carpeting 67 cm wide, if the carpet is laid lengthwise, and costs 68p per metre?

7 How many pieces of French wallpaper, approximately 8·2 m long and 64 cm wide, will be needed for a room 4 m long, 3·5 m wide, and 2·6 m high?

8 How much will it cost to lay a floor 5·1 m long and 4·2 m wide with planks 6 m long and 12 cm wide, laid lengthwise, at 27p per metre run?

9 How much will it cost to paper a room 3·12 m by 2·2 m, and 2·36 m high, with paper at 75p per piece, if there is also a decorative frieze at 25p per metre round the four walls?

10 What is the cost of painting, inside and out, an open rectangular box 1 m long, 70 cm wide and 50 cm deep, at 22·5p per square metre?

11 A man mows a lawn 24 m long and 15·4 m wide with a mower 50 cm wide, going over the surface once only. How far does he walk if he mows (i) lengthwise, (ii) crosswise?

12 How much money does a man lose if a carpet 5·3 m by 4·1 m, made in strips 70 cm wide, at 95p per metre, is laid crosswise instead of lengthwise?

13 A courtyard 8·55 m long and 5·89 m wide is to be paved with the largest possible square tiles which will fit in exactly. How many tiles will there be?

14 A room 14 ft long, 10 ft 6 in wide and 8 ft 4 in high is to be panelled with plywood, sold in sheets 9 ft long and 4 ft wide. If there are no horizontal joins in the panelling between floor and ceiling, how many sheets will have to be bought? What area of wood will be wasted? Allow a width of 7 ft for a door and window, which are not panelled above or below.

15 The bill for a carpet 4·5 m long, made from material 67 cm wide, at £1·25 per metre, laid crosswise, comes to £26·25. How wide is the carpet?

16 How many paving stones, each 1 m long and 80 cm wide, will be needed for a courtyard 13·6 m long and 11 m wide?

17 Twenty-six metres of carpeting 70 cm wide is used for covering a floor 3·5 m wide, and 15 cm of the carpeting is wasted. How long is the floor?

18 'Carpet tiles' are squares of carpet measuring 50 cm each way. If they are used to cover the floor of a room measuring 7·4 m by 4·5 m, find the cost at 65p per tile.

19 A room is 5·3 m long, 4·1 m wide, and 3·2 m high. One of the end walls is papered with paper at 80p per piece, and the other walls with paper at 54p per piece. What is the total cost of papering the room?

20 A room is 4·2 m long, 3·7 m wide and 3 m high. The picture-rail is 30 cm from the ceiling. The walls are to be papered up to the picture-rail with paper at 48p per piece, and that part of the walls above the picture-rail together with the ceiling is to be distempered at 8p per square metre. How much will it cost to decorate the room, if the cost of painting it was £3·74?

Circles and rings

Example 3 *What is the diameter of a circle of area* 3 850 m^2?

$$\text{Area} = \pi r^2 = 3\,850 \text{ m}^2$$
$$\therefore \tfrac{22}{7}r^2 = 3\,850$$
$$\therefore r^2 = 3\,850 \times \tfrac{7}{22} = 7^2 \times 5^2$$
$$\therefore r = 7 \times 5 = 35$$
$$\therefore \text{diameter} = 70 \text{ m}$$

Example 4 *What is the area of a flat washer* 4·8 *cm in outside diameter, the central hole being of diameter* 2·2 *cm?*

$$\begin{aligned}\text{Area} &= \pi(2{\cdot}4)^2 - \pi(1{\cdot}1)^2 && \text{cm}^2\\ &= \pi[2{\cdot}4^2 - 1{\cdot}1^2] && ,,\\ &= \pi(2{\cdot}4 + 1{\cdot}1)(2{\cdot}4 - 1{\cdot}1) && ,,\\ &= \tfrac{22}{7} \times 3{\cdot}5 \times 1{\cdot}3 && ,,\\ &= 14{\cdot}3 && ,,\end{aligned}$$

N.B. Full use is made of factors in order to simplify the arithmetical work: π is taken outside a bracket as soon as possible, and its numerical value is not substituted until the bracket has been simplified. By using the 'difference of two squares' the subsequent cancelling becomes extremely easy.

A slice cut out of a circle from its centre is called a **sector** (Fig. 146).

Any part of the circumference of a circle is called an **arc.**

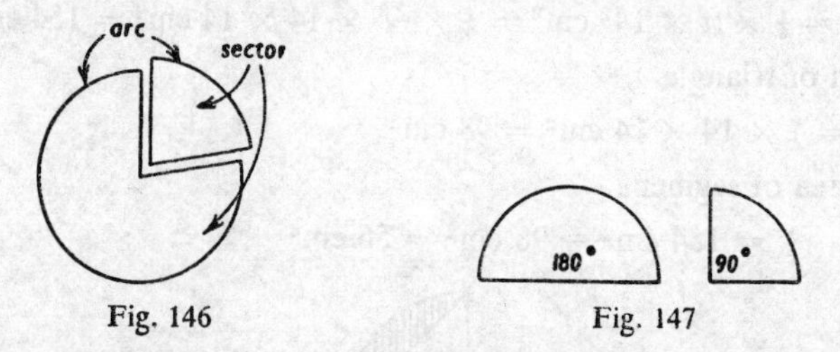

Fig. 146 Fig. 147

The whole angle round the centre of a circle is 360°: if therefore the angle of the sector is $x°$, the length of the arc is $x/360$ of the whole circumference of the circle, and the area of the sector is $x/360$ of the whole area of the circle.

A sector having an angle of 180° at the centre is called a **semicircle,** and one with an angle of 90° a **quadrant** of the circle.

Example 5 *Find the area and perimeter of a sector of a circle of radius* 7 *cm, the angle at the centre of the circle being* 108°.

$$\text{Area} = \tfrac{108}{360} \text{ of } \pi \times 7^2 \text{ cm}^2 = \tfrac{108}{360} \times \tfrac{22}{7} \times 7 \times 7 \text{ cm}^2 = 46{\cdot}2 \text{ cm}^2$$

$$\text{Arc} = \tfrac{108}{360} \text{ of } 2\pi \times 7 \text{ cm} = \tfrac{108}{360} \times 2 \times \tfrac{22}{7} \times 7 \text{ cm} = 13{\cdot}2 \text{ cm}$$

$$\therefore \text{perimeter} = (13{\cdot}2 + 7 + 7) \text{ cm} = 27{\cdot}2 \text{ cm}$$

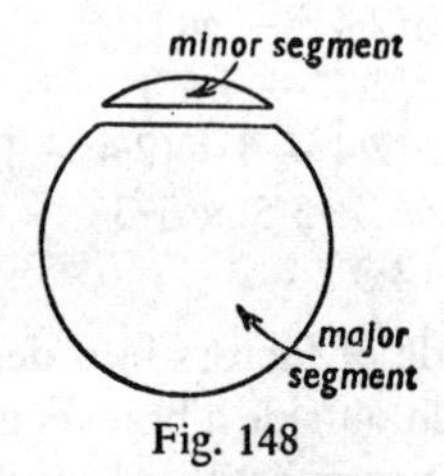

Fig. 148

If a circle is divided into two parts by a chord, the two parts are called **major** and **minor segments** of the circle.

Example 6 *Find the area of the shaded segment for a quadrant of radius* 14 *cm* (Fig. 149).

Area of quadrant

$$= \tfrac{1}{4} \times \pi \times 14^2 \text{ cm}^2 = \tfrac{1}{4} \times \tfrac{22}{7} \times 14 \times 14 \text{ cm}^2 = 154 \text{ cm}^2$$

Area of triangle

$$= \tfrac{1}{2} \times 14 \times 14 \text{ cm}^2 = 98 \text{ cm}^2$$

∴ area of segment

$$= 154 \text{ cm}^2 - 98 \text{ cm}^2 = 56 \text{ cm}^2$$

Fig. 149

Exercise 23b

Throughout this exercise take $\pi = \frac{22}{7}$.

1 Complete the following table for sectors of circles, and give a rough sketch of each.

	Radius	Angle at centre	Arc	Area	Perimeter
(i)	7 cm	90°			
(ii)	35 m	72°			
(iii)	4·2 cm	120°			
(iv)	5·6 cm	135°			
(v)	14 m	300°			
(vi)	21 cm		22 cm		
(vii)		150°	330 m		
(viii)		108°		4 620 cm²	

2 Find the area of each of the rings whose outside and inside diameters are given:

(i) 8 m and 6 m (ii) 22 cm and 20 cm
(iii) 8·6 cm and 8·2 cm (iv) 15 m and 6 m.

3 Find the radii of circles having areas (i) 154 cm², (ii) 1 386 cm², (iii) $86\frac{5}{8}$ m², (iv) 6·16 ha.

4

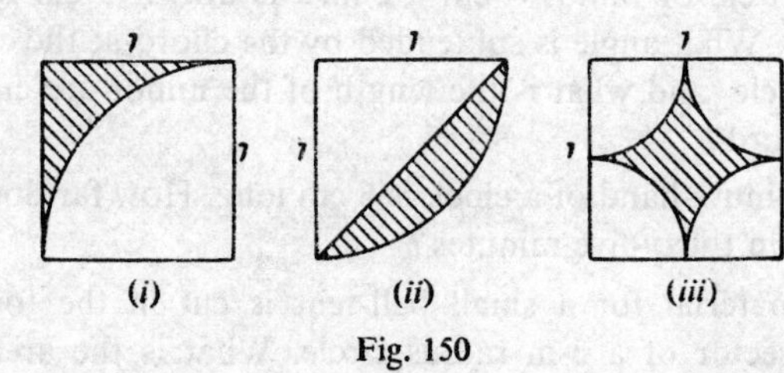

Fig. 150

Find the area of the shaded part of each of the above figures, all dimensions given being in cm.

5 If four pencils, each of diameter 7 mm, are held together in a square by an elastic band, how long is the band in this stretched position?

6 Two circular lead discs of radii 3 cm and 4 cm are melted down and cast into a single disc of the same thickness as before. What is the radius of this disc?

7 A machine-gun with a range of 4 200 m can sweep through an angle of 88°. What area in hectares does its field of fire cover?

8 A piece of wire 22 cm long is bent into an arc of a circle of radius 4 cm. What angle does the wire subtend at the centre of the circle?

9 In order to find the diameter of a wooden roller a piece of string was wound tightly round it for twenty complete turns. The length of the string was found to be 3·96 metres. What was the diameter of the roller in centimetres?

10 What angle does an arc of 10 cm subtend at the centre of a circle of radius 10 cm? Answer in degrees and minutes to the nearest minute.

11 The friction pad in a motorcycle shock absorber is a flat ring of fibre 10 cm in diameter with a 3-cm diameter hole in the middle. What is the area of the fibre?

12 The arm of a beam-engine travels through 35°: if the arm is three metres long, how far does its end travel in one swing of the beam?

13 In a circle of radius 6 cm a chord is drawn 3 cm from the centre. What angle is subtended by the chord at the centre of the circle, and what is the length of the minor arc cut off by the chord?

14 The minute-hand of a clock is 6 cm long. How far does its tip travel in thirty-five minutes?

15 The material for a small bell-tent is cut in the form of a 210° sector of a 3-m radius circle. What is the area of the material used?

16 The pendulum of a grandfather clock can swing through 5° on either side of the vertical. If the tip of the pendulum is 105 cm from the point of suspension, how far does it travel in an hour, one complete swing (back to the starting-point) taking two seconds?

Fig. 151

17 A sheet of corrugated iron is in section a series of arcs of 10 cm radius, each arc subtending 120° at its centre. If there are 14 arcs in one sheet, how wide would the sheet be if flattened?

18 Water is drawn from a well 11 m deep by means of a bucket, the rope winding on to a drum 35 cm in diameter.

(i) Through what angle does the handle turn in winding up one metre of rope?

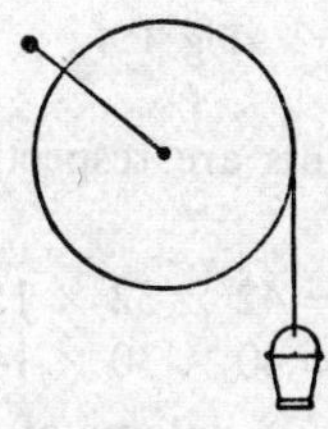
Fig. 152

(ii) How many revolutions of the handle are needed to bring the bucket up the full 11 m?

(iii) If the arm of the handle is 42 cm long, how far does the hand of the winder travel in bringing the bucket up from the bottom?

19 What is the cross-sectional area of a round metal pipe, its outside diameter being 13·5 cm, and the thickness of the metal 0·25 cm?

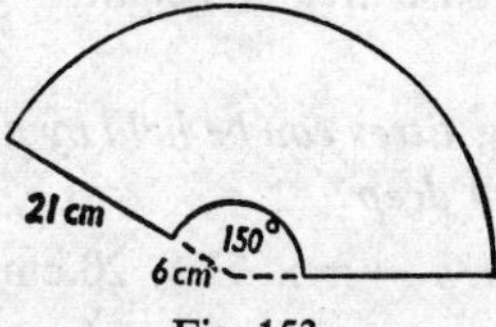

Fig. 153

20 The wind-screen wiper of a car sweeps through an angle of 150°, the blade of the wiper being 21 cm long and the radius of the unswept sector 6 cm. What area of glass is swept clean?

Cylinders, boxes, tanks, etc.

Example 7 *What is the volume of wood in an open rectangular box made of wood 1 cm thick, if the external dimensions of the box are 42 cm long, 32 cm wide and 15 cm deep?*

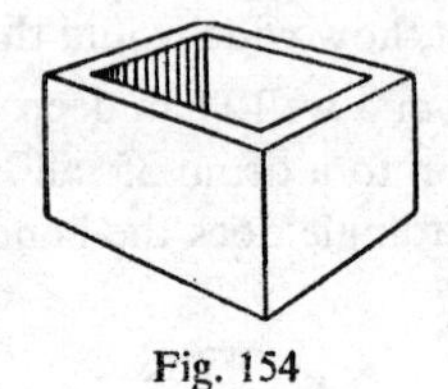

Fig. 154

The inside measurements are respectively 40 cm, 30 cm and 14 cm.

$\therefore$ external volume $= 42 \times 32 \times 15 \text{ cm}^3 = 20\,160 \text{ cm}^3$
internal ,, $= 40 \times 30 \times 14 \text{ cm}^3 = 16\,800 \text{ cm}^3$
$\therefore$ volume of wood $= 3\,360 \text{ cm}^3$

Fig. 155

The volume of a right circular cylinder

$$= \text{base area} \times \text{height} = \pi r^2 h$$

Example 8 *How many litres can be held by a cylindrical can 14 cm in diameter and 20 cm deep?*

Vol. of can $= \pi r^2 h = \pi \times 7^2 \times 20 \text{ cm}^3$

$\therefore$ capacity $= \frac{22}{7} \times 49 \times 20 \div 1\,000$ litres $= 3{\cdot}08$ litres.

Example 9 *A circular sheet of lead 48 cm in diameter and 2 mm thick is melted and recast into a cylindrical bar 6 cm in diameter. How long is the bar?*

Let the bar be x cm long.

Then its volume $= \pi \times 3^2 \times x$ cm³

Volume of circular sheet $= \pi \times 24^2 \times \frac{1}{5}$ cm³

$$\therefore \pi \times 3^2 \times x = \pi \times 24^2 \times \frac{1}{5}$$

$$\therefore x = \frac{\pi \times 24^2 \times \frac{1}{5}}{\pi \times 3^2} = \frac{576}{9 \times 5} = \frac{64}{5} = 12{\cdot}8$$

$\therefore$ bar is 12·8 cm long.

Notice particularly that in Example 9 no numerical value is used for π. *Never* substitute a number for π until it is obvious that such a substitution is necessary.

Exercise 23c

In nos. 1–20 take $\pi = \frac{22}{7}$ where necessary.
In nos. 21–30 no numerical value is to be used for π.

1 An open concrete tank is internally 1 m wide, 2 m long and 1·5 m deep, the concrete being 10 cm thick. What is the capacity of the tank in litres, and the volume of concrete used (in cubic metres)?

2 A pig-trough is in the form of an open rectangular box 2 m long, 30 cm wide and 22·5 cm deep internally. If the trough is made of boards 2·5 cm thick, what volume of wood is required (in cubic centimetres)?

3 What is the volume of a cylindrical steel bar 3·5 cm in diameter and 8 cm long?

4 99 litres of oil are poured into a cylindrical drum 30 cm in diameter. How deep is the oil in the drum?

5 A cylindrical wine-vat is two metres in diameter and three and a half metres deep. How many litres will it hold?

6 A blanket-chest is internally 120 cm long, 75 cm wide and 75 cm deep. It is to be lined on sides and bottom with cedar veneer of negligible thickness. How many square metres of veneer are needed?

7 A tobacco-tin 10 cm long, 7·5 cm wide and 2 cm deep holds 60 g of tobacco. If half a kilo of the same tobacco is packed into a tin 10 cm square, how tall will the tin have to be?

8 A solid concrete cylinder, used as a tank trap, is one metre long and 56 cm in diameter. What is its volume in cubic metres? What is its mass if one cubic metre of concrete has a mass of 2 050 kg?

9 What is the mass in kilograms of a round brass bar 5 m long and 28 mm in diameter, the density of the brass being 8 g per cubic centimetre?

10 How many litres of water will a cylindrical pipe hold if the pipe is one metre long and 7 cm in diameter?

11 The most economical shape for a closed cylindrical tin is one in which the height and diameter are equal. What is the capacity in litres of such a tin 10 cm high? (2 sig. fig.)

12 $2\frac{1}{2}$ litres of oil are poured into a container whose section is a square of side $12\frac{1}{2}$ cm. How deep does the oil fill the container?

13 The cross-section of a gutter is a rectangle 20 cm wide. If water 2·8 cm deep flows along the gutter at the rate of 15 cm/s, how many litres does it carry per minute?

14 A stone sink is in the form of a shallow rectangular tray 60 cm long, 35 cm wide and 15 cm deep internally. The stone is 2·5 cm thick and one cubic centimetre of it has a mass of 2·5 g. What is the mass of the sink?

15 If water flows through a 7-cm diameter pipe at the rate of four metres per second, what is the discharge in litres per minute?

16 A cylindrical water-butt 105 cm in diameter and 150 cm high is full of water. If a leak in the bottom drains away ten litres of the water in one hour, how long will it take to bring the water-level down by 20 cm?

17 What is the mass in kg of a round wooden bar one metre long and 8 cm in diameter if 1 cm^3 of the wood has a mass of 0·7 g?

18 An iron pipe is of the section shown in Fig. 156, the iron being 1 cm thick. The mass of 1 cm^3 of cast iron is 7·2 g. What is the mass of a two-metre length of the pipe?

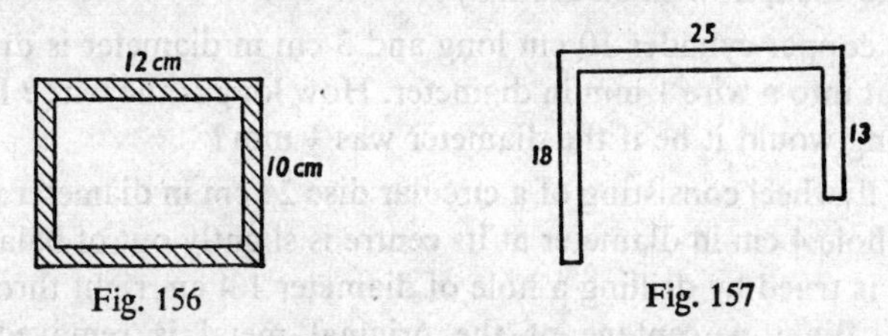

Fig. 156 Fig. 157

19 If the mass of a cubic metre of soil is $1\frac{1}{2}$ tonnes, what mass of soil will have to be excavated in digging a trench of the shape shown in Fig. 157 to a uniform width of 1 m and depth of 1·5 m? Dimensions are given in metres.

20 An open rectangular glass jar used as an aquarium is 30 cm deep, the base being 16 cm by 17 cm (all measurements external). If the glass is 0·5 cm thick and its mass is 3 g per cm^3, find (i) the capacity of the jar in litres, (ii) the mass of the jar in kg.

---

21 A lead disc 12 cm in diameter and 5 cm thick is melted down and cast into a cylindrical bar of diameter 5 cm. How long is the bar?

22 A half-kilo lump of butter is in the form of a solid cylinder approximately 8 cm in diameter and 8 cm long. If the lump is moulded into circular 'pats' 4 cm in diameter and 5 mm thick, how many pats are there?

23 The mass of a circular disc of silver 5 mm thick and 8 cm in diameter is 264 g. What would be the mass of a silver wire 1 m long and 1 mm in diameter?

24 A lemonade jug is 12 cm in diameter and 25 cm deep. If the jug is filled to the brim and the lemonade is poured into glasses 5 cm in diameter, filling them to a uniform depth of 6 cm, how many glasses can be filled?

25 A stick of sealing-wax is 16 cm long and $1\frac{1}{2}$ cm in diameter, and is used for legal documents on which each seal is a disc approximately 5 cm in diameter. If 6 seals can be made out of one stick, how thick are they?

26 A copper cylinder 10 cm long and 3 cm in diameter is drawn out into a wire 1 mm in diameter. How long is the wire? How long would it be if the diameter was $\frac{1}{2}$ mm?

27 A flywheel consisting of a circular disc 24 cm in diameter with a hole 4 cm in diameter at its centre is slightly out of balance. It is trued by drilling a hole of diameter 1·4 cm right through it. What percentage of the original metal is removed by drilling?

28 A circular pond $1\frac{1}{2}$ m in diameter and 16 cm deep is emptied through a 2-cm diameter tube. If the water in the tube is moving at 3 m/s, how long does it take to empty the pond?

29 A circular metal washer is such that the area of the metal is three times the area of the central hole. Prove that the external radius of the washer is equal to the diameter of the hole.

30 A blank for a bolt is made from a steel cylinder by turning away half its diameter for four-fifths of its length. What percentage of the original metal remains?

Chapter 24

Quadratic equations (1)

If the product of two numbers is 0, then one of the numbers (but not necessarily both) must be 0,

e.g. $3 \times 0 = 0$ and $0 \times 5 = 0$.

In general, if $a \times b = 0$

then either $a = 0$ *or* $b = 0$.

Example 1 *Solve the equation* $(x - 2)(x + 7) = 0$.

If $(x - 2)(x + 7) = 0$
then either $x - 2 = 0$ or $x + 7 = 0$

$\therefore x = 2$ or -7.

Example 2 *Solve the equation* $a(a + 3) = 0$.

If $a(a + 3) = 0$
then either $a = 0$ or $a + 3 = 0$

$\therefore a = 0$ or -3.

Example 3 *Solve the equation* $(m - 5)^2 = 0$.

If $(m - 5)^2 = 0$
then $(m - 5)(m - 5) = 0$
i.e. $m - 5 = 0$ twice

$\therefore m = 5$ twice.

Example 4 *Solve the equation* $d(d - 4)(d + 6)^2 = 0$.

If $d(d - 4)(d + 6)^2 = 0$, then any *one* of the four factors of the L.H.S. may be 0,

i.e. $d = 0$ or $d - 4 = 0$ or $d + 6 = 0$ twice

$\therefore d = 0, 4,$ or -6 twice.

The significance of the **repeated roots** in Examples 3 and 4 will be explained on page 280. For the present it should be noticed that

$$\text{if } x - 5 = 0 \quad \text{then } x = 5$$
$$\text{and if } (x - 5)^2 = 0 \quad \text{then } x = 5 \textit{ twice.}$$

Exercise 24a

Solve

1 $(a - 3)(a + 5) = 0$

2 $(b - 2)(b - 1) = 0$

3 $(x + 2)(x + 6) = 0$

4 $y(y - 5) = 0$

5 $(m - 3)^2(m - 4) = 0$

6 $(n - 5)(n + 3)^2 = 0$

7 $u(u + 5)(u + 1) = 0$

8 $(v - 7)(v + 5)(v - 3) = 0$

9 $x^2(x + 3) = 0$

10 $y^2(y - 4)^2 = 0$

11 $5(a + 2)(a - 4) = 0$

12 $4b(b + 6)^2 = 0$

13 $3d^2(d - 7) = 0$

14 $6m^2(m + 3)^2 = 0$

15 $(6 - n)(4 + n) = 0$

16 $(5 + u)(3 - u) = 0$

17 $v(v - 2)(v + 2) = 0$

18 $x^2(x + 5)(x - 5) = 0$

19 $y^2(3 + y) = 0$

20 $a(2 - a)^2(1 + a) = 0$

Example 5 *Solve the equation* $(3a + 2)(2a - 7) = 0$.

If $(3a + 2)(2a - 7) = 0$

$$\text{then either } 3a + 2 = 0 \quad \text{or} \quad 2a - 7 = 0$$
$$\therefore 3a = -2 \quad \text{or} \quad 2a = 7$$
$$\therefore a = -\tfrac{2}{3} \quad \text{or} \quad a = \tfrac{7}{2}$$
$$\text{i.e. } a = -\tfrac{2}{3} \text{ or } 3\tfrac{1}{2}.$$

Notice how these answers may be checked by substitution.

If $a = -\frac{2}{3}$, $(3a + 2)(2a - 7) = (-2 + 2)(-1\frac{1}{3} - 7)$
$= 0 \times -8\frac{1}{3} = 0.$

If $a = 3\frac{1}{2}$, $(3a + 2)(2a - 7) = (10\frac{1}{2} + 2)(7 - 7)$
$= 12\frac{1}{2} \times 0 = 0.$

Exercise 24b

Solve

1 $(d - 5)(3d - 2) = 0$

2 $(2m - 1)(m + 4) = 0$

3 $(a + 3)(5a + 2) = 0$

4 $(4x + 3)(3x + 1) = 0$

5 $(2y - 7)(y + 2) = 0$

6 $(4b - 12)(b - 5) = 0$

7 $(4h - 1)(2h + 3) = 0$

8 $(5 - d)(5 - 2d) = 0$

9 $(5 + 3m)(2 - 5m) = 0$

10 $(3n + 7)(4n - 1) = 0$

11 $(3a + 10)(3a - 12) = 0$

12 $(4b - 3)^2 = 0$

13 $(2c + 1)^2 = 0$

14 $(1 - 2d)(2 + 3d) = 0$

15 $(3e + 5)^2 = 0$

16 $m(3m - 4)(7 - 2m) = 0$

17 $(9 + 3n)(5 - 7n) = 0$

18 $(11 - 4x)^2 = 0$

19 $3y(2y + 9)(5 - y) = 0$

20 $5a^2(15 + 4a)^2 = 0$

A **quadratic equation** is an equation of second degree, i.e. an equation in which 2 is the highest power of the letter (or letters) involved.

An example of a quadratic equation is $m^2 - 5m - 14 = 0$, and it will be noticed that in this case the L.H.S. may be factorised. The equation then becomes $(m + 2)(m - 7) = 0$, which is like those done in Exercise 24b. Quadratic equations which cannot be solved by simple factorisation in this way will be dealt with in Book 3.

The solution can be described as the solution set of $\{m : m^2 - 5m - 14 = 0\}$. If $L = \{m : m + 2 = 0\}$ and $M = \{m : m - 7 = 0\}$, the solution set is $L \cup M$, which is the set containing the possible solutions $\{-2, 7\}$.

Example 6 *Solve the equation* $4y^2 + 5y - 21 = 0$.

$$4y^2 + 5y - 21 = 0$$
$$\therefore (y + 3)(4y - 7) = 0$$
$$\therefore \text{ either } y + 3 = 0 \quad \text{or} \quad 4y - 7 = 0$$
$$\therefore y = -3 \quad \text{or} \quad 4y = 7$$
$$\therefore y = -3 \quad \text{or} \quad y = \tfrac{7}{4}$$
$$\therefore y = -3 \text{ or } 1\tfrac{3}{4}.$$

Check by substitution.

If $y = -3$, $4y^2 + 5y - 21 = 36 - 15 - 21 = 0$.

If $y = 1\frac{3}{4}$, $4y^2 + 5y - 21 = 4 \times \frac{7}{4} \times \frac{7}{4} + 5 \times \frac{7}{4} - 21$

$$= \frac{49}{4} + \frac{35}{4} - 21 = 0.$$

Example 7 *Solve the equation* $m^2 = 16$.

$$(+4)^2 = 16 \quad \text{and} \quad (-4)^2 = 16$$

$$\therefore \sqrt{16} = +4 \quad \text{or} \quad -4, \text{ usually written as } \pm 4.$$

Similarly $\sqrt{m^2} = \pm m$.

Hence, taking the square root of both sides,

$$\text{if} \quad m^2 = 16$$
$$\text{then} \quad \pm m = \pm 4.$$

This result can be simplified. Written at length it means that

(i) $+m = +4$ (ii) $+m = -4$

(iii) $-m = +4$ (iv) $-m = -4$

But (i) and (iv) both mean that $+m = +4$,

and (ii) and (iii) both mean that $+m = -4$.

Hence the result may be written as $m = \pm 4$.

$$\text{Alternatively, if} \quad m^2 = 16$$
$$\text{then} \quad m^2 - 16 = 0.$$
$$\text{Factorising, } (m - 4)(m + 4) = 0$$
$$\therefore \text{ either } m - 4 = 0 \quad \text{or} \quad m + 4 = 0$$
$$\therefore m = +4 \quad \text{or} \quad -4$$
$$\text{i.e.} \quad m = \pm 4.$$

Example 8 *Solve the equation* $a^2 - 3a = 0$.

$$a^2 - 3a = 0$$
$$\therefore a(a - 3) = 0$$
$$\therefore \text{ either } a = 0 \quad \text{or} \quad a - 3 = 0$$
$$\therefore a = 0 \text{ or } 3.$$

Exercise 24c

Solve the following equations. Check the answers to the first ten by substitution.

1 $a^2 - 3a + 2 = 0$
2 $b^2 + 5b + 6 = 0$
3 $c^2 - c - 2 = 0$
4 $d^2 + 2d - 3 = 0$
5 $e^2 - 7e + 10 = 0$
6 $m^2 - 4m = 0$
7 $n^2 + 5n = 0$
8 $p^2 + 7p + 12 = 0$
9 $q^2 + 2q - 8 = 0$
10 $x^2 - 2x + 1 = 0$
11 $y^2 - 5y + 4 = 0$
12 $a^2 - 9a = 0$
13 $b^2 - 9 = 0$
14 $c^2 = 25$
15 $u^2 - 8u - 9 = 0$
16 $v^2 + 2v - 35 = 0$
17 $x^2 - 6x + 9 = 0$
18 $y^2 + 8y + 16 = 0$
19 $z^2 - 4z = 0$
20 $z^2 - 4 = 0$
21 $h^2 - 15h + 54 = 0$
22 $k^2 - 15k - 54 = 0$
23 $2m^2 - 5m = 0$
24 $2m^2 - 5m + 3 = 0$
25 $2m^2 - 5m - 3 = 0$
26 $3n^2 + n = 0$
27 $a^2 + a = 90$
28 $b^2 - b = 72$
29 $3x^2 + 4x + 1 = 0$
30 $9h^2 = 6h - 1$
31 $16k^2 + 8k + 1 = 0$
32 $2c^2 + 5c + 3 = 0$
33 $3d^2 - 5d - 2 = 0$
34 $4e^2 - 20e + 25 = 0$
35 $9f^2 + 12f + 4 = 0$
36 $4a^2 - 11a = 3$
37 $b^2 + 7b = 44$
38 $7m^2 = 3m$
39 $5n^2 + 2n = 0$
40 $2p^2 - 11p + 5 = 0$
41 $5q^2 + 11q + 2 = 0$
42 $25z^2 = 9$
43 $6y^2 = y + 1$
44 $6h^2 + 13h - 5 = 0$
45 $16t^2 = 49$
46 $4r^2 - 49 = 0$
47 $8s^2 + 14s = 15$
48 $6x^2 = 7x + 20$
49 $12y^2 + y - 35 = 0$
50 $63z = 49 + 18z^2$

Example 9 *Find the equation whose roots are* 4 *and* $-1\frac{2}{3}$.

If $x = 4$ or $-1\frac{2}{3}$

$$\text{then either } x - 4 = 0 \quad \text{or} \quad x + 1\tfrac{2}{3} = 0$$
$$\therefore x - 4 = 0 \quad \text{or} \quad 3x + 5 = 0$$
$$\therefore (x - 4)(3x + 5) = 0$$
$$\therefore 3x^2 - 7x - 20 = 0.$$

Exercise 24d

Find the equation whose roots are

1 2, 4	**2** 3, 5	**3** $-2, -4$	**4** $-3, -5$
5 $2, -5$	**6** $-1, 4$	**7** 0, 5	**8** $-4, 0$
9 $1, 1\frac{1}{2}$	**10** ± 2	**11** $2\frac{1}{3}, 3\frac{1}{2}$	**12** $-\frac{3}{4}, -\frac{1}{2}$
13 $-1\frac{1}{2}, 2\frac{1}{4}$	**14** $\pm 1\frac{2}{3}$	**15** $0, 1\frac{2}{3}$	

Sum and product of roots

Consider the equation whose roots are 2 and -5.
If $x = 2$ or -5

$$\text{then either } x - 2 = 0 \quad \text{or} \quad x + 5 = 0$$
$$\therefore (x - 2)(x + 5) = 0$$
$$\therefore x^2 + 3x - 10 = 0.$$

Notice that

(i) the coefficient of x in this equation is $+3$, which is the sum of the roots with the sign changed;

(ii) the absolute term in the equation is -10, which is the product of the roots.

In general, if the roots are h and k,

$$\text{then either } x = h \quad \text{or} \quad x = k$$
$$\therefore \text{either } x - h = 0 \quad \text{or} \quad x - k = 0$$
$$\therefore (x - h)(x - k) = 0$$
$$\therefore x^2 - hx - kx + hk = 0$$
$$\therefore x^2 - (h + k)x + hk = 0.$$

The coefficient of x in this equation is $-(h + k)$, which is the sum of h and k with the sign changed.

The absolute term is hk, which is the product of h and k.

This gives a useful method of checking the answers when solving a quadratic equation.

If the roots are $3\frac{1}{2}$ and $-\frac{2}{3}$

$$\text{then either } x - 3\tfrac{1}{2} = 0 \quad \text{or} \quad x + \tfrac{2}{3} = 0$$
$$\therefore 2x - 7 = 0 \quad \text{or} \quad 3x + 2 = 0$$
$$\therefore (2x - 7)(3x + 2) = 0$$
$$\therefore \text{the equation is } 6x^2 - 17x - 14 = 0.$$

The sum and product of the roots are not $+17$ and -14 respectively; but when divided through by 6 the equation becomes

$$x^2 - \tfrac{17}{6}x - \tfrac{14}{6} = 0$$
$$\text{i.e.} \quad x^2 - \tfrac{17}{6}x - \tfrac{7}{3} = 0.$$

$$\text{The sum of the roots} = 3\tfrac{1}{2} - \tfrac{2}{3} = \frac{21 - 4}{6} = \tfrac{17}{6}$$

and the product of the roots $= \frac{7}{2} \times -\frac{2}{3} = -\frac{7}{3}$.

These agree with the coefficients in $x^2 - \frac{17}{6}x - \frac{7}{3} = 0$.

In general, if the equation is $ax^2 + bx + c = 0$, it may be written as $x^2 + \frac{b}{a}x + \frac{c}{a} = 0$.

$$\text{Then the } \textbf{sum of the roots} = -\frac{b}{a}$$

$$\text{and the } \textbf{product of the roots} = \frac{c}{a}$$

Example 10 *Solve the equation* $2x^2 + 3x - 20 = 0$ *and check by finding the sum and product of the roots.*

$$2x^2 + 3x - 20 = 0$$
$$\therefore (x + 4)(2x - 5) = 0$$
$$\therefore x + 4 = 0 \quad \text{or} \quad 2x - 5 = 0$$
$$\therefore x = -4 \text{ or } \tfrac{5}{2}$$
$$\text{i.e.} \quad x = -4 \text{ or } 2\tfrac{1}{2}.$$

Check. Sum of roots $= -4 + 2\frac{1}{2} = -1\frac{1}{2} = -\frac{3}{2}$.

Product of roots $= -4 \times 2\frac{1}{2} = -10 = -\frac{20}{2}$.

These agree with the coefficients in the given equation.

Example 11 *Find the equation whose roots are* -3 *and* 4.

$$\text{Sum of roots} = +1.$$
$$\text{Product of roots} = -12.$$
$$\therefore \text{ required equation is } x^2 - x - 12 = 0.$$

Exercise 24e

Solve the following equations, and check by finding the sum and product of the roots.

1 $a^2 - 4a + 3 = 0$
2 $b^2 - 5b + 6 = 0$
3 $c^2 + 5c + 4 = 0$
4 $d^2 + 7d + 10 = 0$
5 $m^2 + 2m - 15 = 0$
6 $n^2 - 3n - 10 = 0$
7 $p^2 - 2p - 24 = 0$
8 $q^2 - 3q = 0$
9 $h^2 + 5h = 0$
10 $k^2 + 5k - 24 = 0$
11 $2u^2 - 5u + 3 = 0$
12 $2v^2 - 7v + 3 = 0$
13 $x^2 + 6x + 5 = 0$
14 $y^2 + 6y + 9 = 0$
15 $z^2 - 10z + 25 = 0$
16 $2e^2 + e - 6 = 0$
17 $4f^2 - 8f + 3 = 0$
18 $g^2 - 9 = 0$
19 $m^2 = 36$
20 $p^2 + 3p - 40 = 0$
21 $3q^2 + 5q = 0$
22 $25n^2 - 4 = 0$
23 $4u^2 = 49$
24 $3v^2 + 7v - 6 = 0$
25 $12w^2 - 13w + 3 = 0$

Find the equation whose roots are

26 $2, 3$
27 $2, -4$
28 $1, -2$
29 $-3, -4$
30 $0, 3$
31 $-4, 0$
32 ± 3
33 $\frac{3}{4}, \frac{1}{2}$
34 $-1\frac{1}{2}, 2$
35 $-\frac{1}{3}, -\frac{1}{2}$

Graphical solution

Graphs of functions were introduced in Chapter 10. The present chapter shows how they may be used to solve equations.

Consider the equation $x^2 - 2x - 3 = 0$.

A table of values for the expression $x^2 - 2x - 3$ may be constructed as follows:

x	5	4	3	2	1	0	−1	−2	−3	−4	−5
x^2	25	16	9	4	1	0	1	4	9	16	25
$-2x$	−10	−8	−6	−4	−2	0	2	4	6	8	10
-3	−3	−3	−3	−3	−3	−3	−3	−3	−3	−3	−3
$x^2 - 2x - 3$	12	5	0	−3	−4	−3	0	5	12	21	32

The points whose co-ordinates are determined in this way are plotted on the graph, values of x being measured to right or left, and values of $x^2 - 2x - 3$ up or down (Fig. 158). Common sense suggests that the values (−4, 21) and (−5, 32) will be of little use and need not be plotted.

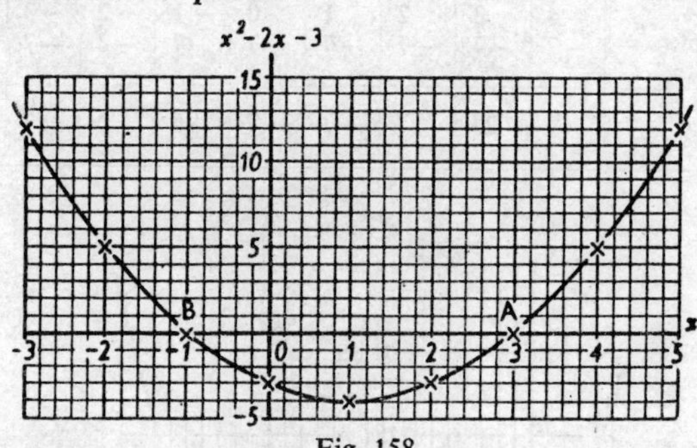

Fig. 158

$x^2 - 2x - 3$ is equal to 0 along the line $0x$, and hence the points *on the graph* where $x^2 - 2x - 3$ is equal to 0 are where the graph cuts $0x$, i.e. at A and B.

At A, $x = 3$; at B, $x = -1$.

Hence $x^2 - 2x - 3 = 0$ when $x = 3$ or -1.

This result may be checked by calculating the roots in the way already familiar.

Thus
$$x^2 - 2x - 3 = 0$$
$$\therefore (x - 3)(x + 1) = 0$$
$$\therefore x = 3 \text{ or } -1.$$

This method would clearly have involved far less work than the graphical method, but if the L.H.S. had had no factors the graphical method would have offered a way out of the difficulty. For example, the equation $3x^2 + x - 7 = 0$ cannot be solved by simple factorisation, but the graphical method will give approximate roots. The accuracy of the results obtained will depend on the scale used in drawing the graph. With the scale in Fig. 159 results correct to one decimal place could be expected. In practice a larger scale would almost certainly be used, such as 2 cm as unit along $0x$, and 0·5 cm as unit on the other axis; also intermediate points corresponding to values of $1\frac{1}{2}$, $\frac{1}{2}$, $-\frac{1}{2}$, etc., for x could be

x	4	3	2	1	0	−1	−2	−3	−4
$3x^2$ $+x$ -7	48 4 −7	27 3 −7	12 2 −7	3 1 −7	0 0 −7	3 −1 −7	12 −2 −7	27 −3 −7	48 −4 −7
$3x^2 + x - 7$	45	23	7	−3	−7	−5	3	17	37

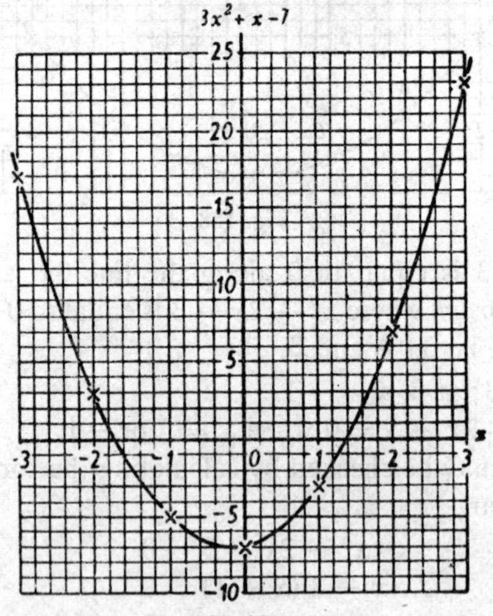

Fig. 159

plotted. These extra points would assist in drawing the curve accurately.

A table of values is constructed, and the graph drawn.

Reading from the graph, $3x^2 + x - 7 = 0$ when $x = 1{\cdot}4$ or $-1{\cdot}7$ approximately.

These results may be roughly checked by taking their sum and product.

Their sum is $1{\cdot}4 - 1{\cdot}7 = -0{\cdot}3$, and their product is $1{\cdot}4 \times -1{\cdot}7 = -2{\cdot}38$. These do not agree *exactly* with the coefficients in $3x^2 + x - 7 = 0$, i.e. in $x^2 + \frac{1}{3}x - 2\frac{1}{3} = 0$, but they are near enough to show that the answer is roughly correct.

Consider the equation $4x^2 - 20x + 25 = 0$. A table of values is constructed and the graph drawn (Fig. 160).

x	6	5	4	3	2	1	0	−1	−2	−3	−4
$4x^2$	144	100	64	36	16	4	0	4	16	36	64
$-20x$	−120	−100	−80	−60	−40	−20	0	20	40	60	80
$+25$	25	25	25	25	25	25	25	25	25	25	25
$4x^2 - 20x + 25$	49	25	9	1	1	9	25	49	81	...	...

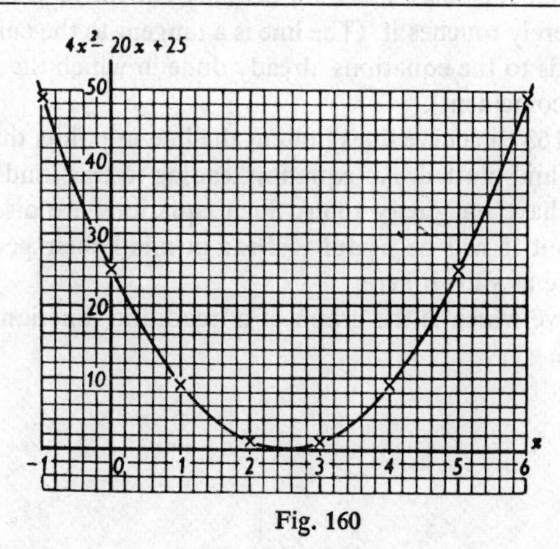

Fig. 160

The graph appears not to *cut* the x-axis at all, but merely to *touch* it where $x = 2{\cdot}5$. This is actually the case, as may be checked by calculation:

$$4x^2 - 20x + 25 = 0$$
$$\therefore (2x - 5)(2x - 5) = 0$$
$$\text{i.e.} \quad (2x - 5)^2 = 0$$
$$\therefore x = 2\tfrac{1}{2} \text{ twice.}$$

Such roots are said to be **coincident.**

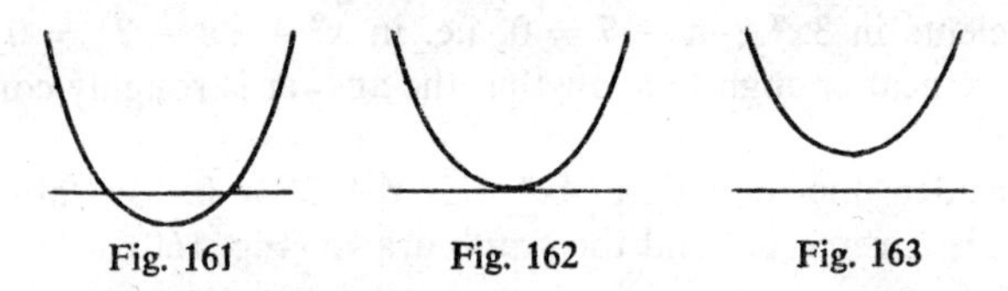

Fig. 161 Fig. 162 Fig. 163

A curve of quadratic type normally cuts a straight line in two points.

In Fig. 161 the two points of intersection are clearly *separate and distinct.* The curve cuts through the line and appears on the other side.

In Fig. 162 the two points are *coincident*, i.e. they are so close together that the curve does not actually cut through the line at all, but merely touches it. (The line is a tangent to the curve.) This corresponds to the equations already done in which the roots are equal (or coincident).

In Fig. 163 the curve does not cut the line in points that can be visualised and plotted. An equation leading to this kind of graph is said to have **imaginary roots.** Such equations are discussed in Book 3, but it will be useful to bear in mind their geometrical significance as shown here.

The curve which is the graph of a quadratic function is called **a parabola.**

Exercise 24f

Solve the following equations graphically. Check the first five by factorising the L.H.S. and thus calculating the roots. In no. 6 onwards give the results correct to one decimal place, and check as common sense suggests by taking the sum or the product of the roots.

1 $x^2 - 2x - 8 = 0$	**2** $x^2 - 4x + 3 = 0$
3 $2x^2 + x - 6 = 0$	**4** $5x^2 - 9x - 18 = 0$
5 $2x^2 - 5x = 0$	**6** $x^2 - 6x + 6 = 0$
7 $x^2 + 2x - 2 = 0$	**8** $x^2 - 2x + 1 = 0$
9 $x^2 - 2x - 1 = 0$	**10** $2x^2 + x - 2 = 0$
11 $x^2 - 3x + 4 = 0$	**12** $x^2 + 3x - 7 = 0$
13 $x^2 + x - 8 = 0$	**14** $x^2 - 3x - 2 = 0$
15 $4x^2 - 12x + 9 = 0$	**16** $3x^2 - x + 2 = 0$
17 $x^2 - 6x + 4 = 0$	**18** $2x^2 - 8x - 11 = 0$
19 $3x^2 + 10x + 6 = 0$	**20** $4x^2 - 9x - 1 = 0$

Easy problems leading to quadratic equations

Example 12 *Find two numbers whose difference is* 5, *and whose product is* 266.

Let the smaller number be x.
Then the larger number is $x + 5$.
Their product is $x(x + 5)$,

$$\therefore x(x + 5) = 266$$
$$\therefore x^2 + 5x - 266 = 0$$
$$\therefore (x - 14)(x + 19) = 0$$
$$\therefore x = 14 \text{ or } -19.$$

The other number is 5 more, i.e. $14 + 5$ or $-19 + 5$
i.e. 19 or -14.

$\therefore$ the two numbers are 14 and 19, or -19 and -14.

Check. $14 \times 19 = 266$ and $-19 \times -14 = 266$.

Compare Example 12 with Example 13 which follows. Notice the use of units, and the discarding of one root because it is not a sensible answer.

Example 13 *The length of a rectangular lawn is 5 metres more than the width, and the area is 266 m². Find the dimensions of the lawn.*

Let the width be x metres.
Then the length is $(x + 5)$ metres.
$\therefore$ the area is $x(x + 5)$ m²

$$\therefore x(x + 5) = 266$$
$$\therefore x^2 + 5x - 266 = 0$$
$$\therefore (x - 14)(x + 19) = 0$$
$$\therefore x = 14 \text{ or } -19.$$

But -19 m is clearly unsuitable for the width of a lawn.
$\therefore$ the width is 14 metres, and the length (5 metres more) is 19 metres.

Check. 14 m $\times$ 19 m $=$ 266 m²

Exercise 24g

Nos. 1 *and* 2 *are connected, also* 3 *and* 4, *and* 5 *and* 6.

1 Find two numbers which differ by 4, and whose product is 221.

2 The width of a classroom is 4 metres less than the length, and the area is 221 square metres. Find the dimensions of the classroom.

3 Two numbers have a difference of 3, and the sum of their squares is 89. Find the numbers.

4 Two square rooms have a total floor area of 89 m², and one is 3 m bigger each way than the other. Find the dimensions of the two rooms.

5 Find two numbers whose sum is 23 and whose product is 126.

6 The perimeter of a rectangular lawn is 46 m and its area is 126 m². Find the dimensions of the lawn.

7 A girl is 6 years younger than her brother, and the product of their ages is 135. Find their ages.

8 The ages of two brothers are 11 and 8 years. In how many years' time will the product of their ages be 208?

9 Find the number which when added to its square makes 90.

10 Twice the square of a certain whole number added to 3 times the number makes 90. Find the number.

11 Divide 21 into two parts whose product is 68.

12 Find two positive numbers differing by 7 whose product is 120.

13 Find two negative numbers which differ by 5, and whose product is 104.

14 The area of a rectangle is 60 cm^2, and the length is 11 cm more than the width. Find the width.

15 The perimeter of a rectangle is 42 cm and the area is 68 cm^2. Find the length and width.

16 Find the number such that when it is successively added to 5 and subtracted from 15, the product of the two results is 96.

17 When the numbers 8 and 13 are both increased by the same amount the product of the new numbers is 204. Find the increase in each.

18 A flower-bed measures 12 m by 5 m, and a path of uniform width runs along one side and one end. If the total area of the flower-bed and the path is 120 m^2, find the width of the path.

19 Find the number such that when it is subtracted from 18 and from 13, the product of the numbers so obtained is 66.

20 A rectangular piece of cardboard measures 17 cm by 14 cm. When strips of equal width are cut off one side and one end, the area of the remaining piece is 108 cm^2. Find the width of the strips removed.

21 When 9 times a certain digit is subtracted from twice the square of the digit, the result is 35. Find the digit.

22 A man is 37 years old and his son's age is 8. How many years ago was the product of their ages 96?

23 Find the number such that when it is successively added to 7, and subtracted from 17, the product of the two results is 128.

24 Find two consecutive numbers whose product is 156.

25 Find two consecutive even numbers whose product is 224.

26 Find two consecutive odd numbers whose product is 195.

27 The square of a certain number is 22 less than 13 times the original number. Find the number.

28 Twice a certain whole number subtracted from 3 times the square of the number leaves 133. Find the number.

29 A lady is three times as old as her daughter, and 8 years ago the product of their ages was 112. Find their present ages.

30 A picture measures 22 cm by 16 cm, and the area of the frame which surrounds it is 368 cm². Find the width of the frame.

Chapter 25

Percentages (3)

Example 1 *A sells some goods to B and makes* 10% *profit; B resells to C at a loss of* 4%. *If C actually paid* £6·60, *how much did A pay for the goods?*

B's cost price is $\frac{110}{100}$ of A's,

C's ,, ,, ,, $\frac{96}{100}$,, B's.

∴ C's ,, ,, ,, $\frac{96}{100} \times \frac{110}{100}$ of A's.

$$\therefore \text{A's cost price} = \frac{100}{96} \times \frac{100}{110} \times £6{\cdot}60$$
$$= £\frac{600}{96}$$
$$= £6{\cdot}25$$

∴ A paid £6·25.

Notice that the working out and cancelling are left until as late as possible.

Example 2 *From a fuel tank* 64% *of the contents are drained away, and this is* 98 *litres more than the quantity left in the tank. How much did the tank hold originally?*

64% is drained away,

∴ 36% is left.

The difference = 28%.

$$\therefore 28\% = 98 \text{ litres}$$
$$\therefore 100\% = 98 \times \frac{100}{28} \text{ litres}$$
$$= 350 \text{ litres.}$$

∴ the tank originally held 350 litres.

Example 3 *A man makes a profit of* 8% *by selling a boat for* £297. *What is his actual profit?*

108% of cost price = £297

∴ 8% ,, ,, ,, $= £297 \times \frac{8}{108}$

= £22.

∴ profit was £22.

Example 4 *By selling a vacuum cleaner for £35·10 a profit of 17% is made. What selling price would have secured a profit of 26%?*

117% of cost price = £35·10
∴ 126% " " " = £35·10 × $\frac{126}{117}$
= £0·30 × 126
= £37·80

∴ selling price should be £37·80.

Exercise 25

Miscellaneous percentages

1 The difference between increasing a number by 8% and decreasing it by 7% is 75. What is the number?

2 If A makes 10% profit in selling to B, and B loses 10% in reselling to C, by what percentage is C's buying price greater or less than A's?

3 If one side of a rectangle is measured 5% too large and the other 10% too small, what is the percentage error in the measured area?

4 If the measurements in no. 3 had been 5% too small and 10% too large, what would the percentage error have been then?

5 A rent collector's commission is 3½% of his takings. If his commission is £4·62, what are his takings?

6 A grocer buys tins of fruit at £1·10 per dozen and sells them at 11p each. Find his profit per cent.

7 A wholesaler buys goods for £350 and sells them to a retailer at 28% profit: the retailer makes a further profit of 35%. What does the customer pay?

8 In no. 7, by what percentage is the customer's price higher than the original price to the wholesaler?

9 If the sides of a square are measured 5% too large, what is the resulting percentage error in the area?

10 A man holds £450 of 4% War Stock. What is his annual income? If he actually paid £420 for this stock, what return per cent is he getting on the money invested?

11 In a certain industry the wages are raised by 6%: as a result, one workman's pay-packet is increased by £1·47. What is his new rate of pay?

12 A man pays 16% of his income in taxation and has £1 058·40 left. How much tax does he pay?

13 If fire-insurance is reckoned at $\frac{1}{4}$% of the value of the property insured, what annual premium is paid on property worth £5 200?

14 A profit of 35% is made on coal bought wholesale for £12·80 per tonne. What is the retail price per tonne?

15 Divide 189 into two parts so that one part is 35% of the other.

16 11 sheep, bought for £95, were sold at a profit of 32%. What was the selling price of each?

17 In 1968 a man's salary was £1 768, and this was increased by 15% in 1969. If he paid $12\frac{1}{2}$% of his salary in income-tax, how much tax did he pay in 1969?

18 A car worth £840 is insured for 65% of its value, and the insurance premium paid is $8\frac{1}{3}$% of the sum insured. What premium is actually paid if there is a 'no-claim bonus' of 40%?

19 If the rate for a 'comprehensive' insurance policy is 27p per cent, what annual premium is paid on a house valued at £5 200?

20 A retailer buys some booklets at £2·16 per dozen, and sells them at a profit of $16\frac{2}{3}$%. Find the retail price of a booklet.

21 If a man gains 5% by selling an article for £1·47, what price would give him 10% profit?

22 A man's salary was increased by 20% in one year, and reduced by 20% in the next. Is his final salary greater or less than the original one, and by how much per cent?

23 When an article is sold for £2·75 a profit is made which is 16% of the selling price. What was the cost price?

24 A retailer marks his goods at 15% over cost price. During a sale all prices are reduced by 4%. What is the cost price of a scarf sold for £1·38 during the sale, and what percentage profit does the retailer actually make?

25 Oranges are bought at 30p a dozen. Half of them are sold at five for 16p, and the other half at four for 11p. Find the gain or loss per cent.

26 In measuring a rectangular field a surveyor's estimate of its length was 4% too great, but the estimated area was correct. By what percentage was the estimated width too small?

27 By selling goods for £5·35 a tradesman made a profit of 7%. If he reduced his price to £5·15, what would his profit be then?

28 A greengrocer buys a 20-kg box of apples for £1·40. 5% of them have to be thrown away: 10% are slightly bruised, and he sells these at 4p per kilo. At what price per kilo must he sell the rest to make 15% profit on his outlay?

29 A man considers that he is 14% overweight when he finds himself turning the scale at 85·5 kg. By how much must he reduce to get back to normal?

30 The cash difference between selling a blouse at a profit of $2\frac{1}{2}$% and of 3% is 2p. What is the second selling price?

31 When goods are sold for £8·61 the profit is 5%. What price will secure a profit of 10%?

32 In one year's trading a company had a turnover of £14 713 and made a profit of £3 835. Express the profit as a percentage of the turnover, correct to three significant figures.

33 A box-manufacturer alters the shape of a certain line of boxes by increasing their length by 25%, breadth by 20%, and reducing the depth so that the capacity is the same as it was at first. By what percentage is the depth reduced?

34 What is the percentage increase in area if a 5-centimetre diameter disc is expanded by forging to 5·5 cm diameter?

35 A man buys a bicycle on 'hire-purchase' and agrees to pay 57p a week in settlement (for one year). If the cash price of the bicycle is £24·70, how much per cent more than the cash price will he have paid by the end of the year?

36 A trader sells 70 toys at 30p each in one week, this price representing a profit to him of 20%. If, in the next week, he sells them at a discount of 5%, how many will he have to sell to make the same profit as before?

37 What percentage profit does the trader in no. 36 actually make on each toy during the second week?

38 A workman's rate of pay per hour is improved by 20%, and at the same time his weekly hours of work are reduced from 45 to 42. By what percentage is his weekly pay-packet improved?

39 A cylindrical bar is turned down to half its original diameter for half its length. What is the percentage reduction in mass?

40 If a balloon is blown up from 15 cm diameter to 18 cm diameter what is its percentage increase in volume?
(*Volume of a sphere* $= \frac{4}{3}\pi \times$ *radius*^{3})

Chapter 26

Simultaneous linear equations (2)

Example 1 *Solve the equations* $\frac{1}{2}x + \frac{1}{3}y = 4$, $\frac{1}{4}y - \frac{1}{3}x = \frac{1}{6}$.

First simplify the equations separately by clearing the fractions: then solve in the usual way.

$$\tfrac{1}{2}x + \tfrac{1}{3}y = 4 \qquad \text{(i)}$$

$$\tfrac{1}{4}y - \tfrac{1}{3}x = \tfrac{1}{6} \qquad \text{(ii)}$$

$$\text{(i)} \times 6 \qquad 3x + 2y = 24 \qquad \text{(iii)}$$

$$\text{(ii)} \times 12 \qquad 3y - 4x = 2 \qquad \text{(iv)}$$

$$\text{(iii)} \times 3 \qquad 9x + 6y = 72$$

$$\text{(iv)} \times 2 \qquad -8x + 6y = 4$$

$$\text{Subtract} \qquad 17x = 68$$

$$\therefore x = 4.$$

Substitute in (iii), $12 + 2y = 24$, $\therefore y = 6$.

$$\therefore x = 4, \quad y = 6.$$

Alternatively

$$3x + 2y = 24$$

$$-4x + 3y = 2$$

$$\therefore \begin{pmatrix} 3 & 2 \\ -4 & 3 \end{pmatrix}\begin{pmatrix} x \\ y \end{pmatrix} = \begin{pmatrix} 24 \\ 2 \end{pmatrix}$$

$$\therefore \frac{1}{17}\begin{pmatrix} 3 & -2 \\ 4 & 3 \end{pmatrix}\begin{pmatrix} 3 & 2 \\ -4 & 3 \end{pmatrix}\begin{pmatrix} x \\ y \end{pmatrix} = \frac{1}{17}\begin{pmatrix} 3 & -2 \\ 4 & 3 \end{pmatrix}\begin{pmatrix} 24 \\ 2 \end{pmatrix}$$

$$\therefore \begin{pmatrix} 1 & 0 \\ 0 & 1 \end{pmatrix}\begin{pmatrix} x \\ y \end{pmatrix} = \frac{1}{17}\begin{pmatrix} 68 \\ 102 \end{pmatrix}$$

$$= \begin{pmatrix} 4 \\ 6 \end{pmatrix}$$

$$\therefore x = 4, y = 6.$$

Check

$$\text{(i)} \ \tfrac{1}{2}x + \tfrac{1}{3}y = 2 + 2 = 4$$

$$\text{(ii)} \ \tfrac{1}{4}y - \tfrac{1}{3}x = 1\tfrac{1}{2} - 1\tfrac{1}{3} = \tfrac{1}{6}.$$

Example 2 *Solve the equations* $\frac{2}{x} - \frac{1}{y} = 3, \frac{4}{x} + \frac{3}{y} = 16.$

Instead of treating x and y as the unknowns, use $\frac{1}{x}$ and $\frac{1}{y}$.

$$\frac{2}{x} - \frac{1}{y} = 3 \qquad \text{(i)}$$

$$\frac{4}{x} + \frac{3}{y} = 16 \qquad \text{(ii)}$$

$$\text{(i)} \times 3 \qquad \frac{6}{x} - \frac{3}{y} = 9$$

$$\text{add} \qquad \frac{10}{x} = 25$$

$$\therefore \frac{1}{x} = \frac{25}{10} = 2\tfrac{1}{2} \quad (\text{or } x = \tfrac{2}{5}).$$

Substitute in (i), $2 \times 2\frac{1}{2} - \frac{1}{y} = 3$

$$\therefore 5 - \frac{1}{y} = 3$$

$$\therefore \frac{1}{y} = 2 \quad (\text{or } y = \tfrac{1}{2})$$

$$\therefore x = \tfrac{2}{5}, \quad y = \tfrac{1}{2}.$$

Alternatively

$$\frac{2}{x} - \frac{1}{y} = 3$$

$$\frac{4}{x} + \frac{3}{y} = 16$$

$$\therefore \begin{pmatrix} 2 & -1 \\ 4 & 3 \end{pmatrix} \begin{pmatrix} \frac{1}{x} \\ \frac{1}{y} \end{pmatrix} = \begin{pmatrix} 3 \\ 16 \end{pmatrix}$$

$$\therefore \frac{1}{10}\begin{pmatrix} 3 & 1 \\ -4 & 2 \end{pmatrix}\begin{pmatrix} 2 & -1 \\ 4 & 3 \end{pmatrix}\begin{pmatrix} \frac{1}{x} \\ \frac{1}{y} \end{pmatrix} = \frac{1}{10}\begin{pmatrix} 3 & 1 \\ -4 & 2 \end{pmatrix}\begin{pmatrix} 3 \\ 16 \end{pmatrix}$$

$$\therefore \begin{pmatrix} 1 & 0 \\ 0 & 1 \end{pmatrix}\begin{pmatrix} \frac{1}{x} \\ \frac{1}{y} \end{pmatrix} = \frac{1}{10}\begin{pmatrix} 25 \\ 20 \end{pmatrix}$$

$$= \begin{pmatrix} 2\frac{1}{2} \\ 2 \end{pmatrix}$$

$$\therefore \frac{1}{x} = 2\tfrac{1}{2}, \frac{1}{y} = 2$$

$$\therefore x = \tfrac{2}{5}, \ y = \tfrac{1}{2}.$$

Check (i) $\frac{2}{x} - \frac{1}{y} = 2 \times 2\frac{1}{2} - 2 = 5 - 2 = 3$

(ii) $\frac{4}{x} + \frac{3}{y} = 4 \times 2\frac{1}{2} + 3 \times 2 = 10 + 6 = 16.$

Example 3 *Solve the equations*

$$2x - 3y + 2 = x + 2y - 5 = 3x + y.$$

If three things are equal to one another, they can be grouped into three equations: e.g., if $a = b = c$, then $a = b$, $a = c$, $b = c$. But these three include only two different equations, because any two of them taken together produce the third.

The method of solution is therefore to pair the three algebraic quantities in two different ways, and then solve the resulting two equations in the usual way.

$$2x - 3y + 2 = 3x + y$$

$$\therefore x + 4y = 2 \qquad \text{(i)}$$

$$x + 2y - 5 = 3x + y$$

$$\therefore 2x - y = -5 \qquad \text{(ii)}$$

(i) × 2 $\quad 2x + 8y = 4$

Subtract $\quad -9y = -9$

$$\therefore y = 1.$$

Substitute in (i), $x + 4 = 2$

$$\therefore x = -2$$

$$\therefore x = -2, y = 1.$$

Alternatively

$$x + 4y = 2$$
$$2x - y = -5$$
$$\therefore \begin{pmatrix} 1 & 4 \\ 2 & -1 \end{pmatrix}\begin{pmatrix} x \\ y \end{pmatrix} = \begin{pmatrix} 2 \\ -5 \end{pmatrix}$$
$$\therefore -\frac{1}{9}\begin{pmatrix} -1 & -4 \\ -2 & 1 \end{pmatrix}\begin{pmatrix} 1 & 4 \\ 2 & -1 \end{pmatrix}\begin{pmatrix} x \\ y \end{pmatrix} = -\frac{1}{9}\begin{pmatrix} -1 & -4 \\ -2 & 1 \end{pmatrix}\begin{pmatrix} 2 \\ -5 \end{pmatrix}$$
$$\therefore \begin{pmatrix} 1 & 0 \\ 0 & 1 \end{pmatrix}\begin{pmatrix} x \\ y \end{pmatrix} = -\frac{1}{9}\begin{pmatrix} 18 \\ -9 \end{pmatrix}$$
$$= \begin{pmatrix} -2 \\ 1 \end{pmatrix}$$
$$\therefore x = -2, y = 1.$$

Check

$$2x - 3y + 2 = -4 - 3 + 2 = -5$$
$$x + 2y - 5 = -2 + 2 - 5 = -5$$
$$3x + y = -6 + 1 = -5.$$

Exercise 26a

Solve the following pairs of equations:

1 $x - \frac{y}{2} = 1$, $\frac{x}{2} + \frac{y}{3} = 2\frac{5}{6}$

2 $x + \frac{y}{2} = \frac{1}{2}$, $\frac{x}{2} - \frac{y}{6} = 1\frac{1}{2}$

3 $3(x + y) = 7(y - x)$, $5(3x - y) = x + 3$

4 $7(a + b) = b - a$, $4(3a + 2b) = b - 8$

5 $f - 2g + 3 = 2f - 3g + 2 = 1$

6 $\frac{3}{a} + \frac{5}{b} = \frac{9}{a} - \frac{5}{b} = 1$

7 $1{\cdot}5x - 0{\cdot}7y = 0{\cdot}1$, $0{\cdot}3x + 1{\cdot}1y = 2{\cdot}5$

8 $2{\cdot}3m + 1{\cdot}8n = 5{\cdot}1$, $0{\cdot}9m + 2{\cdot}4n = 0{\cdot}3$

9 $\frac{2}{e} - \frac{3}{f} = 1$, $\frac{8}{e} + \frac{9}{f} = \frac{1}{2}$

10 $\frac{5x}{8} - \frac{y}{2} = \frac{1}{4}$

$\frac{2x}{3} - \frac{3y}{5} = \frac{2}{15}$

11 $\frac{1}{3}(m - 3n) = 2$

$\frac{m + n}{4} = \frac{1}{2}$

12 $3(3f + 2g) = 5 - f$

$4g + 5 = 2(g - 5f)$

13 $3(2x - y) = x + y + 5$

$5(3x - 2y) = 2(x - y) + 1$

14 $2a + 3b - 1 = 3a + b + 7 = a + 2b$

15 $2{\cdot}32x + 1{\cdot}44y = 15{\cdot}6$

$4{\cdot}8x - 1{\cdot}92y = 2{\cdot}88$

16 $\frac{4s}{3} + \frac{3t}{2} = 4$

$\frac{s}{2} + \frac{t}{4} + 1 = 0$

17 $\frac{3}{c} - \frac{4}{d} = \frac{1}{3}$

$\frac{2}{c} - \frac{5}{d} = 1$

18 $3p - 5q - 4 = 5p + 8 = 2p + q + 7$

19 $3(2h - k + 1) = 2(2h + k - 5) = 5h - k - 2$

20 $\frac{a + 3m}{4} = m + \frac{1}{2}$

$\frac{4(3a - 2m)}{5} = a + m - 2$

21 $\frac{3c}{d + 1} = \frac{2c + 5}{d + 3} = \frac{3}{2}$

22 $\frac{r + 6}{4 - s} = \frac{2r + 11}{1 - 4s} = \frac{1}{3}$

23 $3(x + 2y) = 2(3x - 2y)$

$12(2x + y) = 8(4x - 3y) + 7$

24 $\frac{4u - 3v}{3} = \frac{u - v}{2}$

$\frac{3}{7}(u - 2v) = \frac{2}{3}(2u - 3v) - 3$

25 $4b - 5c + 1 = b = 3b - 4c + 2$

26 $5(3p - 8q) = 3 - 12(p + q)$

$12(p - q) = 1$

27 $2(2e + 3f) + 5(e + 3f) = 0$

$4(3e + 7f) = f + 3$

28 $3d - 7e + 4 = d + 2e - 10 = 2d - 5e + 2$

29 $\frac{4}{a} + \frac{5}{b} = -4$

$\frac{10}{b} - \frac{6}{a} = 13$

30 $1{\cdot}6a + 3{\cdot}3b = 13{\cdot}3$

$2{\cdot}4a + 1{\cdot}3b = 1{\cdot}7$

31 $\frac{3(2m + 3n)}{4} = m + n$

$\frac{2}{5}(2m - 5n) = 2m - 1$

32 $\frac{3}{4}(5x - 6y) = \frac{y}{2}$

$\frac{5}{7}(x + y) = x + 2$

33 $2(x + 2y - 3) = 3x + 5y - 7 = 3(3x - y - 9)$

34 $1{\cdot}24f - 2{\cdot}15g = 1{\cdot}9$

$2{\cdot}17f - 3{\cdot}41g = 4{\cdot}03$

35 $\frac{2}{5}(4s + 3t) + \frac{1}{12} = s + 2t$

$\frac{3(3s - 2t)}{11} = \frac{1}{4}$

36 $\frac{7(3x + 2y)}{4} = \frac{x}{2} + 1$

$\frac{5(2x - y)}{8} = 1 - 6(x + y)$

Harder problems

Example 4 *A number of two digits is such that the sum of the digits is* 11, *and the number is* 27 *greater than the number obtained by reversing the digits. Find the number.*

Let the number be 'xy' (i.e. the tens digit is x and the units digit y).

Then the number is $10x + y$.

The number with digits reversed is $10y + x$.

$$\therefore 10x + y - (10y + x) = 27$$
$$\therefore 10x + y - 10y - x = 27$$
$$\therefore 9x - 9y = 27$$
$$\therefore x - y = 3 \quad \text{(i)}$$

Also $\quad x + y = 11 \quad$ (ii)

Add $\quad 2x = 14$

$$\therefore x = 7$$

$$\text{Subtract} \quad -2y = -8$$
$$\therefore y = 4$$
$\therefore$ the number is 74.

Alternatively

$$x - y = 3$$
$$x + y = 11$$
$$\therefore \begin{pmatrix} 1 & -1 \\ 1 & 1 \end{pmatrix}\begin{pmatrix} x \\ y \end{pmatrix} = \begin{pmatrix} 3 \\ 11 \end{pmatrix}$$
$$\therefore \tfrac{1}{2}\begin{pmatrix} 1 & 1 \\ -1 & 1 \end{pmatrix}\begin{pmatrix} 1 & -1 \\ 1 & 1 \end{pmatrix}\begin{pmatrix} x \\ y \end{pmatrix} = \tfrac{1}{2}\begin{pmatrix} 1 & 1 \\ -1 & 1 \end{pmatrix}\begin{pmatrix} 3 \\ 11 \end{pmatrix}$$
$$\therefore \begin{pmatrix} 1 & 0 \\ 0 & 1 \end{pmatrix}\begin{pmatrix} x \\ y \end{pmatrix} = \tfrac{1}{2}\begin{pmatrix} 14 \\ 8 \end{pmatrix}$$
$$= \begin{pmatrix} 7 \\ 4 \end{pmatrix}$$
$$\therefore x = 7, y = 4$$
$\therefore$ the number is 74.

Check

$$7 + 4 = 11$$
$$74 - 47 = 27.$$

Example 5 *A rowing eight can row* 3 *km upstream in* 20 *minutes, and* 3 *km downstream in* 12 *minutes. Find the speed of the current, and of the eight in still water.*

Let x km/h = speed of current,
and y km/h = speed of eight in still water.

Then speed of eight upstream $= (y - x)$ km/h,
and „ „ „ downstream $= (y + x)$ km/h.

But speed upstream = 9 km/h,
and „ downstream = 15 km/h.

$$\therefore \quad y - x = 9$$
$$\text{and} \quad y + x = 15$$

$$\text{Adding} \quad 2y = 24 \qquad \therefore y = 12$$
$$\text{Subtracting} \quad -2x = -6 \qquad \therefore x = 3$$

$\therefore$ current is 3 km/h, and boat's speed in still water is 12 km/h.

Check Upstream: 3 km at 9 km/h takes $\frac{1}{3}$ h = 20 min.
Downstream: 3 km „ 15 km/h „ $\frac{1}{5}$ h = 12 min.

Exercise 26b

1 A man running for 8 km and walking 2 km covers 10 km in 50 minutes. If he runs 4 km and walks 6 km he takes 1 h 15 min. Find his running and walking speeds.

2 A man bicycles 78 km in 5 hours, travelling at 12 km/h for x hours and at 18 km/h for y hours. Find x and y.

3 A motorist travels for 30 km at x km/h and for 90 km at y km/h, the total time for the journey being $2\frac{1}{2}$ hours. If the speeds had been interchanged the total time would have been 20 minutes less. Find x and y.

4 The difference between the digits of a two-digit number is 1, and the number itself is one more than five times the sum of its digits. The units digit being larger than the tens digit, find the number.

5 Divide 75 into two parts so that one part is $\frac{2}{3}$ of the other.

6 Half of A's money plus one-fifth of B's makes one pound. Two-thirds of A's plus two-fifths of B's makes £1·50. How much has each?

7 A man's age and his son's add to 45 years. Five years ago the man was six times as old as his son. How old was the man when his son was born?

8 The perimeter of the isosceles triangle shown is 28 cm. Find x and y, the sides being given in centimetres.

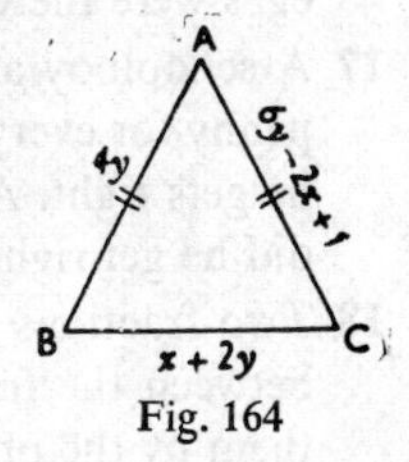

Fig. 164

9 If, in the triangle of no. 8,

$$\hat{A} = 2\tfrac{1}{4}n^\circ + \tfrac{1}{2}m^\circ,$$
$$\hat{B} = 2n^\circ - \tfrac{2}{5}m^\circ,$$
$$\hat{C} = 2m^\circ,$$

find m and n.

10 In a two-digit number the sum of the digits is 8, and the difference between this number and the number with the digits reversed is 54. What is the number?

11 Archie is two years older than Betty. In one year's time he will be twice her present age. How old are they now?

12 Colin's and Diana's ages add up to 29. Seven years ago Colin was twice as old as Diana. In how many years' time will Diana's age be three-quarters of Colin's?

13 A tea-blender has two sorts of tea costing 72p and 90p per kg respectively. How many kg of each sort must he take to produce 36 kg of a mixture at 82p per kg?

14 A gardener makes a rectangular flower-bed square by taking two metres off its length and adding three metres to its breadth. By so doing he increases the area by 20 square metres. What is its final area?

15 If 1 is added to both numerator and denominator of a fraction the fraction becomes $\frac{1}{2}$: if 8 is added to both, the fraction becomes $\frac{2}{3}$. What is the fraction?

16 A bird laid a certain number of eggs in a nest, and a collector took away two-thirds of them. The bird laid some more, and another collector took two-thirds of them. If the bird laid 12 eggs altogether and collectors took 10 altogether, how many eggs were there to begin with?

17 A schoolboy agrees with his schoolmaster that he will pay a penny for every sum he gets wrong if he wins 3p for every one he gets right. After doing 20 sums he is 4p down. How many did he get right?

18 Two fractions have the same denominator 15: the difference between the fractions is $\frac{2}{5}$, and the result of dividing one of them by the other is $\frac{4}{7}$. What are the fractions?

19 When Peter was the same age as David is now, his age was three times David's. When Peter was half as old as he is now, he was eight years older than David was then. How old are they now?

20 Mary is half as old again as Joan was two years ago. When Mary was as old as Joan is now, she was twice as old as Joan was six years ago. How old are they both now?

21 I can normally average 36 km/h in a built-up area and 54 km/h in the country, and my journey from A to B takes exactly 3 hours. On one occasion, owing to fog, I started half an hour earlier than usual, but my speeds were reduced to 27 and 36 km/h respectively, and I arrived 55 minutes late for my appointment. How far apart are A and B?

22 If the larger of two numbers is divided by the smaller, the quotient and remainder are both 4: if fifteen times the smaller number is divided by the larger, the quotient is 3 and the remainder 9. What are the numbers?

23 Alf and Bert want to arrive together at a place 16 km away. They have only one bicycle between them: Alf can walk at 6 km/h and bicycle at 18 km/h, and Bert at $4\frac{1}{2}$ and 15 km/h respectively. They start at the same time, Alf walking. After what distance must Bert leave the bicycle for Alf to pick up, and start walking himself?

24 If hot and cold taps are turned on together a bath is filled in three minutes; but if the cold tap was only half open it would take 1 min 48 s longer. How long would the hot tap alone take to fill the bath?

Revision examples

XXXI

1 Factorise $2mn - 4un - mv + 2uv$, $3x^2 - 8xy - 3y^2$, $4a^2 - 12ab + 9b^2$, $a^2 - (b - c)^2$, $(5a - 2)^2 - 9a^2$.

2 A cylindrical water-butt one metre in diameter holds 1 100 litres of water. How deep is the water (take $\pi = \frac{22}{7}$)?

3 M, N are the mid-points of the sides $\overline{AB}$, $\overline{AC}$ of $\triangle ABC$. $\overline{CM}$, $\overline{BN}$ are produced to X, Y respectively so that $CM = MX$, $BN = NY$. Prove that X, A, Y lie on a straight line, and that $XY = 2BC$.

4 Solve (i) $x(x + 3)(5x - 2) = 0$
(ii) $x^2 - 11x - 12 = 0$

5 Find the angle of elevation of the top of a mast 69 m high from a point 39 m away from its foot on the level ground.

6 An examination paper was taken by 3 825 girls and 5 675 boys. If 64% of the girls passed and 56% of the boys passed, what percentage of the total number of candidates passed? (correct to 3 sig. fig.).

7 Solve simultaneously (i) $x + \frac{1}{2}y = 1$
(ii) $\frac{1}{3}x - y = 5$

8 PQRS is a parallelogram, and $\overline{PX}$, $\overline{RY}$ are the perpendiculars from P, R to the diagonal $\overline{QS}$. Prove that $PX = RY$.

9 A bicycle travelling at 16 km/h takes 7 h 35 min for a certain journey. Find how long a car would take for the same journey if it travelled at 56 km/h.

10 A boy lives d km from his school. If he walks to school at 6 km/h, how many minutes does he take? When he cycles to school at 15 km/h he takes 15 minutes less than when he walks. Form an equation for d and solve it.

XXXII

1 Solve (i) $(m - 6)(m + 3) = (m - 3)^2$

(ii) $\frac{n-1}{2} - \frac{3n+2}{3} = \frac{1}{4}$

2 Find x, y, p, q if $\begin{pmatrix} 3 & 2 \\ 1 & 2 \end{pmatrix}\begin{pmatrix} 4 & x \\ x & y \end{pmatrix} = \begin{pmatrix} 10 & 3 \\ p & q \end{pmatrix}$

3 ABCD is a parallelogram, and X, Y are points in $\overline{\text{AB}}$, $\overline{\text{CD}}$ such that AX = CY. Prove that BY = DX.

4 Solve (i) $h^2(3h + 5) = 0$

(ii) $2k^2 - 3k + 1 = 0$

5 A ladder reaches to a height of 8 m up a wall when the foot of the ladder is 5 m from the wall. Find the angle which the ladder makes with the ground.

6 In the first six months of 1968 a car manufacturer sold 5 817 vehicles. In 1969 the sales for the same period were 4 984. Find the decrease per cent, correct to 3 sig. fig.

7 Out of a group of 71 children, 37 had been to France, 31 to Germany, and 17 had never been abroad. How many of them had visited both France and Germany?

8 PQRS is a trapezium in which $\overline{\text{PS}}$ is perpendicular to $\overline{\text{PQ}}$ and $\overline{\text{SR}}$. The diagonals $\overline{\text{PR}}$, $\overline{\text{SQ}}$ intersect at right angles. Prove that the $\triangle$s PQS, SPR are similar. If PS = 6 cm and SR = 5 cm, calculate PQ.

9 After 13 innings a batsman has an average of 27. Find how many runs he must score in his next innings to bring his average up to 30 (i) if he is 'out', (ii) if he is 'not out'.

10 A cyclist rides for x hours at 20 km/h and then for y hours at 12 km/h. If he goes altogether 90 km in 6 hours, find x and y.

XXXIII

1 Factorise $2am - an - 4bm + 2bn$, $4x^2 - 7x + 3$, $4x^2 - 8x + 3$, $(3b + 2)^2 - 4b^2$, $c^2 - (d + e)^2$.

2 Find the area of a concrete path 2 m wide surrounding a circular pond 12 m in diameter.

3 The average age of a form of 20 boys was 15 years 6 months: when one boy was absent the average age of the form fell to 15 years 5 months. How old was the absentee?

4 Solve graphically the equation $x^2 - x - 3 = 0$, taking values of x from -2 to 3.

5 From the edge of a cliff 227 m high the angle of depression of a fishing-boat is 35° 21′. Find the distance of the boat from the foot of the cliff.

6 Evaluate in the binary scale

(i) $100\,011 \div 111$ (ii) $\dfrac{1\,000\,000 - 1}{11} + 1$ (iii) $\sqrt{1\,001}$

7 Solve simultaneously (i) $5x - 2y = 3$
(ii) $3x - 5y = 17$

8 $\triangle$PQR is right-angled at P, and $\overline{\text{PM}}$ is an altitude. The bisector of $\hat{\text{Q}}$ meets $\overline{\text{PM}}$, $\overline{\text{PR}}$ in X, Y. Prove that PX = PY.

9 Find to the nearest penny the simple interest on £431·25 for 4 years 6 months at $4\frac{1}{2}$% per annum.

10 A cricket ball is thrown vertically into the air, and its height h m after t seconds is given by the formula $h = 30t - 5t^2$. How long after being thrown is it at a height of 40 m? Explain the meaning of the two answers.

XXXIV

1 Solve (i) $(d - 2)(d + 3)^2 = 0$
(ii) $3e^2 - 10e + 3 = 0$

2 The vertices of a regular pentagon lie on the circumference of a circle of radius 5 cm. Calculate the length of a side of the pentagon.

3 PQRS is a square, and H, K, L, M are points in $\overline{\text{PQ}}$, $\overline{\text{QR}}$, $\overline{\text{RS}}$, $\overline{\text{SP}}$ such that PH = QK = RL = SM. Prove that HKLM is a square.

4 Find the equation whose roots are (i) 3 and -5
(ii) $-1\frac{1}{2}$ and 4

5 A vertical section through a roof is an isosceles triangle PQR, $\overline{QR}$ being the horizontal base. $\overline{PQ}$, $\overline{PR}$ are each 6 m long, and make angles of 38° with the horizontal. Find the height of P above $\overline{QR}$ (in m to 3 sig. fig.).

6 A wholesaler sells some clothes to a retailer and makes a profit of 28%. The retailer makes a profit of 35% by selling them for £64·80. What did the wholesaler originally pay for the clothes?

7 Solve simultaneously (i) $2x + 3y = y - 3x$
(ii) $x + 2y = 4 - 2x$

8 Prove that the line joining the mid-points of two adjacent sides of a quadrilateral is equal and parallel to the line joining the mid-points of the other two sides.

9 A car has a faulty speedometer which registers 103 km when the car has travelled 100 km. If the speedometer readings at the beginning and end of a journey are 43 213 km and 43 485 km, find the actual distance travelled (in km correct to 1 dec. pl.).

10 Three times the square of a certain whole number is 3 less than 10 times the original number. Find the number.

XXXV

1 Simplify (i) $5a - 2\{a^2 - 5a(a - 1) + 3(a^2 - 2)\}$

(ii) $\dfrac{3(2m-5)}{8} + \dfrac{5(3m-1)}{6} - \dfrac{11(4m-3)}{12}$

2 A rectangular cistern contains 93·6 litres of water. If the cistern is 65 cm long and 45 cm wide, find the depth of the water.

3 ABCD is a parallelogram and X a point on $\overline{DC}$ such that DX = DA. $\overline{AX}$ and $\overline{BC}$ produced cut at Y. Prove CX = CY.

4 Solve (i) $a(a + 5)^2 = 0$
(ii) $3b^2 + 2b - 8 = 0$

5 A horizontal bar $\overline{AB}$ projects from a wall at B, and is supported by a strut $\overline{AC}$, C being on the wall vertically below B. Another strut $\overline{BD}$, perpendicular to $\overline{AC}$, connects B to $\overline{AC}$. If AB = 100 cm and BC = 75 cm, find the inclination of $\overline{AC}$ to the vertical. Find also BD.

6 A dealer A buys some furniture for £44 and sells to another dealer B at a profit of 15%. The dealer B has to resell at a loss of 15%. What price does the dealer B receive?

7 Solve (i) $\dfrac{a-3}{4} - \dfrac{a+2}{5} + \dfrac{3}{4} = 0$

(ii) $(b-2)(b+5) = (b+1)^2$

8 In the parallelogram PQRS, the bisector of $\hat{P}$ meets $\overline{QR}$ (or $\overline{QR}$ produced) at A, and the bisector of $\hat{Q}$ meets $\overline{PS}$ (or $\overline{PS}$ produced) at B. Prove that AQ = BP.

9 Find the simple interest on £115·20 for 6 years 8 months at $2\frac{1}{2}$% per annum.

10 A certain number of pence is being shared among some children. If they have 11 pence each there are 3 pence left over; but 3 pence more are needed if they are to have 12 pence each. How much money is being shared, and how many children are sharing it?

XXXVI

1 Factorise $2uh + 6uk - hv - 3kv$, $(e + 2f)^2 - 9g^2$, $4x^2 - 13x + 9$, $4x^2 - 37x + 9$, $(5a - 4b)^2 - 9a^2$.

2 A rectangular box with a lid is made of wood 1 cm thick. If the box measures 30 cm by 20 cm by 18 cm externally, and the wood has a density of 0·8 g/cm³, find the mass of the box.

3 M is the mid-point of the side $\overline{AB}$ of a parallelogram ABCD. The line through B parallel to $\overline{MD}$ meets $\overline{AD}$ produced at N. Prove that BC = DN.

4 Solve the equation $3x^2 + x - 5 = 0$ graphically.

5 The roof of a house is sloped so that it rises 5 m vertically for every 3·5 m horizontally. Find its inclination to the horizontal (nearest degree).

6 In 1968 a man's salary was £1 040, and it was increased by $12\frac{1}{2}\%$ for 1969. If he pays $17\frac{1}{2}\%$ of his salary in taxes, how much tax did he pay in 1969?

7 Solve simultaneously $2x - y + 3 = 4x - 3y = 8$.

8 In $\triangle ABC$, P and Q are points on $\overline{AB}$ and $\overline{AC}$ respectively such that $A\hat{Q}P = A\hat{B}C$. $AB = 12$ cm, $BC = 8$ cm $= AQ$, $AC = 9$ cm. Calculate PB and PQ.

9 For a group of 10 girls the average mark in an examination is $53\frac{1}{2}$ out of 100. The marks for 9 of them are 65, 37, 46, 81, 55, 49, 23, 77, 58. Find the marks of the other girl. How many marks should she have scored to bring the average for the group up to 55?

10 A boy has to go 5 km to school. He cycles for n km at 14 km/h but then has a puncture. He walks the remaining distance at 7 km/h and arrives at school $22\frac{1}{2}$ minutes after starting. Form an equation for n and solve it.

XXXVII

1 Simplify (i) $6 - 3\{(m^2 - m) - (m - 1) - (m^2 - 1)\}$

(ii) $\dfrac{a+1}{3} - 2 - \dfrac{2a-1}{5} + \dfrac{1}{3}$

2 Two circular metal discs of radii 3·3 cm and 5·6 cm respectively are melted down and cast into a single circular disc of the same thickness. Find the radius of this disc.

3 In an orchard of 100 apple trees the crops of individual trees were as follows:

Crop (kg)	1-5	6-10	11-15	16-20	21-25	26-30	31-35	36-40
Frequency	2	7	8	18	31	21	10	3

Calculate the mean crop. Draw the cumulative-frequency curve to find the median. If the lower quartile shows the number of trees due for replacement, what is the lowest acceptable crop per tree?

4 Solve (i) $m(3m + 2)^2 = 0$
(ii) $4n^2 - 7n + 3 = 0$

5 From a point 10 m away from the base of a building the angles of elevation of the top and bottom of a window are 41° and 31° respectively. How tall is the window?

6 Divide 174 into two parts so that one part is 45% of the other.

7 Solve simultaneously (i) $2(x - y) = 2 - 3y$
(ii) $4x - 3(2x + y) = 4$

8 In the parallelogram ABCD, X and Y are points on $\overline{CD}$ (produced each way if necessary) such that $\overline{AX}$ bisects $\hat{A}$ and $\overline{BY}$ bisects $\hat{B}$. Prove that DY = CX.

9 In a class of 40 pupils, 7 take French and German, 5 German and Spanish, 6 Spanish and French. 17 take German, and the number taking French only is twice that taking German only. 5 take Spanish only. How many take all three languages?

10 When 48 is divided by a certain number, the result is the same as when 10 is added to the number and the sum divided by 2. Find the number.

XXXVIII

1 Simplify
(i) $-12d^4e^3 \div 4de^2$ (ii) $(-2a^2b^3)^4$ (iii) $\sqrt{12uv \times 3u^3v}$

2 A yacht sailed 3 km on a bearing of 015°, and then 4 km on a bearing of 064°. Find by means of an accurate scale drawing the final distance and bearing of the yacht from the starting-point.

3 M is the mid-point of the side $\overline{AB}$ of a parallelogram ABCD. $\overline{CM}$ produced meets $\overline{DA}$ produced at N.
Prove that DN = 2BC.

4 Solve (i) $3x(4x - 3) = 0$
(ii) $4y^2 + 8y + 3 = 0$

5 The altitude of an isosceles triangle is 25 cm and the length of its base is 18 cm. Find the vertical angle.

6 If a profit of 11% would be obtained by selling an article for £3·70, find the percentage profit or loss if it is sold for £3·10.

7 Solve (i) $\dfrac{3(2m - 1)}{4} - \dfrac{5(m - 2)}{3} = \dfrac{5}{6}$

(ii) $(x + 3)(4x - 1) = 2x(2x + 3)$

8 X, Y are the mid-points of the sides PS, QR of the parallelogram PQRS. $\overline{QX}$, $\overline{YS}$ meet $\overline{PR}$ in H, K. Prove that $\overline{QX}$, $\overline{YS}$ are parallel, and that $\overline{PR}$ is trisected at H and K.

9 $A = \begin{pmatrix} 1 & 2 & 3 \\ 3 & 0 & 2 \\ 2 & 1 & 4 \end{pmatrix}$, $B = \begin{pmatrix} 2 & 0 & 0 \\ 0 & 3 & 0 \\ 0 & 0 & 5 \end{pmatrix}$.

Find $A \times B$ and $B \times A$.

10 The lengths, in cm, of the sides of an equilateral triangle are $m + n$, $3m - 5n$, $m - 2n + 3$. Find the values of m and n, and hence find the perimeter of the triangle.

XXXIX

1 Restate the equations $4x + 5y = 7$, $3x + 4y = 5$ in matrix form, and solve them.

2 A man went 10 km at 10 km/h, 10 km at 20 km/h, 10 km at 30 km/h and 10 km at 40 km/h. What was his average speed for the whole distance?

3 A rectangle 6 cm by 4 cm is placed in a semi-circle as shown in Fig. 165, one of the long sides being along the diameter of the semi-circle. Find the radius of the semi-circle, and also what percentage of its area is occupied by the rectangle. (Take $\pi = \frac{22}{7}$.)

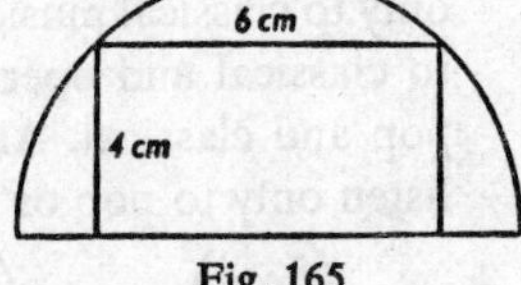

Fig. 165

4 A floor to be carpeted 'wall-to-wall' is 6·4 m long and 4·6 m wide. The carpeting used is in rolls 750 mm wide, and costs £1·25 per metre. Is it cheaper to lay the carpet lengthwise or crosswise, and by how much?

5 $A \cup B = \mathscr{E}$, $n\{A \cap B\} = 5$, $n\{A \cup B\} = 28$, $n\{B'\} = n\{B\}$. Find $n\{B\}$.

6 ABC is a triangle having AB = AC. P is a point on $\overline{BC}$ such that PA = PB. $\overline{CA}$ is produced to X so that A is between C and X. Prove that $X\hat{A}B = A\hat{P}C$.

7 The sum of n terms of the series 19, 16, 13, . . . is known to be $\frac{1}{2}n(41 - 3n)$. How many terms add up to 55?

8 '$2x$' is a two-digit number (x being the second digit). If $2x$ is in base 4, express it as a denary number: similarly if it is in base 9. If one of these denary numbers is one less than twice the other find x.

Show that the number 'xx' in base 4 is exactly half 'xx' in base 9, whatever x may be.

9 A man made a profit of $12\frac{1}{2}\%$ by selling a horse for £108. What profit or loss per cent would he have made if he had sold the horse for £97·20?

10 1 litre = 1·76 pints. Draw a graph from which metric equivalents of capacities up to one gallon can be read off. What are the equivalents of 1 pint in cm³ and of $3\frac{1}{2}$ litres in pints?

XL

1 Solve the equations (i) $3x^2 - 5x = 0$ (ii) $3x^2 - 5x = 2$.

2 In a club of 142 boys the same number listen only to pop and only to classical music: 3 are interested only in opera. 23 listen to classical and operatic music, 24 to pop and opera, 28 to pop and classical. Altogether 34 listen to opera. How many listen only to pop or only to classical music?

3 $A = \begin{pmatrix} 3 & 4 \\ 1 & 2 \end{pmatrix}$, $B = \begin{pmatrix} 4 & 5 \\ 2 & 3 \end{pmatrix}$. Find $A \times B$ and $B \times A$.

Evaluate the determinants of A and B.

4 Find x and y in Fig. 166, all lengths being in cm.

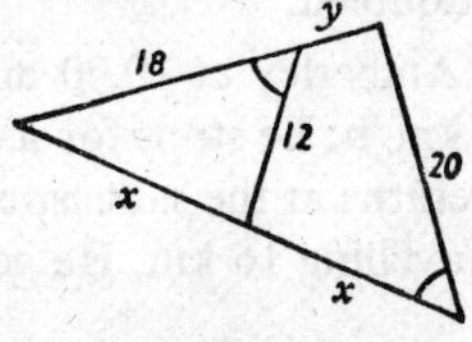

Fig. 166

5 After a boy had spent 32% of his pocket-money he had 17p left. How much had he to begin with?

6 A father's age added to twice his daughter's age amounts to 60 years. Five years ago he was seven times as old as his daughter. How old is each of them now?

7 The two solids shown (Fig. 167) have the same volume, one of them consisting of 3 discs of diameters 2, 4, 6 cm, each 1 cm thick; the other being a cylinder of diameter 2 cm. How long is the cylinder? (Do not use any numerical value for π.)

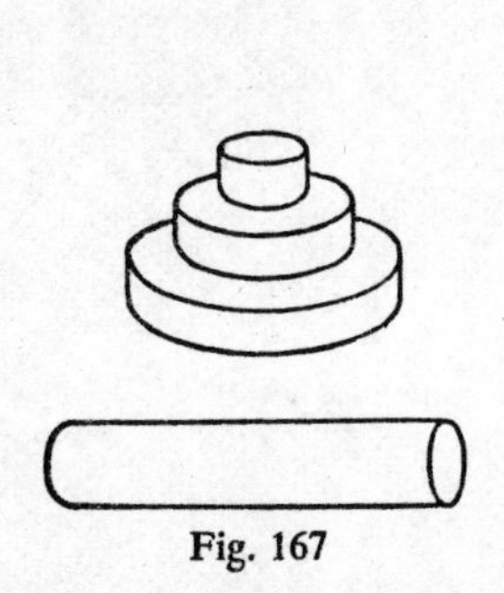

Fig. 167

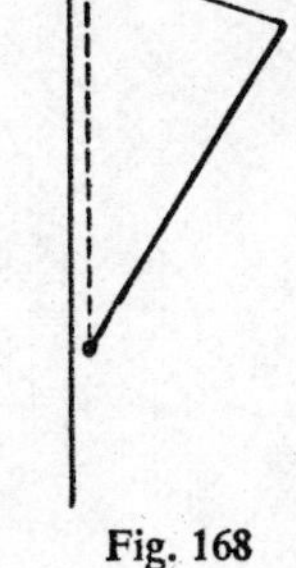

Fig. 168

8 ABCD is a parallelogram: $\overline{BC}$ is produced to E and M is the mid-point of $\overline{BE}$: $\overline{AM}$ is produced to F and AM = MF. Prove that $\overline{DF}$ and $\overline{CE}$ bisect one another.

9 A window 1 m high is hinged along the bottom edge, the opening being controlled by a cord from the top edge of the window which passes over a pulley in the frame (Fig. 168). Calculate (i) the angle to which the window is open when

40 cm of cord is let out, (ii) the extra length of cord needed when this angle is doubled.

10 A motorist leaves Amberley at 10.00 and travels to Buckby, 48 km away, at 64 km/h: he stops for a quarter of an hour in Buckby and then returns at the same speed, but is held up for 20 minutes after travelling 16 km. He gets back to Amberley at 12.00 exactly.

A cyclist leaves Buckby, also at 10.00, and rides towards Amberley at a steady 16 km/h.

How fast did the motorist travel for the final stage of his journey, and at what times did he meet or pass the cyclist? (Solve graphically.)